一切都是最好的安排

加措 〈著〉

中国友谊出版公司

图书在版编目（CIP）数据

一切都是最好的安排 / 加措著 . —北京：中国友
谊出版公司，2014.1（2017.10 重印）
ISBN 978-7-5057-2923-0

Ⅰ . ①一… Ⅱ . ①加… Ⅲ . ①随笔－作品集－中国－
当代 Ⅳ . ① I267.1

中国版本图书馆 CIP 数据核字（2014）第 008433 号

书名	**一切都是最好的安排**
作者	加措
出版	中国友谊出版公司
发行	中国友谊出版公司
经销	新华书店
印刷	河北鹏润印刷有限公司
规格	700×990 毫米　16 开
	20.5 印张　220 千字
版次	2014 年 3 月第 1 版
印次	2017 年 10 月第 20 次印刷
书号	ISBN 978-7-5057-2923-0
定价	39.80 元
地址	北京市朝阳区西坝河南里 17 号楼
邮编	100028
电话	(010) 64668676

如发现图书质量问题，可联系调换。质量投诉电话：010-82069336

既不要扰乱他人的心，也不要动摇自己的决心。

——上师法王如意宝晋美彭措

推荐序

加措活佛是一位很有才华的年轻僧人，早在北大上学的时候，就给我读过他写的一些诗，既有天然画意又有深邃哲理，相当感人。这本《一切都是最好的安排》，则是他开示人生智慧的感悟随笔。每篇文字不多，然不乏触动你心灵的警言，让你与他一起去面对人生生命、生活中的种种问题，以及由此而悟得的解脱智慧。

人生是苦，这是佛教的一个基本教义。然而，没有乐又哪来苦，没有苦又哪来乐？苦中有乐，乐中有苦；苦尽甘来，乐极生悲。苦乐无常，全在一念之转。佛陀开示众生说：执取名相，执我为本，乐亦为苦；看破名相，放下自我，苦亦为乐。在生活中修行修心，面对人生的种种苦难，让自己的心智成熟起来、坚强起来，不为苦纠结，不为乐陶醉，自主自在。

我相信，读者在读了加措活佛这本书后，一定能从中得到智慧的启示，从而增长自心内在的力量，破除生命历程中的困惑和无常，以无畏的勇气去面对日常生活中的无尽磨难。

楼宇烈

二〇一三年十一月

自序：内在的力量

　　心是人生的鼓点，不同的律动带来不一样的人生。生活的一切都是历练，笔直平坦，曲折坎坷，得来惊喜，失去惶恐，用不同的心来丈量，结果也会完全不一样。这个世界很大，你今天能有幸见到这本书，并且能够对你有所帮助的话，且不管这种帮助有多大，都源于很深的佛缘和福报，我们是幸运的有缘人，这一切都是最好的安排。

　　我的童年与大多数的藏族儿童一样，在神山边、溪流中、蓝天云间的坡地上，和来来去去的牦牛、羚羊，绕着那间破旧的小木屋，自在快乐地生活着。我总是喜欢一个人静静地思考，唯一爱干的事就是捏糌粑做曼扎供品。姐姐、姨妈找我干活，都被我拒绝了，我说："我已经老了，不想干活了，想休息休息……"就这样，一直休息了好几年。终于有一天，我瞒着家人，偷偷去了色达佛学院，拜见了生命中最重要的上师法王如意宝晋美彭措。就在那一年，我成为了法王的弟子，找到了我这几年休息时一直思考的问题：心灵的归宿及内在的力量。

　　一个普通人想要凭借羸弱的肉身去守护自己的梦想，是不容易的，再强的人，也总有布满创伤的一天。人始终是在变故中才能成长，而能够依照初心，做好自己的，总是那些不断修正内心、充满正念的人。人往往少年轻狂时才敢妄谈梦想，不顾一切地去实现它，因为我们输得起，无所牵挂。可随着年龄的增长，很多人会心存挂碍，可这并不能阻止那些可怕的事情发生。这时候我们最需要的是一个怦怦跳动、坚韧而有力量的内心，不怕，不慌，不因一时的迷失迷惘一世。要知道，他人与世界并不由我们改变，却是我们心灵成长的最好土壤。人生永远都是一场选择，真舍利不用死抓不放，好机会或许就在放手之时，你修好了内心，也就看清了前路。世事无常，风雨再大，你也能开好自己的花。

　　有多少无常，就有多少修行。我们要做的是发挥自己内在的力量，用一颗慈悲与友爱的心，与无常共处。只有这样，我们才能拥有长久的快乐、幸福与爱！修行是一个由内而外的过程，有两种方式：一种是外修，一种是内修。外修多是生存技能的修炼，而内修则是我们内心的领悟与净化。我不知道你是否想过，我们在这个世间赖以生存的动力之源在哪里，是谁给你源源不断地提供了渡过生命难关的各种力量，是父母和朋友吗？很多人或许给过我们物质上的支持或言语上的鼓励与安慰，但真正让你迈过心里那道坎儿的只能是你自己。当下，一个人内在力量的大小往往成为他在这个世界里能否安乐的重要条件。如果能有一颗坚韧的心，那么所有外在的困难都只是你内在修行过程中的一种检验。你要成为怎样的人，你期待怎样的世界，我想这一切都由你的心决定。

CONTENTS
目录

▶ 第三章 **快乐是一种能力**

▶ 第六章　**智慧源于生命的起伏**

▶ 第七章　**生活需要一种姿态**

第八章　爱是人生最好的营养

第九章　信念是菩提

第一章

我们该如何与这个

世界相处

心中有痛，也要舍得

　　很多事情不是逃避可以解决的，很多东西不是掩饰就可以抹去的。没有谁能做到让所有人满意，就算你再圆滑。在利益的冲突下也不可能将一切做到皆大欢喜，总会有人受伤。当出现矛盾，需要取舍时，我们一定得清楚自己要的是什么，该舍的哪怕痛也要舍掉。若心存侥幸，也许最后原本想留下的却已回不来了。

　　我曾经遇到过一个这样的修行者，他说他修行是为了逃避现实，逃避现实中的喧嚣、嘈杂和人生中诸多不好的东西，这显然是对修行的误解。我告诉他，修行和生活一样，不是为了逃避，而是为了面对。如果是为了逃避而修行，那么你已经离修行十分遥远了，而且会越来越远。

　　前进的路上有汗水和泪水，难免为了某个人或者某件事而伤心难过，但我们绝不能沉迷在已经成为过去时的伤心难过中，更不能逃避。事情并不会因为我们的逃避而得以化解，就算可以躲过一时，存留在内心深处的阴影却始终挥之不去。

就如同世界上始终存在阳光照耀不到的地方，无论怎样努力，都不可能皆大欢喜，总会有人得到，也总会有人失去，这是世界运行的根本规则之一。我一直都认为，人生中真正的喜乐来源于对痛苦的领悟，没有经历过痛苦的人，不可能感受到快乐。正确地面对得到和失去，得到应该得到的，失去应该失去的，而不是心存侥幸地百般挽留。只有经历过这些，并且有了很深的感悟，人们才会懂得珍惜。而这种珍惜，正是人生中的宝藏，可以给我们带来一个快意无悔的人生。

一个人在修行的时候，是无法回避那些给我们带来痛苦的人与事的，无论是逃避还是掩饰，都不是生活的本质。苦难从来都是我们精神的上师。只有精神上得到了，才会达到一个高境界。

你是自己的人生参照物

　　不要以和人相比判定自己的价值，正因我们彼此有别，才使每个人显得特别。不要以别人的标准作为自己的目标，只有你自己知道什么最适合你。不要将最贴心的人视若当然，请珍惜他们，如同对待你的生命。不要因为沉湎过去或憧憬未来而使时间从指缝中溜走，过好今天，把握当下，你便精彩了生命的每一天！

　　总有人问我如何才能成功，面对这样的问题，我只能反问："你是失败的吗？"

　　"是的，活佛，我是失败的，我没有他人活得好。"

　　每当面对这样的抱怨之时，我总是告诉他们："你要有自己的活法。"

　　不要用别人的路标来确定自己的方向，那只会让你迷失。如果你是一条鱼的话，就不要想着像飞鸟一样在天空中翱翔，那不是你的路。什么样的路是独属于你的，什么东西是最适合你的，这些只有你自己才知道。

人们习惯于把别人的关怀和温暖视作理所当然，习惯于追寻遥远的温暖，却看不到最近的阳光。父母、爱人、朋友的无私关切和帮助是我们最大的财富，是让人备感温暖的太阳，一旦失去，你会感觉到侵肌入骨的寒冷，所以请珍视他们，如同珍视你自己那样对待他们。

过去的已经过去，不要总是沉湎在其中无法自拔。时间就好像指间的细沙，会在我们对将来的憧憬中不知不觉地溜走，到最后什么都剩不下。相对于那些已经经历过的过去和无法预测的将来，珍惜眼前的温暖和关切，活出最好的自己，才是最有价值的事。

沉
默
的
人
生
才
厚
重

　　微笑和沉默是两个有效的武器，微笑能解决很多问题，沉默能避免很多问题。不被贪婪所诱惑的人最没有负担的，因为没有人与他结怨，他也没有心机和别人计较，这种日子最轻松，这样的人生也最快乐。选择其实很简单，往自己心里感到踏实的地方走就不会错。日子，因为爱而博大，因为爱而温馨，因为信任而厚重。

　　我经常独自沉默，这是为了感受曾经的过往，是为了守住自己的本心，是为了用睿智的目光内视自我。沉默的时候，不会被世间的纷繁扰乱，可以明心见性。

　　就如同微笑可以解决问题一样，沉默可以避免问题。一个人不应该热衷于在嘈杂中彰显自己，也不要用激烈的争辩来证明什么。寂静是安守本心的一种很好的方式，用这种方式，我们可以以稳健厚重的姿态抵御突如其来的诱惑。诱惑少了，才可以活得轻松。

　　沉默是不争，是不计较，是对自己负责，也是对别人负责。内心厚重之人，往往看起来都是慈祥的，因为他们的心是微笑的。与这样的人相处，不需要太多的言语，却是最轻松的。就像我的上师法王如意宝一样，我每次见到他，内心都有一种由衷的喜悦。他经常对我说：只有往自己心里感到踏实的地方走，才不会出错。

　　沉默，是浮华喧嚣的尽头最美的声音。

　　沉默，是在嘈杂中与自己宁静地交谈。

人生经不起太多的耽搁

　　我们常常会想，以后我要怎样怎样，可是等我们假想的以后来到时，一切可能已不是当初的模样。从当下出发，想了就去做，不论是对事，还是对人，不要只是空想。做的过程中也许会有很多障碍，只要越过了就是成功。想对之好的人，父母、爱人，抑或朋友，去爱他们吧，因为人生常常是来不及告别就会分离。

　　至今还清楚地记得，当黑色的牦牛驮着阿妈走向往生净土之路的时候，我是何等悲伤。想对阿妈好，想更多地爱阿妈，可惜已经来不及了。很多人总是会不由自主地这样想：等我功成名就的时候，一定好好地爱他们。殊不知，时间从不为人美好的愿望作丝毫停留。当我们所想象的"以后"变成"现在"的时候，一切已经时过境迁，物是人非，早已寻不回当初的模样。不要让心中的想法始终停留在

"想"的阶段，那并不能解决什么问题。只有真正去做了，才会明白要做的事情到底有多么重要。如果你想对谁好，如果你想对那些深爱的人表达自己的爱心，就勇敢地去表达，尽快去把你对他们的爱告诉他们，让他们和你一样欢喜。

命运无常，人生苦短，一旦耽搁下来，可能连告别的话语都来不及说出，就真的分别了。

人与人的相遇是用几世修来的，相识即是有缘。所以，凡事不必斤斤计较，退一步海阔天空。要记住，不要轻易伤害别人，更不要去伤害身边的人。我们不要以为伤害了别人，受伤的仅仅是别人，其实最大的受害者还是自己。因为别人只有恨，而我们却要受到良知的拷问，心中充满懊悔与内疚，永远永远。

以爱己之心爱人，

莲花会在冰雪中绽放。

学
习
即
修
行

　　学会知而不言，因为言多必失；学会自我解脱，因为这样
才能自我超越；学会一个人静静思考，因为这样才能让自己清醒、
明白；学会用心看世界，因为这样才会看清人的本初；学会放下，
因为只有放下了才能重新开始；学会感恩，因为拥有一颗感恩
的心能帮助我们在逆境中寻求希望，在悲观中寻求快乐！

　　藏区的孩子，很多都有出家的经历。相对于孩子们而言，出家
的意义除了修行，更主要的是学习知识。这种学习，并不仅仅是对
文字的认识，还是一种充实人生的经历。其实学习并不需要特定的
场所，也不需要特定的形式。人从咿呀学语，到蹒跚学步，一直都
在学习的过程当中。因为学习，我们会了很多，懂了很多，也明
白了很多。

　　在路上走了很远之后，很多人学会了用心去看世界，因为这样

不会被五光十色所迷惑，能更容易看清楚一些最本源的东西。人生是一条不断自我发现、自我完善的道路，我们现在所拥有的经验来源于对以前所犯错误的总结。在和人交往的过程中有了言多必失的经历，才学会了知而不言；在一次次舍与得的考验中，才知道人生该做怎样的选择……只有不断学习、不断进步，才能够超越昨天的自我。修行之路在脚下一直延伸到生生世世的轮回，为了脱离轮回，为了得到解脱，众生唯有以生命不息、修行不止的意志，如海绵吸水那样吸取世间珍贵的能量，方可在修习中抵达圆满！

短板决定生命的容量

　　人，总是喜欢要求别人，却很少去想自己是否也是按照这个准则在要求自身；人，总是容易发现别人的错误，却很难发现自己的错误。有时，明知错了，却很难克服，喜欢找出各种理由让自己一再犯错。把握正确的方向，坚守做人的原则。如果发现错了，一定要止步。

　　严于律己、宽以待人的道理很多人都知道，不过大多往往是说到却做不到。人们总是喜欢按照自己理想中的样子去要求别人，却忘记审视自己有没有达到同样的标准。每个人都有这样那样的不足，身上也肯定会存在短板，在修行的过程中这些不足便会暴露出来，不过只要我们对自己有足够多的内观与自省，是不难发现它们的。无论做什么事情都不要随波逐流，你不去沉淀自己，心必然会浮躁。

　　严格要求别人的前提是我们必须严格要求自己，如此，我们和他人才能共同进步。否则，我们的要求在别人看来可能就是无理的挑剔。能够通过别人的行为修正自己的人，才是真正的智者。能够看到错误是一方面，但重要的是要知道如何去改正、去避免。把握好方向、坚持住原则，不仅是心安的最基本前提，也是消除错误最厉害的武器。

人们对待事物的时候，往往以自己想到的、看到的为参照，用自己的价值观和角度去看待事物，这就产生了在同一件事情上的双重标准：在指责别人的时候，即便是愚蠢的人，也会显得清醒而又智慧；而那些自以为聪明的人，在原谅自己的时候，总是迷迷糊糊、模棱两可。这种做法，除了证明自身浅薄之外，还往往会被同一块石头绊倒。一个人修为的多少，完全取决于他身上的那块短板。

不争不辩，不闻不见

　　不要轻易和人发生争执，当有人和我们争执时，就让他赢，因为我们并没有因此而损失什么。所谓的赢，他又能赢得什么、得到什么呢？所谓的输，你又输了什么、失去了什么呢？争来争去只会伤了彼此的和气，还会平添无谓的烦恼。谨慎地、沉默地、精明地回避，以平常心应对无常的人生。

　　姨妈在我年幼时曾讲过这样一个故事：有三个持刀的武士，彼此站在距离对方一步远的地方进行决斗，以决定谁是最厉害的武士。他们的刀都很锋利，可以保证一下子就把对方杀死，而且绝对不会失手。在这种情况下，谁才会是最厉害的那个武士呢？若是三个武士争夺第一的虚名，肯定会全部死去，也就无所谓谁是第一了。唯一的办法就是不争，放下手中刀。
　　不争不辩、不闻不见是大境界，或许俗世中的人们难以贯彻始终，却可以在生活中充分运用不争的智慧，不轻易和别人发生争执。当争执无可避免的时候，忍一时退一步，让对方赢，又有何妨？争来争去的结果往往是两败俱伤，伤了一团和气，还平添了无数烦恼，甚至由此引发灾祸。

不争并不是理屈词穷，也不是让对方闭嘴，而是以柔克刚、消除分歧的智慧。它不仅是我们宽厚之德的外化，同样也是与他人相处的根本。放下争执之刃，持不争之戒，就会免受纠结之苦，而且以淡然的平常心应对无常的人生，这本就是修行的目的之一。唯有不争，才能做到不执。当别人与你争吵时，你无论是用沉默来表达自己的观点，还是选择精明地回避，都是慈悲的开始。

自我疏导的法则

　　多花些时间和能让你快乐的人在一起，少一些时间和那些让你感到有压力的人相处；不要说别人的梦想是不可能的，当他们用成功证明你错的时候，那将是一件难堪的事；不管你犯了多少错或者进度多慢，你仍然比那些没有开始的人领先；一个人幸运的前提，是他有能力改变自己；心境可以归于平和，但不能趋于死寂。

　　快乐是可以互相感染的，和那些能让你快乐的人在一起，你也会变得快乐起来。用别人的良好心态来改善自己的心态，不失为一种方法。任何站在"过来人"的角度去指责别人，用自己的经验去说服别人这样做不行的做法，都是不可取的。每个人都有自己的经历和感受，都有自己独一无二的人生之路，很多在大多数人看起来不行的事情，对于某些人而言就未必真的不能实现。

　　无论何时出发，走了多远，只要我们向前看，总会发现前方有人比我们更努力，比自己更加接近目标。可这并不是我们怀疑自己能力的理由，只能说明，有人比我们行动得更早或者跑得更快，理所当然比我们更加靠前一些，所以不要为此感到不公。其实，不管我们在途中跌倒过多少次，也不管速度有多慢，比起那些还站在起跑线上的后来者都要领先。

　　生活中的诸多智慧，就如同我们人生路上那些不知名的花朵，没必要去强求它们是否名贵、是否芬芳，每一朵花的存在都是对世间最好的装扮。

做人不需要解释

　　解释，有时候确实可以消除误会，获得理解，然而有时候，别人也可能将你的解释理解成一种掩饰。不是每做一件事都必须向旁人解释，不停地解释会限制自己的人生道路，你所做的一切，只要自己认可、心安就好。所以，给人以帮助，只要伸出温暖的手；证明自己正直，只管端端正正做事情；原谅别人，只须露出笑脸。

　　在很多时候，解释并不是必要的。对于信赖你的人，不需要解释；对于不信赖你的人，解释是无用功；而那些懵懂的人，你的解释反而会让他难解。

　　经常有信徒问我什么是佛，对于这样的问题，我通常是不回答也不解释。佛的博大精深，佛的微言大义，又怎会是几句话能解释得清楚的？如果没有亲身经历，没有感悟，解释再多也无法理解。

如果真的有了深刻的感悟，到达了一定的境界，自然会佛光普照。很多高僧的大彻大悟根本就无法用言语的解释来和别人分享，因为众生的经历不同，境界也不同，愿的程度深浅不一，行的程度更有不同，并不是每个人通过佛法的开释便能了解佛学的真谛。

天不解释自己的高度，依然高远无涯。解释虽然可以在一定程度上将误会消除，可有时解释并不是必要的，甚至会被直接理解为掩饰。做人做事，只要自己认可，只要问心无愧，也就足够了。做错事情的时候，踏踏实实地用行动去改正，比解释更直接更有效。面对他人的错误和误会之时，或许一个微笑比解释一百次都要好。

驾驭自己的欲望

　　如果我们没有刻意追求的欲望，就不会在意别人的眼色，也不会违心地去讨好，生活自然会轻松很多。不要做欲望的奴隶，不然永远静不下来。有些人非常善于窥视别人的心思，他们会利用别人的欲望和所求，以达到自己所期望的目的，要想不被这种人牵着自己的鼻子走，就要学会散去心中的不良欲望。无欲则刚！

　　"无欲"并不是一无所有的意思，而是要去掉那些虚无缥缈的、不切实际的贪念。

　　无欲是生命在退去了喧嚣和浮躁之后所展现出来的真谛，是人生意义之根本，只有在修行中真正洞察这些，才不会被欲望所迷惑。只有无欲才会刚强，但这里的刚强并不是指争强好胜，而是对自我的克制。驾驭自己的欲望，不做违背天理良知的事情，并且坚守下去，使之成为自己生命当中不可更改的准则。

那些执着于对欲望追逐的人，才会在意别人的看法与自己的得失，才会昧着本心去讨好钻营，斤斤计较，难以平静。世俗中的一部分人最善于察言观色，他们很清楚别人的欲望，也知道别人想要得到什么，这种人是非常危险的，因为他们会利用别人性格中的弱点有针对性地做出一些事情，以达到他们自己的目的。一旦被这种人掌控，就会一直被牵着鼻子走。在那些存在诱惑与陷阱的境地，散去那些不良的、不切实际的欲望，看清楚方向，才能在诱惑面前保持自己的品格。俗语说，苍蝇不叮无缝的蛋，只要自己的心不变质，外人是很难伤害到我们的。修好自己的，才是自在的开始。

世上没有过不去的坎儿

　　生活中不可能事事尽如人意，学说三句话，时刻拥有乐观的心态和快乐的心境。第一句是"算了吧"，生活中有很多事，只要你努力过、争取过，其实结果已经不重要了；第二句是"不要紧"，因为积极乐观的态度是解决和战胜困难的第一步；第三句是"会过去的"，无论遇到什么困难，都要以积极的心态去面对。

　　世间之事在那些没有修行过的人看来往往是纷纷扰扰、千头万绪，有很多是他们不希望看到也不希望遇见的，但生活本身并不以人的意愿为转移，万物自有其运行的规律，你我都强求不得。佛经中有"缘合固有缘尽则灭，业集随心相现果起"的教导，就算是精深的修行者，也会遇到扰乱忧怖、厄恼不吉之事，任何人的一生都不可能只遇到欢喜与美满。回过头来想想我们这些年所走过来的路，那些让我们刻骨铭心的，其实往往都是我们不希望发生的。经历坎坷并不可怕，可怕的是我们因此失去思考与抵制磨难的勇气与力量。

　　在面对生活中的那些不如意的时候，时时刻刻都怀着乐观的心态，用快乐的态度去迎接它们，方可化悲痛为力量。淡然地对自己说一句"算了吧"，因为只要你努力过，就已经得到了整个过程。如果此刻你对生活充满失意与忧伤，那么现在就仔细想想生活最坏还能怎样。其实每个人都应该明白一个道理：任何我们在失去后所得到的领悟，都远比失去本身更值得珍重。用积极的心态把自己从失去的痛苦中拯救出来，才能战胜更大的困难。佛法或者上师的开示，并不是让我们得到不可能得到的，也不是让我们获得已失去的，而是教我们如何去面对不如意的人生，当遇到挫折的时候如何对自己的内在做出及时的调整。

勿因喜而轻诺

　　很多时候我们习惯去承诺，在违背诺言的时候，又会指责对方对自己不信任。那么信任是什么？信任是由一个个坚定的承诺堆砌起来的，你遵守的承诺越多，信任的塔就越牢固。而一旦违背诺言，就会危及塔的坚固，就需要用更多的时间去修补。所以，当你明知道自己做不到的时候，不要随意承诺，否则，伤人伤己。

　　在听着格萨尔王的故事和舅舅一起放牧牦牛的那段时光，有一天，舅舅很高兴地说有位同修者要来拜访他，舅舅为此做了精心的准备，结果那位同修者并没有来。虽然舅舅并没有怪他，但无形中却受到了伤害，于是就在那时我给自己定了一个原则：如果答应了别人，就一定不要失信。

　　诺言如砖石，信任似高塔，很多兑现的诺言才能堆砌出一方信任的高塔，但某一块或者某几块砖石的缺失，可能会使高塔倒塌。修补信任的高塔是一件费时费力的事情，所以不要因为一时的冲动便不假思索地轻许诺言。

为了让别人相信，一些人习惯于对他人做语言上的承诺，但是现实中的很多限制往往会造成身不由己的局面，以至于诺言无法实现。面对这种状况，去指责对方并不能解决问题，而且也不是一个慈悲之人该有的做法。不能因为一个人一次未能履行承诺，便对其加以否定，或许问题出在自己的身上，抑或这种承诺原本就不应该发生，你与对方都是在勉强自己。

对于别人的许诺，人们应该怀着一颗平常心去对待，不必为一时的允诺而欣喜，更不必为了一时的失言而愤怒。它就像是一杯清水，简单平淡而又清澈透明，不需要去刻意渲染，也不需要去刻意遮掩。

每
一
个
自
己
都
是
独
一
无
二
的

　　不要将自己和他人比，因为每个人都是这世上独一无二的个体。不要将他人追逐的理想变成自己的目标，因为你有你的路，与其眼看着别人的美好，不如用心经营好自己的幸福。当你还可以给予时，不要轻言放弃；当你还可以努力时，不要告诉自己"不可能"；当你主动停止尝试前，没有任何一件事是已经结束的。

　　牧区有个阅历丰富的老人，我很喜欢听他讲述过去的故事。有一次，我跟随老人到了一座小山的脚下，我急于爬上山顶，老人家却摇着转经筒对我说："爬得慢一点，这里的每一块石头都是独一无二的，一定要好好看。"后来我去了很多地方，但始终记得那座无名小山，记得山上那些独一无二的石头。

　　和独一无二的石头一样，世间的每一个人都是独一无二的个体。

与其只看到别人的成功和圆满，还不如低下头看自己的路，走向自己的方向，追寻属于自己的那份独特。

也许脚下的路布满了坎坷，也许前方被荆棘阻碍，在我们还可以付出的时候，就不要放弃，只要还在努力，就没有什么是不可以实现的。不放弃就有希望，有希望就不算是失败，只不过是暂时没有成功而已。最大的失败不是没有获得成功，而是放弃获得成功的可能。只要我们还在主动地尝试，一切就不会结束，只是还没有到达目的地而已。

战胜自己的才是强者

要用行动控制情绪，不要让情绪控制行动；要让心灵启迪智慧，不要让耳朵支配心灵。思想会变成语言，语言会变成行动，行动会变成习惯，习惯会改变性格，性格会影响人生！我们无法改变世界，但可以改变观念；我们无法改变别人的看法，但可以改变自己的想法！

我见过很多人，他们一遇到自己不如意的事，首先会去埋怨别人，之后才轻描淡写地把责任放到自己身上去衡量。在这类人的想法中，功劳是自己的，坏事往往是别人做的，这不仅是一种逃避责任的表现，更是不能正视自己的表现。不自我反省，不在反省后改变自己，一味要求别人做出改变，会让世界多出很多不必要的摩擦。

"改变别人，不如改变自己"，如果我们不能改变别人的观点，那就改变自己的想法。既然无法改变这个世界，那就改变自己的思维观念，以更好地适应世界。在改变自我的过程中，可以从智慧人生的大方向着眼，但具体到细节上，却要从宽人严己的小处入手。

内修心性，外炼品行，用质朴的心灵、最本源的智慧去改变行动和语言，就是用心灵支配我们的耳朵和嘴巴。性格决定命运，但性格的改变并非一朝一夕，先从小处着手，改变语言和行动，进而改变习惯，最后才可以重塑性格，敢于担当。

得
失
之
间

　　有时，我们以为赢了，其实，我们输了！因为，我们赢了"面子"，却输了"里子"！我们生活在社会里，懂得赢，也要懂得输；懂得竞争，也要懂得包容。因为，我们不能一直只赢不输！我们必须懂得适时地包容、退让与感恩。常常，包容与退让不一定是"我输"，反而可能是"双赢"！

　　总有人把人生当成战场，一定要分出个胜负输赢，不过到最后，往往伤痕累累，就算是赢了对手，得到了想要得到的财富和地位，但如果因此输掉了友谊和尊重，那这样的赢其实是真正的输。人的一生重要的不是输赢，而是有没有得到自己想要的，别到最后赢了光鲜的"面子"，却输掉了实实在在的"里子"，那就真的从赢家变成了输家，得不偿失。

　　不要把竞争当作你死我活的战争，人生并没有注定辉煌的胜利，谁都会品尝失败的滋味。学会退让与包容，人生才会拥有更加广阔的天地。那些把"赢"当作终极目标，为了一点点利益就争得面红耳赤的人，通常已经输了，因为他们在赢得蝇头小利之时已经失去了更加宽广的世界。反之，也不要把输当作洪水猛兽，输赢之间也没有明确的界限，有时候你以为你输了，其实你赢得更多。只要站在更高的高度，换一个角度去面对输赢，我们就会发现，任何所经历过的事情都不会是一无所获。无论是输还是赢，只要你做过了，能够用正确的心态去看待，结果都一样精彩。

膨胀的人都是轻飘的

　　如果我们常想着别人对自己的好处，就会善待对我们好的每一个人，就愿意为他们付出，就会使友谊不断巩固发展；如果我们常想着自己对别人的好处，就会让自我优越感不断膨胀，就会因他人的一点点过失而感到委屈和不平衡，就难以宽容地对人，这样对完善自身不利，也不利于友谊。一念善，皆是善；一念恶，皆为恶！

与人善，
福虽未至，祸已远离；
与人恶，
祸虽未至，福已远离。

佛教是讲究布施的，无论是物质上的还是精神上的。修行的人总是与人为善，把别人的好处谨记心中，存着感恩的心善待每一个人，并且愿意为他们付出更多。

有善因才会有善果。很多抱怨之所以发生，根本原因是我们只记住了我们对别人的好，而未能记住别人对我们的好。所以当一个人总是念念不忘自己曾经给予他人的一些东西时，就会开始自我膨胀，轻飘飘地浮在半空中，以为自己高人一等，以为自己可以俯视众生，这对自我的完善非常不利。因为你把布施给别人的好处当作一种筹码，无法忍受他人哪怕一丁点儿的过错，会为了一些微不足道的事情而感觉到委屈，认为别人以怨报德，当这种想法产生的时候，宽容的心态已经离你而去了。

与人为善会收获善缘，与人为恶则会收获孽缘。如果把给别人的好处当作一种施舍，当作谋求后报的手段，如果善良地对待别人是为了索取，那么这种善则是世间最大的恶。善与恶的分界在于我们的本心，如果我们心存不善的念头去帮助别人，哪怕是戴上了善的面具，也终将瞒不过别人。

情绪是可以调节的变量

要记得抖落肩上的尘土

　　不要害怕做错什么，即使错了，也不必懊恼，人生本来就是对对错错，这次错了，下次别犯同样的错就好。不要在流眼泪的时候做任何决定，情绪负面的时候话越少越好。无论遇到什么事情，都要对自己说这是正常的，而不要说"我怎么这么倒霉"，因为比你倒霉的人多的是。积极、阳光的心态能助你走出逆境！

因为地球是圆的，
所以乌云不可能永远都遮蔽同一个地方。

　　"金无足赤，人无完人"，这句俗语很准确地道出了世间万物不完美的本质。因为不完美，所以会犯错误，而犯错、试错、纠错的过程本就是生活的一部分。所以，即使真的做错了什么，也没有必要捶胸顿足。就算是圣者，也做不到万无一失。人生本来就在磕磕绊绊的对错中度过，所以也不必刻意地抵触错误。错误的存在恰恰可以提醒我们，生命道路上哪些是陷阱哪些是蜜糖，怎样的人生取舍与定位是可取的，免得下一次再被同样的石头所绊倒。

人之所以犯错，是因为认识不够，准备不够充分，而不是因为足够"倒霉"。如果"倒霉"这个理论真的成立的话，那么你肯定不是最"倒霉"的那个人，因为还有很多人比你更"倒霉"。

我们所犯下的错误不是"命中注定"的，更不是上天安排的，每个人都在一个又一个错误中成长。面对犯下的错误时，最重要的是及时改正，尽快走出负面的情绪，而不是在懊恼和自责中停滞不前。

清醒的智慧

　　一个人或事会令你不舒服，一定是有原因的，有些原因要过很久你才有可能知道，而有些原因你可能永远都不会知道。但这些并不重要，重要的是它使你不舒服，它会影响你的心情，影响到你的判断，也影响到你的生活。输什么也不能输了心情，既然不舒服，就放了吧，给别人一个重新认识你的机会，有什么不好呢？

　　人生五味俱全，一切都值得我们去品尝。

　　有些人有些事，或令人沮丧，或令人难堪，然而等一切过去，回头再看的时候，只不过是人生激流中一朵微不足道的小浪花。这些是非对错并没有当初所想的那么重要，真正重要的是这些人或事让你有了不舒服的感觉。

　　不舒服的感觉虽然不是常态，但也应该尽快将其消除，否则内在的不顺畅将对我们的身体机能的良好运行产生影响。负面的情绪会蚕食人的理智，让人做出不正确或者不恰当的判断。世上没有任何美好会在抱怨中产生。远离并消除负面情绪，是一切良好开端的基础。

　　不如意的人与事，大多是没有意义的过眼云烟，它能左右我们一时，但不能左右我们一世，虽然早晚都要消散离去，但若能尽早将之从内心里取出来扔掉，或许可以免受很多枉苦。尽早出离，功德便越丰厚。不让外界无谓的纷扰影响到自己的心情，不让那些无谓的人或事左右自己的情绪，便不会因愤而生乱。当我们不再执着一件事物或一种习惯，它就失去了指挥摆布我们的能力，我们也就获得了自由。

人心如水，静则澄澈

　　即使再清澈的水，如果在一个杯子里不停地摇晃，它都不会清澈；即使再浑浊的水，如果静静地放着，也自然会变得清澈。我们的心也是如此，如果你没有给它时间去沉淀，而总是摇晃不停，那它就会处在一种浑浊的状态。——静下心来！

　　心静，
　　便无杂念，
　　心静，
　　则大自在。

　　每当看到众生的心难以平静，就想起上师如意宝在去往净土之前留给我的话："不要扰乱他人的心，也不要动摇自己的决心。"
　　人心如水，不论水如何清澈透亮，若是不停地摇晃，也会渐渐浑浊；而再浑浊的水，只要经历了长时间的静止后，杂质会逐渐沉淀下来，再次恢复清澈。世俗之人，看着前方人如潮涌，总是漫无目的地跟着飞奔；看着远方的群山巍峨，总以为攀上去便是幸福。有的人奋进一生，其目的就是希望拥有更大的成功，拥有更多的财富，能站在更高的山峰上看风景。可是，这是唯一的幸福标准吗？拥有了这一切便能真的幸福吗？

　　是时候让心灵静下来了，是时候沉淀一下自我了。让自己闲下来，给心一个安静的瞬间，仔细留意生活中的每一个细微之处，方知什么是一花一世界、一木一浮生。只有静下心来，人和心才能一起沉下去。生命中除了向前跑，还有急流勇退的闲适和很多种其他的快乐值得我们去珍重。

一切都是最好的安排

当遇到一件事，已无法解决，甚至是已经影响到我们的生活、心情时，我们通常喜欢一味地在原地踏步、绕圈、抱怨，让自己陷在痛苦的深渊中。此时，何不停下脚步，想一想是否有转换的空间，或许换种方法，换条路走，事情便会简单点。生命中常常会有挫折，但那不是尽头，只是在提醒我们：该转弯了！

挫折就像一张巨大的网把心困在其中，越是努力向前冲，就越被勒得遍体鳞伤。抓住挫折不放手，就只能拥有痛苦，只有放开手，才能有机会选择别的。心若死执，那么人的智慧也只能达到某种程度而已。

佛陀在楞严会上对大众说法时，曾经举起自己的手来问阿难："阿难！你看我的手是正的还是倒的？"阿难道："我也不知道究竟如何为正，如何为倒。"佛陀说："手臂就是手臂，哪有一定的正或倒？

只是世间之人一定要执着上竖为正、下垂为倒，这是执迷不悟的看法。"

世间没什么事情会注定成为挫折，换一个角度去看，坏事未尝不是好事。佛云："吃苦是了苦，享福是消福。"说的正是如此。秋叶飘落是无法阻止的，零落成泥碾作尘是悲，但化作春泥护花则是感动。没有暴风骤雨，哪里会有雨后长虹？一条路行不通，但它绝对不是生活中必须要撞破的南墙，换一个方向走下去，一切也许都将迎刃而解；换个角度再尝试一次，或许可以开辟出一条崭新的路径。

去留无心，随意最好

　　有时，我们并不知道自己在忙些什么，仿佛一切都是为了生活，为了最简单地活下去。可是，在无意中，我们像花一样散发香味，感染了别人，那是我们无法预知的，也是无须刻意追寻的，那香味或许会永远留在别人心里，或许什么也没留下。因此，我们不必为某些事或大喜或大悲。随意是最好的，那才是生命的本真！

　　这是一个快节奏的时代，每个人都步履匆匆，但如果生活只是单调而又重复地奔忙，那也就没有意义了。

　　很多东西无须刻意去追寻，反而是在无意当中，会留下很多闪光点，会留下最甜美的芬芳。无心插柳柳成荫，很多随性而为的事，达到的效果往往是最好的。就像很多没有目的地的旅行一样，往往能够收获到更大的快乐，看到意想不到的景致。这是上天带给我们的意外惊喜，是在预想之外的收获。

生活的芬芳或许会长久地留在心中，或许会随着岁月的流逝而渐渐消散，最后什么都没有留下，可我们无须为此遗憾，因为这根本就是期望之外的礼物，得到固然欣喜，没得到也在情理之中。随意而为才是最好的，简单明了，不会有太多的纠葛和牵绊。停下脚步欣赏路旁的无名野花，在感受到一份闲适之后再次起程，不为生活而去，不为生活而留，这才是真正的生活。

烦恼，没什么大不了

　　我们生活在尘世中，什么人都可能遇上，什么事都可能碰上，会有人说你好，也会有人说你不好。但只要我们做人做事问心无愧，就不必执着于他人的评判。当有人对你施不敬的言语，请不要在意，更不要因此而烦恼，因为这些言语改变不了事实，却可能搅乱你的心。心如果乱了，一切就都乱了。

　　生活是一个由无数个体组成的群体世界，每个人总会和别人产生交集，难免会有磕磕碰碰，哪怕是全心全意替人着想，也有人不但不领情，还恶言相加，就更不用提因为立场不同、角度不同而导致的诸多批评和指责。

　　如果因为别人一个有意无意的批评或不敬，让我们的心情变坏，而我们又将这种坏心情带到工作和生活中，那么无形中我们就充当了坏心情的传染源，伤害了身边的亲人和朋友。像在湖面上投入了无数个小石子，以每一个人为中心，向周围扩散，最终导致整个湖面波澜不断。生活在荆棘丛中的人都是戒备心十足的刺猬，稍稍一动，彼此都被刺得遍体鳞伤。

用平静的心态，去包容生活中突如其来的批判和指责，那时候才会发现，尽管还是生活在同样的环境之中，每天面对的也是同样的人与事，但是所有的一切却因为感知不同而有了另一番模样。也许有的事情、有的人还是不尽如人意，但如果懂得包容，我们自己的心情会轻松很多。其实，没有什么大不了的。

欣赏他人，才能成就自己

事物本身没有快乐与痛苦之分，一件事究竟是快乐还是痛苦，关键是看我们抱着怎样的心态、用怎样的眼光去看待。如果我们对周遭的事物感到不舒服，那也许只是我们的感受造成的。学会用欣赏的眼光、欣赏的心态去欣赏我们身边的人和事，人生就会因为这份欣赏与被欣赏而更加和谐、灿烂！

欣赏者心中，
有朝霞、露珠
和常年盛开的花朵。

世间赏心悦目的人和事，常人大多都能用欣赏的眼光去看待，但对那些让人不舒服的人和事，该如何去看待呢？是去批判吗？你有没有想过这些恰恰更要用欣赏的眼光去看待吗？

　　小孩子经常因他人考试成绩比自己好而暗生妒忌，觉得是那些人抢了本属于自己的风光，很少真正去想，正是因为这些比自己优秀的人存在，才让自己有了前行的方向与努力的动力。能用欣赏的眼光去看待比自己优秀的对手，并不会让我们变得不如人，相反会因此而发现他人身上许多自己所没有的优点。

　　看世界不光要用眼睛，还要用心。失去欣赏能力的人是可悲的，他的心已经变得衰老。一个人的胸怀是否宽阔，很重要的一点就是看他是否能欣赏他人，又是如何欣赏的。如果视别人如冤家，看他人一无是处，最终自己也将难有大的作为。社会是一个大舞台，也是一个竞技场，人生是场表演，也是种奋斗，每个人都需要别人的喝彩。

　　欣赏可以让人看待事物的眼光更加高远。不要把每天的时间安排得紧紧的，留下一点空间，想一想如何做自己的主人，这才是重要的事。我们有机会来到这个多彩多姿的世界，不妨学做一个旅行家，不只要跋山涉水，更要懂得铭记。

痛苦需要清理

　　我们每天经历的开心或不开心的事都会在心里安家，心里的事多了，就会杂乱无序，然后心也会随之而烦乱。那些痛苦的情绪和不愉快的记忆充斥在心中，如果不及时清理，便会令人纠结迷茫。所以我们要时常整理，这样才能告别烦乱。凡事要往好的方面想，丢掉那些无谓的痛苦，这样，才会有更多空间让快乐进驻。

　　谁都会遇到不开心的事情，只有及时放下无谓的痛苦，心才不会生病。

　　痛苦因人而异，每个人都不一样，一个穷苦人一天三顿能有饭吃就感到幸福了，而一个富翁会为待客时餐桌上的酒不够高档而感到懊恼和痛苦烦躁。人们在希求幸福降临的同时，往往造的是苦痛的因。痛苦源于内心过多的欲望。人有欲望是正常的，但应该是有限度。欲望并不可怕，可怕的是贪欲。贪欲生起时，使人远离真正的自利心和利他心，远离诸圣贤所享受的真常之乐，使人对自心和所贪着的对象愚痴不明，直至自害。

诸苦所因，贪欲为本。放下贪欲，才会知足常乐。小孩子一生下来，手总是攥得紧紧的，而当一个人走完一生，却总是要撒手而去。人活着的目的，并不是要得到多少，而是要通过不断的修行来提升自己的人格修养，用人性的光辉照亮生命中那些阴暗的角落。一味地向外求取，只会使自己丧失信心，人格堕落。

"万法皆空，唯有因果不空。"布施是放下贪欲最好的办法，不计回报，心无所求地去帮助别人，只有善的能量能让我们体会到作为一个人的真正快乐。

生活就像是一个瓶子，只有把里面的痛苦减少到最小，开心的空间才会越大。

能断才能得到

握在手里的，不一定就是我们真正拥有的；我们所拥有的，也不一定就是我们真正铭刻在心的！其实人生很多时候需要自觉放弃，放弃一个心仪却无缘分的朋友，放弃某段投入却无收获的感情，放弃某种选择……也许会因放弃而伤感，但伤感并不妨碍我们重新开始！安然一份放弃，固守一份洒脱！

人们总想把握住能够看得到的所有机会，将所有希望得到的都握在手里，所以拼命去争夺。一些人总是强调：这是我的，那也是我的，这些那些都是我的……一旦"我的"东西被侵犯，就会很痛苦，或是很愤怒。他们从来没有想过，若想拥有，首先要学会放弃。上天对每个人都是公平的，他关闭了你的一扇门，必然为你打开一扇窗。

我们拥有的或者极力试图拥有的，并不一定就是内心中最希望得到的，也不见得就是我们最想要的。人生中，很多时候需要我们自觉地放弃一些东西。放手，虽会带来伤感，但这份伤感仅仅是放手之后的一种感受，并不意味着不能重新开始。

世间最珍贵的，莫过于眼前的幸福，对于那些不属于自己的，我们只需要放开手，便能得到快乐。固守固然值得钦佩，但放手何尝不是一种洒脱？安然放弃那些不属于自己的东西，也就不会被牵绊住。心无挂碍地生活，才是生命中该有的最好追求。

一切天长地久，其实不过是萍水相逢。你什么时候能断，什么时候才能得到。

不要抱着得到的目的做事

　　我们常常会努力地做一些事情，只为了某些人的夸奖或者开心，但如果做了以后看不到我们所期望的态度，委屈、抱怨的情绪马上会显现出来，最后原本好的发愿反而弄得大家不欢而散。所以，要么就做了不去期望回报，要么就干脆不做或者少做一点。抱怨不仅会毁掉别人的好心情，更会毁掉自己的好心情。

世间的一切，
原本就不是我们的。
我们来的时候两手空空，
日后无论得到多或少，
都是意外的惊喜。

　　有四个孩子，把捡到的钱包交给老师后受到了表扬。为了继续得到表扬，第二天，这四个孩子纷纷旷课去街上找钱包。孩子这样做是因为天真，可在很多事情上，大人也在犯同样的错误。有时全力以赴去做某些事的时候，其实并不是为了最初的美好愿望，而是希望事成后获得领导或者其他什么人的夸赞。这和专门捡钱包的小孩子并没有什么不同，因为早已经违背了我们的初心。

　　事情做得好，得到赞赏，是一件可喜的事。如果抱着得到额外回报的心思做事，通常都会大失所望，还不如当初就不去做，因为事后的抱怨会极大地伤害我们自己。优秀的人，都是不抱怨的人，他们总是会把消极的想法从自己内心中扫除殆尽，让内心充满阳光、充满希望。为什么很多人过不上自己想要的生活？很大一部分原因在于抱怨使他与成功相背离。任何众生都有资格得到他们想要的东西，但前提是不要替自己找借口，需要认识到自己的不足，不四处发泄内心的不满。

　　抱怨是最消耗能量的无益举动，与其喋喋不休地去抱怨，不如静下来寻找解脱。流年似水，正是那些刻骨铭心的痛让我们懂得了珍惜生活、珍惜身边的人。生活中，被朋友戏谑或遭人误解时，过多的言辞申辩往往徒劳，此时，莫不如留下一抹微笑，给人更多遐想的空间。痛而不言是智慧，笑而不语是豁达。

别让情绪操控了你

　　往往我们控制不好情绪，一是修行不够，二是接触实际让我们产生了负面情绪。当我们的情绪受到影响时，适当的远离负面的环境，让自己平息下来，冥想一些快乐的人与事；或者来一次远行，让心胸开阔起来，再回头看之前的是是非非，一切也就释然了。很多矛盾的起因都是一些小事，不懂得退就会越搅越大！

　　人活得好不好在于心态，有没有好好活在于情绪。虽然人类不是为了情绪而活着，却始终活在情绪当中。人往往不能很好地控制情绪，尤其是那些不好的情绪，究其根本，主要是因为修行的境界还不够高。

　　情绪就像是一个不定性的孩子，虽然时时处在变化之中，但它仍然是可以掌控并管理的。管理情绪不是要去除或压制情绪，而是在觉察到情绪后，去调整它。情绪虽然有正面、负面之分，但真正的关键不在于情绪本身，而在于情绪的表达方式。用适当的方式在适当的场合中表达适当的情绪，才是情绪管理的最佳选择。

很多事或许我们无法改变，却可以改变自己看待事物的角度与方法。受到负面情绪侵蚀的时候，停下手边的事情，闭上眼睛冥想那些让我们快乐的东西；或者是做一点运动，听一些舒缓的音乐，让疲惫的身心得以放松；或者干脆做一次远足之行，去没有去过的地方，看看没有看过的风景；哪怕只是心平气和地喝一杯水，有时候也能让不好的情绪得以改观。

修行就是修心

　　没有过不去的事情，只有过不去的心情，很多事情之所以过不去，是因为心里放不下。门槛是什么？过去了是门，没过去就成了槛。可许多人就是过不去心里的槛。其实只要把心情变一下，世界就完全不一样了。修行就是修心，怎么修都是修的这颗心！

　　万物由心。
　　心存，则万物存；
　　心灭，则万物灭。

　　万法由心而起，万事由心而灭。不要对已经发生过的事情耿耿于怀，因为所有的事情都会过去，让我们感觉过不去的仅仅是过不去的心情本身。我们或许留恋一些人，或许无法忘怀一些事，但内心的喜怒哀乐、爱恨情仇只是心中所想、心中所念，归根到底都是因为心里还没有放下，无法越过横亘在心头的这道门槛。

对于阳光，如果我们想到的是炙烤和燥热，阳光将会成为不好的、需要躲避的东西；如果我们想到的是温暖，就会享受它。同一个东西，心情不同也会产生不同的结果。只要把心情转换一下，这个世界也就变得很容易接受。

很多人都问我修行是在修什么，真正的修行，不是寄希望于修行得来一个辉煌灿烂的未来，也不是要按照我们的意愿改变一切，而是为了我们的内在更加完美。修行就是修心。心，人人都有，但并非人人都识，它永远跟随你我，但很多人却常常忽视它。心是世间法，它的安乐与否决定着你人生幸福的额度。

心窄了，一切都会远

要学会调整情绪，凡事尽量往好的方面想。很多人遇到一些难以解决的事情时，就会有很多抱怨，很烦躁，结果因为把握不好情绪，往往将简单的事情复杂化，复杂的事情变得更难。当我们遇到棘手的事情时，一定要先控制好情绪，让自己能够冷静思考。并且你越往好的方面想，心就越宽；越往坏的方面想，心就越窄！

岁月本长，忙者自促；

天地本宽，卑者自隘。

恼人的雨水总是会让很多东西霉变，但若没有了雨水，就不会有茂盛的牧草，反而会酿成更大的灾难。一切都是相对而言的，缺点可能成为优点，害处也有可能转化为好处，事物本身的缺陷恰恰就是某种特色。

就像人们的情绪，一方面它是人生的调味品，但同时也是毒品，既能治病也能致病，主要是取决于我们对它的态度和方法。生气，被人们称之为坏情绪，但你知道吗，生气也有它的另一面，它使大脑的左侧被激活，而这部分常常是负责积极情绪的。对心理健康的人来说，应该是乐观多于悲观，积极多于消极，即使遭遇无常，也总是能调节自己，以饱满的精神和乐观的态度面对生活。

情绪总是由一定的刺激所引起的，当引起情绪的刺激消失之后，人的反应也应该逐渐平复。这个时候，就更加需要在认真的观察和冷静的思考中，以豁达的心态和广阔的心胸去应对，不能只看到事物的一个方面。遇到大事难事时，不要被事物表面的复杂所困扰，多往好的方面想，很多事情远没有自己想的那么糟糕，很多障碍甚至会成为我们的助力。就如同月亮的亏盈一样，凡事都有利有弊，看到事物圆满和有利的正面，你才会乐观起来。

心窄了，一切都会远。

有些错误，一生最多只能犯一次

　　我们常常会冲动地说出一些话，做出一些事。是否想过，我们的每个思想、每句话语与每个行为都已带上各自的印记——无法逃脱。若我们制造了某些不太好的事，便永远无法收回，因为它已经进入未来，并将制造一连串的作用与反应。所以，在做任何事情之前一定要慎重考虑，以免将来后悔。谨言，慎行！

　　藏区的冬天非常寒冷，藏民尤其是在大雪之后，牧区和农场的工作都会停止下来，这时有些藏民则会开始他们的另外一份工作——向导。藏区的向导不像旅游景点的导游，这是一个收入较高但风险更高的工作，来自世界各地的登山者和探险家都需要向导。一个经验最丰富也最有名气的老向导曾经对我说过：一个合格的向导，必备的品质绝对不是勇敢，而是谨慎！这个行业非常特殊，一生最多只能犯一次错误。对于不熟悉地理状况的探险家和登山者而言，向导就是他们的眼睛，哪怕向导出现一次最细微的错误，也有可能造成毁灭性的灾难。

或者是因为冲动，或者是因为心情不好，世人往往会"不假思索"地说出一些话、做出一些事，而这很可能就是一连串连锁反应的源头。说出去的话，泼出去的水。很多时候，我们也需要像谨小慎微的向导那样为人处世。着急的心，叫嗔心，是恶法，是不善。以冲动的心态去办事，多半效果不好，甚至可能办错事，将来必定后悔。人心焦躁时，双目所视、双耳所闻的人与物，都会让我们产生错误的判断。要谨记：有些错误，一生最多只能犯一次。做事要三思而行，说话切莫逞心头一时之快。

不要让内心变成野马

我们每个人的心灵，都需要一方净土。面对外面世界的浮躁与喧嚣，我们的内心时常会疲惫、会厌倦。所以，时常要给自己创造一个静的空间，思自己所思，想自己所想；或者燃一炷香，调匀呼吸，打坐禅定，将身心放空，给内心以清明。也唯有静下心来的时候，才是我们和自己贴得最近的时候。

在这个繁华而纷扰的世界里，每个人其实都需要静下心来，听一听内心深处的声音，用一双虔诚的手，缝补自己偶尔会有漏洞的生活。

万物生于静而归于静，不仅身体需要静下来，心灵也需要找到一方宁静的净土。静，不是无所作为，也不是懈怠懒惰，而是创造，不为外物所动。思自己之所思，想自己之所想，是为了真正的定下来修养心性反省自身，这是对疲惫的身心做一次常规保养。对一个禅修者而言，世间最冒险也是最不能让人心安的事情，便是冒着失去心灵永久安宁的危险去享受尘世的幸福。

放下忧虑打坐冥思，进入禅定之境界，内心空明无我无物。排除一切曾经牵着我们的鼻子让我们走上歧途的欲望，专心致志地将智慧和灵光调动起来，才能有所创造，有所成就。在冥想中筹划未来，积蓄前行的动力；在宁静中贴近自我，倾听最真实的心声，才能以博大的心胸稀释忧伤，驱散心中的困惑。

能让内心保持宁静的人，才是最有力量的。当世界上所有人都在努力奔跑的时候，记得要缓慢行走。

成熟的心智是磨炼出来的

　　心智是需要经过磨炼的。要想让自己充满智慧，就必须去体验生活，这样悟出的道理才是真理，也更容易为自己所接受。很多人不理解这一点，总是把希望寄托到外界的事物上，不好好去反思自己，总结自己，展示自己，最终却一事无成。耕好自己的心田，用自己的智慧去耕耘人生，去启发别人，从中收获生活的回馈！

　　人，如果无法在逆流中坚定方向，就只能被淹没。

　　人生的路有千万条，每个人都选择了不同的路，但是结局只有一个，所不同的是每个人走向这个结局的过程，而这个过程的不同是由人心造成的。顽铁只有被炉火反复熔炼，反复捶打，才能化为精钢。人的心智也只有被反复磨炼过，才可展现出人性的坚韧和刚强。也许不是每个人都会变得伟大，但每个人都可以成为内心强大的人。

　　用智慧的心态去面对生活，以学习的心态去体验生活，我们会发现原来生活在赋予我们苦难和艰险的时候，也带来了喜乐和强大。人生中的意外，并非不可跨越的天堑，只要我们比困难更强大，便可以冲破藩篱。所有的失败都是为成功做准备的。在艰难和失意中感悟本心，发现强大的自我，这才是生活的智慧。抱怨无法改变现状，拼搏才会有希望。

　　佛法不能代替我们去面对实实在在的困难，它只能赋予我们战胜困难的勇气。如果期望别人或者别的事物可以改变自己的窘迫境地，却没有在困境中总结经验奋发图强，看不清楚自己，不自救，到最后谁也帮不了你。

贪心的人终将一贫如洗

　　我们从出生就开始被欲望所驾驭，要做到无欲无念、超凡脱俗是很难的。我们可以有欲念，可以去满足自己，但是不能贪。不管是面对什么样的欲望，只要过了界，就是累己累心。很多时候，我们总想知道山那边是什么，克制不住欲望拼命爬，其实那边并没有什么，一旦爬上去了，才发现原来还是这边比较好。

　　欲望本身并没有善恶的属性，在正常情况下，那些基本的欲望反而可以促使我们步步向前，这就是佛常说的正欲。不是不能有欲望，而是不能过于贪婪，不能执于欲望。一旦心中的欲望超越了界限，就变成了贪婪。欲望就如同海水，喝得越多就越口渴，越口渴就想喝更多，于是形成了无解的死循环。

　　贪婪是第一大心障，无节制的贪欲让人的内心过度膨胀，让人生超载。有太多的人就是因为欲壑难填而被置于危险的境地，这方面的例子很多了。正欲过了界，就成了贪婪的逆欲，甚至可能招致灾祸，不但自己无法承受，往往还会累及他人。

贪欲并非与生俱来，它多是受后天环境的影响而逐渐累积而成。把心态放平，克制住拼命朝上攀爬的想法，不要太在意那些功利的外在，心平气和地面对人生中的每一次起伏，才会真正做到祥和超然。

贪心是最大的贫穷，贪婪者终将一贫如洗。

第三章

快乐是一种能力

痛苦与快乐同在

人生的苦与乐如同一个硬币的两面，一面是苦，一面是乐。失落时是苦，希望时是乐；经历时是苦，回味时是乐。今日以为苦之事，却为明天回味之乐。人生没有永恒的苦与乐，苦与乐常常只在人心的一瞬之间！所以，我们不要因为得到而欣喜若狂，也不要因为失去而痛苦不堪。

人生有八苦：生、老、病、死，爱别离、怨长久、求不得、放不下。唯有身心放空，方能人离难、难离身，一切灾殃化为尘。苦，只不过是因为我们还奔赴在乐的途中。

因为修养和心理状态不同，有人在最差的条件下，也能感到快乐；有人纵使在最好的环境里，也是不知足，痛苦难当。这个世界上，苦与乐常常形影相随，有时互相交替，有时互相融合。没有谁永远都是快乐的，也没有谁一生都是痛苦的。快乐时，懂得享受；痛苦时，学会化解。想过得幸福快乐，首先要把不幸和痛苦读懂。判断一个人是否能够得到幸福，其标准不是他能接收到多少别人的祝福，而在于他能否勇敢地接受自己所面临的无常。苦与乐，常常在于内心的一瞬之间。快乐与否，都取决于我们那颗不平凡的心。佛曰：我是一切根源，一切根源在我。只有当一个人心念清净时，才能感受到绝对的快乐。

心念是因，苦乐是果。无论遇到任何逆境，只要放大心量，常存慈悲、感恩和欢喜，便可以化苦为乐。

梦想成真的喜悦

　　我们的一生中什么最重要？比如，当一个人做一件好事的时候，别人考虑的可能是他这样做值不值得，这种付出有没有回报。其实，这些问题并不重要。殊不知，当一个人拥有了他想拥有的，这份开心是别人无法体会的。所以，在人生的所有事情中，没有什么比达成心愿更重要。

　　上学的时候，我每隔一段时间都要回农场去看望阿妈，帮着阿妈做一些事情。其实也帮不上多大的忙，但还是愿意去做，哪怕走很远的路，感觉也是值得的。牧区的生活很艰苦，很多孩子都没有机会读书，我不希望家乡的孩子们失去接受教育的机会，所以后来我才在家乡办了一所学校。当学校建成的那一刻，自己从心底流露出的喜悦，恐怕是其他人所不能理解的。然而，对于那些没有学上的孩子来说，那一刻，是他们开始放飞梦想的时刻；而对于我来说，那是多年心愿实现的时刻，没有什么比这更令我开心的了。

做事的时候，不要去想回报，最好的回报莫过于内心的喜悦。衡量一件事情应该不应该去做的标准，绝非"值得"或者"不值得"，而是我们内心的感受。如果这件事对别人有益，同时可以让自己得到一份温暖恬静的心境，给自己的人生增添一段可以随时驻足倾听的声音，那就放手去做吧，因为这就是我们得到的最大回报。

帮助了别人，也完成了自己的心愿，收获了喜乐和满足，这就是"值得"！

每一个有良好愿望的人的责任，就是要尽其所能，在他自己的小天地里做坚定的努力，使纯粹的人性光芒成为一种有生命的力量。

活得丰盛才不会被湮没

　　每个人都有自己的事要做,不论是开心的事,还是悲伤的事;每个人都有自己的人要遇见,不管是携手的人,还是擦肩的客。所以,不要羡慕别人的生活,不要评判别人的对错,不要计较自己的付出与收获。宠辱不惊,去留无意,只要快乐,你就什么都不缺了。

　　人生是一场无法回放的绝版电影,不管过去是辉煌还是糟糕,都已经不再停留。唯一值得拥有的,就是当下的时光。

　　人生究竟是为了什么?是为了寻找前世的因缘,还是为了某种特定的使命,还是为了各自的追求与信仰?不论答案是什么,有一点很重要,那就是活出自己,生命才有一切可能。当一个人在现实中碰到限制与捆绑时,要向自己的内在看去,这是我们随时可以取用的能量场。

世事无常，结局总是出乎意料。为了一件事情，耗费了很多时间和精力；为了一个不值得的人，付出了大半个青春……可这种种经历难道就不会成为人生中宝贵的财富吗？无须计较，也无须抱怨，荣枯无意，聚散随缘，守着一颗安静平和的心，努力让自己活得丰盛才好。

一些人在工作和生活的压力驱使下，做事都希望速成，甚至期待没有过程的成功，恨不得可以一步就从起点迈到终点，如此痴念，就如同不修行、不持戒便想直接成佛一样虚妄。没有生根发芽，如何才能开花结果？人生的精彩不是因为结果这个句号勾画得足够圆，而是在于这个句号之前的所有内容。

你拥有自己人生的选择权

　　放弃其实也是一种美，它并不代表逃避，因为这只是一种选择，是另一种美丽。生命给了我们无尽的悲欢，也给了我们选择的权利。安然一份放弃，固守一份超脱，不管红尘世俗生活如何变迁，不管选择的结果是错是对，我们虽逃避但也勇敢，虽伤感却也美丽。因为，生活本无常，前路更精彩！

　　佛法是讲因果的，一切际遇和平生所遇的事物，都是因果所致，没有谁可以改变。有些东西注定会得到，而有些东西也注定需要放弃，因为那本就不属于我们。尤其是在面对诱惑的时候，放弃会成为不得不面对的选择。

　　世事如云，变幻莫测，无常无时不在，而无常的世事正是不得不选择放弃的外在因素。生活给予世人痛苦和磨难的同时，也把选择的权利交到我们手中。放弃，并不是主动逃避，而是取舍的智慧，生命中总有一些东西是我们抓不住的，知取舍、懂进退方能有所成。如果说执着坚守是勇气的话，那么适时放弃就是魄力，就是脱离红尘喧嚣的大觉大悟。

放弃只是一种选择，同对与错没有关系。与执着地坚守相比，前者考验的是人的毅力，后者衡量的是生命的气度。危难中的船长把不必要的货物丢弃，是为了减轻船的负重，是为了迎接更大的风浪。同样放弃一些东西，不是为了停靠，而是为了更远的航行。

别和自己过不去

　　用单纯的眼光看待人生，你将少掉许多莫名的烦恼；用幸福的脚印丈量生活，你的步履会轻盈洒脱；用感恩的心去面对帮你的人，你会发现人间真的有许多无私与美好；用宽容的心去面对伤你的人，你会觉得他们其实也都不容易。人生，总有许多沟坎要跨越；岁月，总有许多遗憾要弥补；生命，总有许多迷茫要领悟。

缘合故有，
缘尽则灭。
无令疑悔，
退修善业。

弟子问师父："如何理解永远？"师父答："人人都觉得永远会

很远，其实它可能短暂得无法看见。"

弟子又问："怎样叫作脚踏实地？"师父答："只要你的脚还在地面上，就别把自己看得太轻；只要还生活在这个世上，就别把自己看得太大。"

人，只是茫茫天地中的一粒尘埃，可以微不足道到忽略不计。你我都是这天地间的匆匆过客，很多事都无法做主。很多人和物，我们越想抓牢，往往离开我们的速度越快。

凡事不必太较真、太在意。用单纯的眼光来看待人生，一切随缘随心，缘深多相聚，缘浅一笑随它去。唯如此，我们的心智才会成熟。一颗成熟的心，要像大海一般宽容，在委屈面前，一笑了之。用感恩的心去面对帮助我们的人，用宽容的心去面对伤害我们的人，多一些感激，少一些抱怨，人生的路上才会步履轻盈洒脱。我们要始终相信：人生，总有许多沟坎要跨越；岁月，总有许多遗憾要弥补；生命，总有许多迷茫要领悟。凡事缘到则聚，缘尽则散，顺其自然，无所谓得失。

你的快乐，与别人无关

　　人生的快乐在于我们对生活的态度。快乐是自己的事情，只要愿意，你可以随时调换手中的遥控器，将心灵的视窗调整到快乐频道。持续的快乐来自内心深处的精神快乐，我们之所以生活得比较愉快，是因为我们学会了放大美好。学会快乐，即使难过时，也要微笑着面对。

　　在所有表达祝福的语句中，"快乐"应该是使用频率最高的一个词。但究竟什么才是快乐呢？快乐是一种感受，它是精神层面反映到现实世界的感受，不能用物质来衡量。在绝大多数情况下，快乐与否，同外部环境没有必然的联系。每一个人都有一些只属于自己的东西，没有必要一味地瞧着别人的财富与地位而羡慕不已。真正的快乐，与金钱和其他外在的评判准则无关，因为快乐是内心的律动，来自我们对自身所拥有物的满足，来自对生命的依恋。只要你愿意，随时随地都可以快乐起来。

　　每个人都是生命的主角，是喜剧还是悲剧，决定权在我们自己手中。学会快乐，即使难过，即使现在的你并不容易，也要保持一颗积极的、快乐的心，微笑着面对生活。快乐源于每天的好感觉，把每一天过好即是幸福。如果总是忧虑明天的风险，总抹不去昨天的阴影，今天的生活怎能快乐？总攀比那些不可攀比的，总幻想那些不能实现的，今天的心灵怎能安静？任何不切实际的东西，都是痛苦之源，生命的最大杀手是忧愁和焦虑。痛苦源于不充实，生活充实就不会胡思乱想！

没有不幸福的人，
只有不肯快乐的心

　　我们应该学会在自我满足中找到快乐。怀疑自我是人性的一大弱点，怀疑自我的人常常无法集中精力做事，更不可能做好一件事。他们很难摆脱失望情绪的纠缠，自然很难得到快乐。其实，世上没有不幸福的人，只有不肯快乐的心。

　　曾经有个很苦恼的信徒向我倾诉，说这段时间运气很不好，无论做什么都不成，不管怎么做都是错，于是他怀疑自己原本就不是那块材料。我笑着告诉他，不要总是否定自己，应该在做事情的过程中找到自信，而不是哀叹命运的不幸，更不能被动地等待"转运"。命运有时会和人开玩笑，甚至会搞出一些恶作剧。人生中需要不断地自我反省，而不是自我怀疑。不断地怀疑自己，会让我们无法集中精神，做错事就在所难免。对于出现在岁月之歌当中的那些不协调的音符，应该用勇气和智慧去消弭掉。真正能让转变出现的不是命运，而是我们自身的开悟。

在忐忑中怀疑自我、否定自我是人性的弱点。如果连自己都不信任了，那还有什么值得信任呢？人，可以虚怀若谷，可以沉默寡言，可以低调行事，但绝对不可以不自信。不要因为自己已经很努力了，却依旧没有成功而感到沮丧、失望，要始终相信，有失必有得，上天赐予我们的不会太多，也不会太少。世上没有不幸福的人，只有不肯快乐的心。

给予，永远比索取快乐

　　当他人忧伤、困惑时，请给予一份亲切的抚慰；当他人遇挫、失意时，请给予一个真诚的鼓励；当他人成功、顺意时，请给予一声由衷的喝彩。为别人的心添一份温馨，也使自己的心收获一份快乐！很多时候，给予，不是取决于我们给了多少，而是取决于我们在给予的过程中投入了多少爱！给予，永远比索取快乐！

　　劝人向善是佛教一直以来的根本，所以我们做了很多善事，给贫穷的人们送过生活物资，给艰难中的孩子送过学习用具。给予的人总是很快乐的。有些人也有善念，却很少把善念化为实实在在的善举，究其原因，无非是"能力不足"。

　　给予是一个动词，真正的意义不在于这个动词的后缀，而在于这个动词的本身。在很多时候，给予不一定需要大量的物质作为修饰，一次及时的搀扶、一个鼓励的眼神、一句关切的话语，都是慷慨的馈赠。只要能让需要帮助的人感受到关心、温暖和宽慰，给予的意义就已经实现了，而自己的内心也会收获一份快乐。

给予别人并不在于我们付出了多少物质，而在于我们献出了多少爱心。爱心到了，给予的目的也就实现了。

在别人成功时送上一声喝彩，在别人失意时送去一句鼓励，都会让别人快乐，也会让自己快乐，这就是给予的本质。给予和能力无关，为灾区屡次捐款的乞丐，身上闪耀着比所有人都灿烂的光芒。给予，永远比索取更快乐。

消化痛苦的能力
决定你的快乐指数

　　人生中，快乐带给我们愉悦，痛苦带给我们回味。真正的快乐，我们很难记起，但痛苦却往往难以忘却。既然痛苦不可避免，我们又无法抗拒，为什么不学会面带微笑应对痛苦的来临呢？时间会告别过去，痛苦会告别回忆，学会接受，学会忍受，学会珍惜，这样的人生将会更加美丽。平和的心态，胜于一切！

　　岁月总是不经意间悄无声息地流逝，曾经的成功与失败，曾经的奋进与收获，终将成为过去式，留给人们的只是或愉悦或痛苦的回忆，以及在回忆中产生的对生活的感悟。人生原本就是这样的，由不得我们有太多的选择，可以任意选择的是面对所有这一切的心态。

　　在所有曾经的过往中，那些快乐的、愉悦的总是会随着时间而变得越来越模糊，甚至很难记起，而那些伤和痛会深深地埋藏在心底，长久地伴随我们，因此，一个人的幸福指数的高低取决于他处理消化伤痛的能力。面对痛苦之时，是伤痛欲绝还是微笑应对，很大程度上决定了我们人生道路上的天气。当生命把如花一般的笑容绽放在心头，照耀在我们身上的也将是温暖的阳光。

人都是哭着来到这个世界上的，而笑是后来才学会的。可以说忧伤是一种低级的本能，而快乐才是难能可贵的高级能力。把周围的人看作恶魔，我们生活的地方便是地狱；把周围的人看作天使，我们才能走进天堂。所有的一切终将过去，所有的一切也终将到来。一颗平和之心，可以造就无量功德。

不要用别人的错误
来惩罚自己

　　我们之所以不快乐，大都是因为不自觉地让别人控制了自己的心情。也许只是一件小事、一句话，就令自己很生气。一个真正懂得快乐的人，是不会拿别人的错误来惩罚自己的，他会将快乐掌握在自己手中。活着已经很不容易了，放下执着，碰到烦恼的事尽量绕道行，当快乐来临时就尽情拥抱它吧。愿你快乐！

　　忍得一时之气，
　　免得百日之忧。

　　遭到误解或者无端责难之时，生气会成为常人最"自然"的反应，很多人觉得："我还没有开悟到佛的境地，没有佛的心胸，所以我生气，这是无可厚非的。"

虽说不是每一个人都有佛的境界，但可以换一个角度去看待。你生气、愤怒的时候，已经自觉不自觉地被外界的人和事控制了情绪，随便一句不顺心的话，或者是一件微不足道的小事，就让你愤怒地失去了自我控制能力，这岂不是得不偿失？

生气就是用别人的错误来惩罚自己。生活当中免不了遇到朋友之间磕磕碰碰，争论几句，怒从中来，互相攻击，到最后伤害的还是自己；工作之时遇到同事没有做好，惹得你怒火如涛，声色俱厉，其实还是自己没有控制好情绪，更不可能从根本上解决问题。

很多事情未必要争吵、生气才能解决，既然错误不在我们，而在他人，那我们为什么要生气呢？别人犯了错，自己却生闷气，用别人的错误来惩罚自己，始终不是智者该有的心态。

放下气恼，放下计较，人才会活得精彩。遇到矛盾，要理智地去克服，不要钻牛角尖，不要为难自己。

在生活中寻到生命的价值

　　幸福是用来感觉的，而不是用来比较的；生活是用来经营的，而不是用来计较的；感情是用来维系的，而不是用来考验的；爱人是用来疼爱的，而不是用来伤害的。幸福的人总在营造好心情，快乐的人总在找寻好心情，智慧的人总是在传播好心情，觉悟的人总是在制造好心情。生命的价值在于你怎样勇敢地活着！

　　幸福是什么？其实这是一个见仁见智的问题。幸福是对生活本身的感悟和品味，可以是温暖，可以是宽容，可以是感激。每个人都有独属于自己的幸福，因为是独属，所以不能拿来比较。比较你的幸福多一点还是我的幸福多一点，这本身就是一个伪命题。幸福的人总是生活在阳光中，总是可以感觉到温暖，总是有非常好的心情，并且善于把快乐传播到四方。

当挫折降临在自己的头上时，不管苦有多大，都别让人生因此而停滞，只有顶着风雨勇敢熬过来的人，才能承担更大的责任。每个人都要勇敢，勇敢的意义就在于对幸福、对生命的执守，即使自己已经变成一捧泥土，也要把它铺在通往真理的大道上，让别人大踏步地冲过去。

幸福不是我们的房子有多大，而是房子里有多少欢乐的笑声；幸福不是我们开的车子有多么豪华，而是能不能平安顺利地到达目的地；幸福不是我们的爱人有多么漂亮，而是爱人的脸上有多少满足的笑容。

生命的意义在于感受，生命的价值在于我们怎样勇敢地去追寻这种感受。

内心充实，人生才能完整

　　一个心胸开阔的人，能够正确地看待自身与他人的差别。他既不会自轻自贱，把任何人都看得比自己优越；也不会盲目自信，无谓地贬低他人。他没有时间幸灾乐祸，没有时间评论别人，他只是忙于自己所追求的事业与生活。他不会计较在每件事情上是否公平，他在乎的是自己的内心是否快乐与充实。你是这样的吗？

　　偶尔听到一些信徒说起自己的烦恼，无非是"我怎么样""别人怎么样"。佛教把世界分为"人"和"我"，其实只是一个内心世界和外部环境的区分，而不是去强调自身和别人的种种差异。总是强调这种差异，就是没有开悟的缘故。任何一个拥有了智慧灵光的人，都可以正确看待"我"与"人"的差别，做一个心胸开阔的人，不把别人看得比自己更加优越，也不盲目而又无来由地拿自己的长处和他人的短板对比，也就不会轻视他人。

生活中的强者，总是埋头奋进在自己的道路上，根本就没有闲暇时间去品评别人。斤斤计较每一件细微的小事，试图在其中寻找出"不公"的蛛丝马迹，这是对自己生命的无端浪费。

把每一天都当作一个值得享受、值得追求的日子，时时刻刻审视内心是否充实，是否因为这种充实而快乐。走好每一天该走的路，做好每一天该做的事。不轻贱自己，也不贬低他人，在每一个日出日落间活出真实的自我，埋首于自己认为对的事情，努力让自己的生命充实，努力让自己的人生丰富多彩，用心感受生命的快乐，正确对待"我"与"人"的差别……这样的人生，才算完整。

世间所有美好都在于心

　　每天见很多人，说的大都是不快乐的事。事业成功的说压力大，工作清闲的说没前途，没有结婚的说怎么还遇不到合适的人，结婚的却说遇到的人不适合自己。幸福像皮球一样被踢来踢去，烦恼却像宝贝一样谁都不肯撒手。我们往往以为通过外界的满足才能使自己快乐，其实，真正的快乐是需要通过内心来寻找的。

　　快乐不会隐匿自己的踪迹，之所以难以找到快乐，是因为真正的快乐都是内在的。它只有在人类的心灵中才能被发现。真正的快乐不受外界环境的影响。

　　无论我们是什么人，或是我们拥有什么，只要改变自己内心的想法，世界便将因你而改变。幸福快乐不是一个结局，而是一个方向，没有终点，只要一直往那个方向走，不回头，每个人都可以领受这世界最美的恩赐。

那些找不到自我的人，往往总是在仰望别人的幸福，从来不去思量自己究竟有什么，而是每天都在问自己"我还没有什么"。知足才能常乐，世间有太多需要追逐的事物，而这些事物往往不会全都属于我们，我们也不可能得到世间所有的美好。

不快乐的原因，就是自己内心的平静发生了动荡，迫使自己去追寻不可能得到的东西。要想发现快乐，必须让心中的浮躁不安消失，不和别人攀比，找准自己的目标，做自己喜欢的事，从内心去寻找。

看破才能放下

　　出现误会时，聪明的人会放弃解释，因为敌人不信你的解释，朋友无需你的解释。也许，天不晴有时就是因为雨没下透，下透了就好了。只要你做事，就会出错，就可能引起某些人的不满。不要因为别人的误解而伤心，他完全可以有他的看法，这是他的自由，与你无关。只要你尽心了，就看破放下，赶路要紧。

　　当年净空法师问章嘉活佛什么是学佛的秘诀时，章嘉活佛答曰："看破放下。"短短的四个字，却将所有的道理说明白了。可我要说的也是，不管是学佛还是生活，一定要懂得这四个字，不然，我们的人生会过得很苦。一直执着于虚幻，就会在虚幻的生死里无休止地轮回。

　　红尘看破了不过是浮沉，生命看破了不过是无常。生活原来没有烦恼，当我们总是试图解释清楚一切的时候，烦恼也许就会找上门来；生活原本也没有痛苦，当我们开始计较得失、贪求更多时，痛苦便紧随我们了。有人活了一辈子都不明白什么才算是有意义的事情，很多人以为自己在这万物中显得太过渺小，根本就干不了什么惊天动地的大事。其实我想说的是，一件事有没有意义，并不在于事情本身的大小。不要因为这件事很小，就不去做了。

放不下的不是事物，而是本心的执守。一切看不破放不下的，终究会归于乌有。亲情也好，事业也好，爱情也罢，都逃不掉这个规律。路在前方，我们不可能为一件事情停留太久，而忘记赶路。

带着微笑行走

快乐的人不是没有痛苦，而是不会被痛苦所左右。人生难免会和痛苦不期而遇，其实痛苦并不可怕，可怕的是我们的内心背叛我们自己，成为痛苦的帮凶。整理一下自己的心情，忘记那些不愉快的事，听听音乐，看看风景，说能说的话，做可做的事，走该走的路，见想见的人。带上微笑，和快乐一起出发！

世界上快乐的人有很多，他们之所以快乐，并不是没有痛苦，而是不会被痛苦掌控。

那些不可计数的坎坷与艰难，带给人痛苦，但也给人以磨砺和洗礼的机会。在很多情况下，痛苦反而是成功的前提条件。痛苦并不可怕，真正可怕的是被痛苦打倒在地，在煎熬中向痛苦臣服。要想不被痛苦打败，我们需要调整自己的心态，不要让那些凌乱的琐事牵绊自己的脚步，影响自己的情绪。忘记那些不愉快的人和事情，听一听想听的音乐，看一看想看的人。要想在如火一般的痛苦世界中快乐地生活、成长，就应该忽略一些应该忽略的东西，做自己可以做到的事情，简简单单地存在。

做一件事，爱一个人，心总会有所期待，期待一种自己喜欢的结局。可现实有时很残酷，经常偏离预想的轨道，让我们在期望中失望。世人常常以为结果是最重要的，可有时它仅仅是事物的收尾方式罢了，更多的幸福与快乐是存在于前行路上的，而在终点迎接我们的任何结果，都应坦然接受。

摊开你的双手

　　我们越执着，对自己的伤害越大。如果我们不执着于快乐，快乐自然而然就来了；如果我们不逃避痛苦，痛苦自然而然就远了；如果我们不沉迷于欲望，压力自然而然就小了。心放平了，一切都会风平浪静；心放正了，一切都会一帆风顺；心放下了，快乐与幸福也就随之而来了。

　　如果你感到困惑，请摊开你的双手。虽然什么都没有，但什么也都有。我们的思想在手纹中延展，我们的希望在指尖上蔓延，我们的经历被印刻在厚厚的茧上。人在一无所有的时候，才能真正知道自己的财富到底有多少。真正放下了包袱，不再执着于对欲望的追逐，快乐才会顺理成章地到来。人们所感受到的压力与痛苦，大多是因为沉迷在欲望之中，执着于追求。把执着放下，一切都会平息。

累与不累，完全取决于我们自己。放下，对于很多人来说很难，难的是你一直在为难自己，总是试图抓得更紧而无法放开双手。当我们真正摊开握紧的拳头，看看手心中究竟抓住了什么的时候，一定会有所领悟，握紧的双手再也不可能抓住别的东西，而放开双手却可以得到整个世界。

如果有一天，你失去了心爱之物，请打开你的双手。如果左手是过去，右手是未来，那么合在一起就是现在，而我们便在这一开一合中存在。当一切尘埃落定，当一切旧事回放，当一切归于平静，才会真正懂得放下执着的深层意义，其实那才是一种厚实广博的丰硕收获。

第四章

幸福是一种独特的属性

幸福从不偏爱任何人

　　有的人本来很幸福，看起来却很烦恼；有的人本来该烦恼，看起来却很幸福。很多人都会认为幸福总围绕在别人身边，烦恼总纠缠在自己心里，其实常常看到的景象却是：当你仰望和羡慕别人的幸福时，一回头，却发现自己正被别人仰望和羡慕着。所以每个人都是幸福的，不要老觉得自己不幸福，要有一颗感恩的心！

　　鞋穿在脚上，
　　舒服不舒服只有自己知道。

　　有人问我："对于地位和财富的追求是不是一种错误？是不是就不能得到幸福？"我告诉他："对于地位和财富的追求并没有错，错的是不能直接把这些东西当作幸福本身。"财富、地位其实都是一种实体的具现，本身不能和幸福画等号。那些东西只是能引发幸福感的一种因缘，因为幸福不是一个固定的实体，而是一种内心的感受。得到财富和地位固然会引发幸福的感受，但得到这些东西的人并不全都是幸福的。究其根本，这就是一个白马与马的问题。

在物质文明高度发达的今日，充分享受物质生活，却依然感觉不到幸福的人比比皆是，这就是因为没有弄清楚幸福的实质，没有弄明白幸福到底是物质的还是精神的，而陷入一种盲目的状态。有些人具备了幸福的属性，但是看起来似乎并没有那么幸福；而有些人本应该是烦恼的，但给人的感觉却是他很幸福。之所以会出现这种现象，就是因为幸福具有无数种属性，不同的人对于幸福的理解也完全不同，而不同的人生又可以对应不同的幸福。有些人喜欢在险象环生、风高浪急的潮头打拼，在风险和机遇的碰撞中感受幸福；有些人喜欢追求超越，认为领先才是幸福；但也有些人生性恬淡，喜欢悠然宁静的生活，认为清心寡欲、平安祥和才是幸福。幸福可以是激烈伟大的，也可以是朴实平凡的，不同的人有属于自己的幸福，甚至同一个人在不同的人生阶段也会对幸福有不一样的理解。很多时候，我们的烦恼就是别人的幸福。

生命不能透支

　　我们要经常整理一下自己的生活，看看哪些是我们已拥有却常常忽视的，哪些是我们得不到却一直苦苦追寻的。那些被我们忽视的一旦失去，会不会令我们追悔？那些苦苦求来的一旦拥有，是否真的值得去珍惜？思考过后，或许你就会明白你现在正在做的是什么，有没有选择了错误的方向。及时调整，幸福就会来敲门！

感到自己是人们所需要的和亲近的人，
这是生活最大的享受、最高的喜悦。

　　很多人踏入社会之后，往往会主动与单纯划清界限，以此来应对多变的社会，可社会真的很复杂吗？不是的。复杂，只是我们的所想。心若单纯，世界又怎么会不澄清？！

　　人应该有所追求，但绝对不应该追求所有，总有些东西是要做出取舍的。我们应该静下心来好好地审视一遍自己，看看是不是忽视了一些曾经拥有的。生命中有太多的美好，但总有些东西不值得我们放弃健康、透支生命去追逐，比如金钱、权势；总有些东西一旦失去，定然会让人扼腕而叹、追悔莫及，比如说你的亲人和你的爱人。如果你忽略了这些宝贵的东西，那就不是在追寻幸福，而是被幸福所负累。

　　如果一个人所追求的事物不值得他永远珍惜，那他就不是在追寻幸福，而是在追寻虚荣。如果你追寻的方向出现了偏差或者干脆就是错误的，就应该及时准确地做出调整。只有方向对了，目标才不会出错，幸福才会来敲你的门。

淡定是幸福的『新娘』

　　走过的路长了，遇见的人多了，经历的事杂了，不经意间我们会发现，人生最曼妙的风景是内心的淡定与从容、头脑的睿智与清醒。人生最奢侈的是拥有一颗不老的童心、一个生生不息的信念、一个健康的身体、一个永远牵手的爱人、一个自由的心态、一份喜欢的工作、一份安稳的睡眠、一份享受生活的美丽心情。

　　关于"幸福是什么"的问题已经被提起过无数次，其实这是一个仁者见仁、智者见智的问题。因为幸福从来就没有标准的答案，也没有可以作为参考的标志物。

　　当自身犯了错误给别人带来伤害的时候，得到一个谅解而又释然的微笑；前途无路时忽然柳暗花明；远足之际聆听亲人的反复叮咛；健康的体魄、智慧而又清醒的头脑、自由自在的心态……所有的这一切都是幸福最直接的表现形式。世间有千万人，幸福就有千万种。

不过很多身在幸福中的人却不自知，在失望、浮躁和焦虑中主动远离幸福，更有人把堆砌金钱当作幸福，把成为名利的俘虏作为向往和追求，岂不知自己在纸醉金迷中浪费生命、感叹幸福难觅之时，那些贫困山区的孩子还在为一本字典、一个书包而苦恼。在我给山区的孩子们送去书包的时候，至少我是幸福的，孩子们也是幸福的。从某种程度上来说，帮助别人不仅仅是一种布施，也是自我收益的举动。

如果你还要再一次问我幸福是什么、幸福在哪里，那我只能告诉你，天地间的一切都是幸福的源泉，幸福就在你我心里，幸福就在你我的生活当中。当我们把手里的幸福给予别人的时候，我们会更加幸福。

别给自己的冷漠找理由

　　当我们心中有佛时，所见的都是光明，所说的都是善良；当我们心中有魔时，所见的都是黑暗，所说的都是邪恶。如果我们对这个世界充满了怨气，那么这个世界怎么可能给予我们快乐与幸福？所以，不要给自己的冷漠找理由。不管有多少障碍，也应该坚持我们善良的本初；不管有多么无奈，也应该敞开我们宽容的胸怀！

　　关于人性本善还是人性本恶的争论已经延续了千百年，在可以预知的未来还会继续延续下去。有信徒问起我对此的看法，我更倾向于：人性本是洁白如纸，在上面涂画了什么就是什么。在人性的纸上留下了善，那就是善；留下了恶，那就是恶。关键在于后天培养，这也正是世人需要修行的原因之一。心中有佛，整个世界就都是佛光普照，所见皆是光明，所闻皆是善良；若心中存魔，所见所闻当然会是黑暗和邪恶的。

若我们的心里始终存留着对世界的怨气，则这种怨气会给自己的目光涂抹上带有怨恨属性的色彩。戴上有色眼镜，看到的一切都是扭曲变形的，那么这个世界反馈给我们的绝对不可能是喜乐和幸福。找不到喜乐，得不到幸福，并非是因为世界上根本就不存在这两种东西，而是我们的目光已经看不到它们了。

用热情的目光、积极的心态去看待整个世界，用美好的心去迎接所有的一切，所得到的必然是美好和幸福。不要用一个个客观或者主观的借口来遮掩内心中的冷漠，不管遇到什么样的障碍艰难，都要坚守住最本初的善良；不管世界留给我们的是无奈还是艰难，都要敞开心胸以广阔的胸襟去接受，然后才能愉快地与这个世界和平相处。

心是幸福的温度计

　　有的人对幸福熟视无睹，有的人对幸福习以为常，有的人对幸福梦寐以求，有的人对幸福求之不得……幸福是我们每个人永不疲倦的追求。只要不把幸福的期望值提得高不可及，只要不把自己的幸福建立在别人的痛苦之上，以一种平常的心态求之，就会发现：幸福，其实就在俯仰之间；幸福，其实就在你我身旁。

　　小时候，幸福是一件东西，得到了，就是幸福；长大了，幸福是一个目标，达到了，就是幸福；成熟后，幸福是一种心态，领会了，就是幸福。幸福就在当下，只有一个个当下串成的幸福，才是一生一世的幸福。

　　对幸福的期待值过高，想要收获世间所有的美好，追寻幸福的心就变成了永远都不能填满的欲壑，我们不仅无法体会满足的快乐，还会超负荷地负重，最终与幸福分道扬镳。

保持平和的心态，才会得到满足。喝下一杯水可以解渴，又何必强求一壶？不能把幸福指数无限拔高，也不能把自己的幸福建立在别人的痛苦之上。当我们内心平静、心态平和之时，会惊喜地发现，幸福就在自己眼前触手可及的地方。

幸福，是近在咫尺俯仰可得，还是远在天涯永不能接近，取决于我们以什么样的心态来期待幸福的到来。心永远都是幸福的温度计。

轻易得到的幸福没味道

　　许多人都在刻意追求所谓的幸福，有的虽然得到了，却付出了很大的代价。智者说：幸福是种感觉，就如同"佛"在你我心中。幸福的感觉随满足程度而递减，与人的心境、心态相关。得之愈艰，爱之愈深。拥有幸福，常思艰难。一个人总是感觉不到幸福，是自己最大的悲哀。幸福是种感觉，不知足，永不会幸福！

　　苦难如同惊雷，总是带着轰轰烈烈的威势让人猝不及防；而幸福就好像春雨，经常是以润物细无声的方式出现。幸福就好像照耀荒原的月光，就如同拂过水面的微风，虽然可以感觉到，却又抓不住。

　　幸福的多少往往与一个人对幸福的敏感度相关，若一个人比较容易满足，幸福感就会十分强烈；要是很少知足，或者根本就不可能被满足，即便已经得到了幸福，感觉也不明显。只有知足的人，才更容易觉察到幸福的临近。幸福的距离，有时近，有时远，以为就在咫尺，转眼间却还在天涯。平静的生活就像一杯白开水，喝起来淡而无味，却不知道正是它的纯净无瑕才让人的生命更有容量，也只有懂得生活的人，才会在这份平淡中品出甘甜和幸福的滋味。

幸福的"大"与"小"，幸福的"多"与"少"，取决于人的心态。苦苦寻觅，经历千万艰险、付出很多努力之后才得到的幸福，就好像经历过日晒风吹的果实那样分外甘甜；轻易得到的幸福，就好像过早成熟的果子，就算嚼在嘴里也不会有什么味道。一个内心麻木、感觉不到幸福存在的人，将是最可悲的。

莫让错过变成过错

　　当遇到合适的人，彼此可以融洽地生活，不管这生活简单也好，复杂也好，只要快乐轻松，就不要犹豫，赶紧抓住它并珍惜。因为，犹豫之间，它就有可能成为别人的幸福，最后令自己追悔。不要贪图物质的享受，也不要贪图精神的高尚，世间没有十全十美的人，也没有十全十美的生活。贫贱富贵，舒心就好！

　　在对的时间遇到错的人，注定是一场心伤；在错的时间遇到错的人，最多只是一场荒唐。所以，若是在对的时间遇到了合适的人，一定要万般珍惜。只要意气相投、彼此契合，只要快乐和睦，不管生活是简单还是复杂、清贫还是富足，都应该知足。

　　千万个善果才有一次相遇的机会，不要在意物质上的贫乏与丰足，也不要贪图外在的音容。日月尚有圆缺，人又怎会完美？如果我们总是放大他人的过错，终究有一天会把过错演变成错过。别把彼此的伤害当作是某种壮举，到了那个时候，除了追悔莫及，可能你什么都做不了。美好的风景，如果没有人与自己分享，一样会了无生趣。过错可以纠正，但是错过就只能是遗憾。

彼此相爱，是世间最大的因缘。它是那么简单，又是那么艰难，不要过于天真，总是幻想前方还有更好的爱情在等待。即使有，也不一定就属于你，或许那只是擦肩而过的缘分，不值得如此执着。

心冷了，一切都会遥远

　　有的人你可能认识了一辈子，却忽视了一辈子；有的人你也许只见了一面，却影响了一生；有的人默默地守在你身边，为你付出，却被冷落；有的人无心的一个表情，却成了你永恒的牵挂……我们常常是努力追求未得到的，而遗忘了已拥有的。不要向远方寻找幸福，它也许就在你的手中，你只要安然握住。

　　在很多人的心目中，爱情和幸福都是非常遥远的事物，远得如同天上冷月，只能远远地看到，却无法触及。在这里我想说的是：爱情不遥，幸福也不远，远的是对于幸福的冷落和忽略。生活中，有些人会陪伴我们一辈子，一直到终老，却常常被忽视；有的人与我们只是萍水相逢，却可以影响我们的一生，甚至一个无心的问候也会成为长久的牵挂。这就是因为我们总是习惯于把眼光投向遥远之处，而没有珍惜近在咫尺的珍宝。前方或许有更加美丽的存在，但它可能是毒药。

人生就像难驯的野马，总是带着狂乱的气息向前狂奔，茫然不知地看着远方模糊的风光。

因为"得不到"，所以才"更宝贵"，这是人性中的弱点，所以人们总是奋力争取那些还没有得到的东西。殊不知，伴随你走过漫漫人生长路的幸福已经拥有了，只不过被你忽视被你遗忘了。

不要总是犯骑着快马追逐快马的错误。

难得平常心

　　不管我们在尘世中处于什么样的位置，有钱或没钱，有名或没名，生活对于每个人都是一样的，都离不开柴米油盐酱醋茶，都得在同一片天下，呼吸着同样的空气。人生无常，有时起，有时落，不论处于怎样的状态，都要用平常的心去包容生活，用感恩的心去拥抱幸福。当我们心里想着幸福，幸福就不会远了！

在财富、权力、荣誉和独占的爱当中去探求幸福，

不但不会得到，

反而还会失去。

　　在凡尘俗世当中，人们以占有物质的多寡区分出富人和穷人，以地位和权势的高下人为地分出高贵和低贱。但是真正的贫穷和富

有，在于内心丰盈与否，而不在于金钱、地位的拥有程度。在佛的面前，穿着黄金打造的盛装的人，和赤身裸体的人是平等的。

不管是富可敌国也好，还是身无分文也罢，名动天下或者是籍籍无名，对于生活本身而言，都是一样的，没有任何分别。无论一个人有多少金钱、有多少物质，终究离不开最基本的生活所需。哪怕他占据了广阔的陆地和海洋，在去往净土的路上，也只能占据身体那么大的一块地方。

不管在俗世中拥有多少财富，处于多么高的地位，都同在阳光的照耀之下，呼吸着一模一样的空气。人生无常，世事多变，拥有的身外之物终究会失去，高高在上的地位也不是永恒的，起起伏伏本就是人生的基本状态。看开一些，看淡一些，不管现实生活中的我们是什么样子，都要用平和的心态去接受。

不再被俗世中的财富、地位所负累，以平常心待物，才是人生中最富有的时刻。

超然物外，心无挂碍

　　我们是负荷前行的，总觉得人生苦短，春天难留。背着重重的行囊，我们一路都在喘息，何曾在意身边的风光？其实，那偌大的行囊中，有很多是可以摒弃的，如那些世俗的偏见、物欲的躁动、追逐的劳累、取舍的烦忧。超然物外是境界，只要身上无疾病，心中无块垒，我们就会发现，生活原本如此美好、轻松！

　　人们总是习惯于带上不达目的绝不罢休的执着去追逐梦想，总是把永远都无法填满的欲壑横亘在现实与梦想的中间。身上背着沉重的包袱，又怎么可能飞跃？疲惫的身躯，又如何能生出自在之心？即便在筋疲力尽的状态下到达目的地，也会丢失太多值得珍惜、值得品味的东西。

　　其实你背负着的那个行囊本没有必要那么沉重，其中所装载着的东西有很多是完全可以摒弃的。浮躁让心无法灵动，世俗的偏见让人失去平和与从容，取舍间的犹豫、得失时的忐忑……都是可以放下的。人生的幸福和烦恼是等量的，老天给予每个人同样多的幸福，就看我们能感受到多少。抛下那些阻碍我们前进的东西，轻装上路，才能达到超然物外的心境。

行走在人生道路之上，其实没有必要携带太多，只要身体健朗、精神充盈，就已经足够，其他都不是必需的。人生能走多远，完全要看包袱的大小。

人生需要目的地

　　欲望太多会增添烦恼，可并非只有无欲无求才能幸福。有一个明确的能带来快乐和意义的目标，然后努力去追求，只有这样，才会给你带来真正持续的幸福感。因为，幸福不是拼命爬到山顶，也不是在山下漫无目的地游荡，幸福是向山顶攀登途中的种种经历和感受。

　　佛说众生皆苦，是因为人们有太多与自身不相符合的欲望，而欲望正是一切烦恼的根源。无欲无求固然是大自在的境界，但很难到达。追求幸福的过程，为了不迷路，就非常需要一个指引前进、确保方向始终如一的灯塔——目标。在不可预知的前进道路上，目标如同灯塔一样在远处显示着航向。

　　离目标越近，心里就会越踏实。生命可以安于途中，但不是说就不需要一个目标。毫无目的的人生与一只无头苍蝇又有何异？目标的确立，让欲望不至于肆意放纵，这是一个非常智慧的选择。在拉近与目标的距离的过程中，最重要的是要把握好速度和尺度，控制好节奏。越过一个又一个障碍，可以极大地锻炼自我的身心，收获更多满足和喜乐。

无论我们的目标是远还是近，有没有最终到达，只要走得坚定、执着、安然，就已经是胜利者了。

与美好不期而遇

生命是一种缘，你刻意追求的东西也许终生得不到，而你不曾期遇的灿烂，反而会在你的淡泊从容中不期而至。我们马不停蹄地寻找幸福，蓦然回首，幸福其实就在身边，我们需要做的是停下来，慢慢感受。一生中，想要追求的东西太多了。殊不知，有舍才有得，这是一种智慧，而我们更需要这样一份心境。

不幸的源头，
总有一桩意外。
幸福的起点，
总是发生巧合。

世间的所有痛苦和喜乐都是因缘相互作用的结果。缘从来都不会凭空出现或者消失，只有前因，才能有后缘，而追求只是在因和缘的过程中行走而已。生命本身就是一种缘分的载体。人们费尽千辛万苦所追求的东西并不一定就可以得到，因为追求和得到的中间不存在必然的因缘联系。

当我们手持淡泊的花朵，以从容的心态面对最终的结果之时，反而会和预料之外的美好不期而遇。这看似是一桩巧合，但每个巧合都不是只发生一次的偶然，每个偶然的背后都有必然的影子。

奇迹时时刻刻都在发生，不需要刻意期待，也无须祈求。美好的人和事总会和我们不期而遇，不过这需要我们在挥汗如雨的工作或生活中，不失时机地抬头或者回望。

放缓脚步，别走得太匆忙，舍掉遥不可及的奢望，抓住现在所拥有的。对自己负责，这不仅仅是生活中历练出来的智慧，也是内心浮躁者最好的镇静剂。

停下匆匆的脚步，用心看看这个世界。

得把自己活开了

　　很多时候我们的痛苦来源于不甘心，不甘心为什么自己付出了这么多，得到的却不是自己想要的。于是时常沉迷在这份痛苦中，越想得到更多，得到的却是越多的失落，这样的人生怎可能幸福！期望是需要的，努力也是应该的，可结果有时候却要看因缘，何必执着于最后自己得到了多少，其间的过程才是幸福！

小时候，
幸福是一件很简单的事；
成熟后，
简单是一件很幸福的事。

　　每个人都会犯错误，错误并不可怕，因为正确的结果往往是从很多个错误中总结出来的，可怕的是对于错误的坚持而不知做任何改正。在很多时候，人们坚持错误的方向或者是错误的做法，并不是因为不知道对错，而是因为不甘心，而这也是人陷入痛苦的原因之一。

现实和理想、实际和预期之间存在差异，所以事物最终的结果往往与想象的并不相同。希望越大，失望就越大；想要得到的越多，失去的也就越多。

获得幸福最大的障碍就是期待更多的幸福。

期待和希望都是需要的，付出的努力也是必需的，但事物的最终结果取决于因缘的相互作用，没有前因的情况下，付出得再多也只是徒劳无功。刻意想要得到幸福，反而常常收获失败与忧伤。不要执着于最终的结果，更不要陷在不甘心、不接受的泥潭中不可自拔，那会让我们的痛苦加倍。放下得到的执着，仔细体会追求的过程，这才是正确的抉择。

贪婪的人内心最贫穷

　　幸福的"福"字就是一件衣服一口田，告诉我们够吃够穿就好，知足者常乐。有些人通过物质上的满足换来幸福，那种幸福非常短暂；如果我们能时时刻刻微笑，拥有一颗安详的心，就会拥有永恒的幸福。佛曰：笑着面对，不去埋怨。悠然，随心，随性，随缘。注定让一生改变的，只在百年后，那一朵花开的时间。

人之所以不幸福，

不是因为拥有的太少，

而是想要的太多。

　　人们常说：生活水平提高了，幸福感觉却降低了。这是因为人们心中的欲望越来越高，想要得到的东西也越来越多，变得越来越难以满足。殊不知，依靠物质堆砌起来的幸福感受只是昙花一现，并不能持久。随着物质的减少和变更，这种幸福感会大大地减少，随之而来的痛苦便会更加凶猛。

越来越多的欲望，即便是全部都得到了满足，那也不是幸福，而是对于自我的肆意放纵。贪婪的人心中是最贫穷的，而懂得知足的人才是最富有的。

拥有安详平和的心态，从容笑看得失，淡定地面对取舍，才是大自在的境界。要微笑面对，持花而行。不要把幸福定位在那些得不到的事物上，而让最简单的幸福从我们身边溜走。只有一个人感觉到满足的时候，才会身体轻松，内心从容。

幸福的"福"字就是一件衣服一口田，简单到了极致。而你的幸福也可以同样简单明了，吃得饱、穿得暖、睡得香、走得动，足矣。

随缘、随性、随心，笑对得失，不去埋怨，则幸福久远。

沉默的美丽

　　独乐，是一个人独处时也能欢喜，因为有心灵与生命的充实；独醒，是不为众乐所迷惑的生活方式，但往往不一定适合我们。每个人都有伤心的时刻，但是每个人的伤心都会不一样。每一朵花都是安静地来到这个世界，又沉默地离开，如若我们倾听，也许会发觉，在安静中仿佛有深思，而在沉默里也似有美丽的雄辩。

　　只有当一个人独处的时候，他才可以完全成为自己，找到内心真正的平和与宁静。

　　你可能会有这样的经历，自己莫名其妙地被人误解了，或者某一天清晨醒来后，关于自己的一些谣言四起，而只有你知道，这事根本与你无关，那么你的第一反应会是什么？争辩，还是与散布谣言的人大打出手？

　　留一份沉默给自己，即使有人散布你的谣言，说了你的坏话，你也大可不必反唇相讥，歇斯底里地乱吵一通。对于一个心灵纯洁有修养的人来说，任何流言都会显得苍白无力。无论流言的影响力有多大，它也只是一块迟早要风化的石头，终究会有水落石出的那一天。智者往往是那些懂得在沉默中思考的人。

　　沉默并不是教人缄口不语，而是希望人们能深思熟虑，三思而后言。沉默之所以是金，在于它是一种难得的心理素质与可贵的处世之道。形式上的静止，并不代表思考的停滞，而是一种力量的蓄积。那些深邃的思想，皆来自那些沉默的思考过程。反之，夸夸其谈之人往往浅尝辄止，难以看清事物的本质。

慈悲无边，慈航普度

　　我们常常用慈悲为别人祈愿，常常用慈悲的心去帮助他人。当有一天我们发现别人没有丝毫改变的时候，我们还是很欣慰地告诉自己：我很努力，这个人不可救药，与我无关。殊不知，也许不是他无可救药，而是我们的慈悲心不够。

　　何为慈悲？并没有一个硬性的标准。慈悲是佛家的一种大境界，是助人为乐拯救众生的情怀，是在痛苦着别人的痛苦之时由内而外散发出来的光芒。慈悲是不必相识、不必拥有，是给予不求回报，是只有关爱没有所求。

　　常怀慈悲之心，把痛苦自己承担，把快乐与众人分享，祈愿世间美好，乐于帮助别人，并且将之视为义务。但有些时候，我们的慈悲并没有改变什么，并没有让别人放下虚妄的执着，也没有将别人从痛苦迷茫中拉出来。这个时候，很多人会用宽慰的语气告诉自己："我不是佛，也不能度尽世间众生，总有些人是无可救药的，还是算了吧。"这是懒惰和懈怠的想法，不能用慈悲感化他人，是因为我们的慈悲之心比较单薄，做得还不够。

宏法普传，佛魔同度，这才是大慈悲的境界。救可救之人，也救不可救药之人，连恶魔都能被佛法普度，还有什么人是无可救药的呢？一滴水扑不灭熊熊烈焰，一朵花也描绘不出灿烂的季节。只有付出更多的慈与悲，才能出现更多、更大的改变。当一个个小水滴汇集成江河海洋，灼人的烈焰才会熄灭。慈悲不是出于勉强，它像甘露一样从天上降下尘世；它不但给幸福于受施的人，也同样给幸福于施与的人。

第五章

人生是一场修行

拥有未必就是充盈

　　生活有时会逼迫你，不得不交出权力，不得不放走机遇，甚至不得不抛弃爱情。我们不可能什么都得到，所以，在生活中应该学会放弃。不想丢掉我们手中的东西，却又想要拿起更多的东西。拿得起就得放得下，只有放得下，才能将该拿得起的东西更好地握住，才能抓住最重要的东西，我们的人生才会更加精彩。

　　佛教总是讲布施，过去说布施更多的是精神的布施，当然这也非常重要，我们的终极目标还是精神的布施。但是现在所有的人都更关注一件事情，那就是物质，所以我们佛家必须学会与时俱进，来通过物质去布施，这件事情是非常重要的。我发起过一些慈善活动，比如"温暖玉树—雪中送炭"。那是玉树地震后的第一个春节前夕，玉树的灾民都住在救灾帐篷里，很冷，我们就号召大家为玉树灾民送温暖，每一户送一吨煤，让他们过上一个温暖的春节。后来是"情系盈江—爱心书包"，给盈江地震灾区的学生送书包和学习用具。短短的时间里，在大家的爱心传递下，四万多个灾区学生背上了新书包。确实，对于一个城市里的孩子来说，一个书包不算什么；但对于刚刚经历过大灾难，本身家庭就不算富足的孩子来说，一个书包、一个铅笔盒，也许就可以扫去他们心中的阴霾，让笑容重新在他们的脸上绽放。后来我们又做了一个叫"慈爱轮椅"的活动，我们将一万辆轮椅送到了一万户家中有残疾人的贫困家庭，在那一刻，我们看到了这个轮椅带给他们的希望。

一个有追求的人，或许一生都要奔波在路上，无论是为了生活中的必需品而忙碌，还是为了心灵的解脱而探索，都是为了获得。可我们想过没有，我们真需要两套以上的住房吗？真的需要很多辆车吗？这种数量的增加，是否就是我们心底所渴望的极乐？外物带来的只是虚假的荣耀，并不会让我们的生活更加坦然。我并不觉得一个富豪就一定会比一个穷人过得快乐。如果某种得到会伴随着心理上的不安，还不如失去的好。拥有并不一定就是幸福，失去的未必就是不快乐。很多人一生只做一件事，从结果来看，却是一种最好的选择。与一生碌碌、不可终日相比，这种一直走下去的态度是我最为推崇的。时间有着永恒的执着魔力，它会洗涤荡尽世间所有的虚无，只有经受住时间的洗礼，不改本色，人生才会历久弥香。

别把心底的美好榨干

　　人生再多的幸运，再多的不幸，都是曾经，都是过去，一
如窗外的雨，淋过，湿过，走了，远了。曾经的美好留于心底，
曾经的悲伤置于脑后，不恋，不恨。学会忘记，懂得放弃，人
生总是从告别中走向明天。悄悄告诉自己，没事的，一切皆如此，
漫漫人生，淡然对待，一切也都会过去。阳光总在风雨后。

如果不忘记许多，
人生将无法再继续。

　　有人说："师父，看到您的时候我就忘记了伤痛和苦恼。"我说：
"这是对的，人的一生太短暂，有太多不能承受的东西，记住该记
住的，忘记该忘记的。"
　　每一个人都经历了太多的苦乐悲欢，有着太多的幸与不幸。人

生就是一次长途跋涉，能够遇到什么，是无法预料的，唯有让自己的内心变得强大，才可以抵抗住世间的种种风波与诱惑。学会忘记，才能懂得放弃。世间之事，无论是美若琉璃，还是清风苦雨，都不可能成为人生的常态，告别过去，才能更好地安于当下。

人生本就是一个吐故纳新的过程。曾经的过往，就如同车窗外的风雨，不能因为惧怕被淋湿，就拒绝前行。昨天的悔恨不能解决今天或者明天的任何问题。淡然地面对曾经的失意和窘迫，不要把明日黄花当作眼前的美景，也不要让流逝在身后的云烟占据心头。

昨日的坎坷和风雨，不恨；过去的成功和美好，不恋。漫漫人生本就如此，只要淡然面对，一切都会成为过去。

得到过，失去过，彷徨过，无奈过，用淡忘的智慧让自己洒脱一点，就会看到更加美好的风光。告别经历过的坎坷和苦难，不要掩面叹息，也不必伤感挂怀，不然，就只能永远停留在昨天。

忘记花开的喜悦，忘记花落的叹息。安静，超然。

生命无常，内心柔韧

　　有些事不管我们愿意不愿意，都要发生；有些人不论我们喜欢不喜欢，都要面对。人生中遇到的所有事、所有人，都是不以我们的意志为转移的。愿意也好，不喜欢也罢，该来的都会来，该到的都会到，没有选择，没有逃避。我们能做的就是接受，就是相处，默默地做好自己的一切，用善良感染生活、感染人生。

不管是怎样的事情，都请安静地接受吧！
勇敢地、大胆地，而且永远微笑！

　　也许人生从来都不会因人的意志而有丝毫改变，愿意也好，不愿意也罢，都会毫不停留地发生。很多人觉得自己的人生境遇十之八九都是不能让人满意的，每时每刻都要面对挫折、困境和失败，其实这些都是上天对我们的考验，也是人生当中一种必然的存在，并且人都是在种种考验中从成长奔向成熟的。

接受，并不是甘于认命，而是主动以平和的心态承担起来，为将来的改变做好准备。一味地逃避，不仅会误人误己，还会失去磨炼自己的机会。很多不能让人满意的人或者事，在以不可改变的状态降临之时，这本身就是一种考验、一种磨炼。我们要学会与磨炼相处，并且渐渐习惯。

在那些大灾难中，很多勇于接受的人们，他们没有嗔恨，没有恐惧，只是默默地为明天的生活做着准备，并且以善良而又向上的心态感染着别人，照亮了人生。

佛说的"无常"是指事物不会因为个体的喜欢或者不喜欢而有丝毫改变。圆满本就是一个不断接受、不断修改、不断完善的过程。面对这些的时候，就应该勇敢地接纳，如同大海接受河流来充实自己一样。做好自己，欢喜必会源源不尽。

只笑自己看不穿

　　与我们相处最多的人其实是自己，可是多少人能正确认识自己呢？只有知道自身的优势与不足，我们才能不断地修正自己。如果我们常常以诚恳、虚心的态度听听身边朋友对自己的看法，坦然面对自身的问题并积极去改变，人生一定会简单、灿烂。问佛："世间为何多苦恼？" 佛曰："只因不识自我。"

在了解佛之前，

人，必须先了解自己。

　　佛曰："天地并生，物我为一。"但是在现实生活当中，人们很少能够正确地认识自己，也就是人们常说的难有"自知之明"。
　　对于自我认知的缺乏，更多来自人们的自卑或者自负的心理暗示，缺少了对自己的审视、发现和反省的机会，甚至时常被自己所蒙蔽。

在不断地躬身自省当中，人可以不断地修正自我，可以不断地充实自我。以真诚而又谦虚的心态，仔细聆听身边的人对"自我"的看法，感受他人对"自己"的态度，从中发现自己的不足和更多需要改进之处。坦然面对自身的种种不足，以积极主动的心态去改正，就可以通透地明白自我的意义，履行自我的责任，更好地改善自我，更好地与他人相处。

只有知道了自身的长处与不足，才能避免内心世界的膨胀和萎缩，才能得到心灵的充实和精神的进一步提升。

正确地认识自我，不仅是一种卓然的能力，是一种高尚的品德，更是一种人生的境界。

世间为何多苦恼？只因不识自我。

真正的悲哀是对自己的放纵

　　很多时候，我们一直在路上奔跑，一直在追逐那仿佛永远达不到的目标，很累很辛苦。但只要我们稍微停下来回头看看，也许会发现当初的目标早已在身后了，而且引诱我们的是不断升级的欲望。欲望就像是一条锁链，一个连着一个，永远都不可能满足。而真正可悲的是：人们永远都会为自己的欲望找到借口。

人生是只能出发一次的旅程，
我们其实一直在路上。
如果只能携带两件行李，
我愿是无畏与无执。
如果只能有一个牵挂，
那一定是众生。

　　在我的理解当中，人的一生就好像一盏酥油灯，欲望则是灯光。当灯火燃烧得太过剧烈之时，酥油就会枯竭。人的欲望，可谓千姿百态、光怪陆离。比如说人口渴了要喝水，肚子饿了要吃饭，这些都是欲望，能禁止得了吗？其实根本就不需要禁止，因为这些都是正欲。

　　正是因为有了这些正欲，才能奋发图强，才能推动事业和生活的发展，不过很少有人能做到真正的"无欲则刚"。当人们在实现了自己的目标之后，通常都不会停下脚步，而是被各种诱因所迷惑，变得不知满足，并且轻易地就能为放纵的欲望找到借口，这是非常可悲的。

　　层出不穷的欲望就是一片光怪陆离的茫茫苦海，无边无际之后才是彼岸。被过分的欲望所折磨的人，注定是不快乐的。放弃对某种欲望的追求，才能脱离苦海，才能离开滋生烦恼的土壤。

　　若能把欲望控制在合理的范围之内，不时停下追逐的脚步回头看看，就能很好地驾驭它们。

　　有所求，并求之有度，才不会迷失自我。

人生需要放手

　　其实，没有什么东西是不能放手的。曾经以为不能放手的东西，只是生命瞬间的一块跳板；所有不能放弃的事情，不过是生命里的一个过渡，你跳过了，一切就变得更精彩。人在跳板上，最痛苦的不是跳下的那一刻，而是跳下之前，心里的挣扎、犹豫、无助无法向别人倾诉，闭上眼睛，鼓起勇气，跳了，就过去了。

　　生命当中有很多东西需要坚守，也有更多的事情需要勇于放手。

　　永不放弃的坚守确实顽强，但明智的放手也并不代表懦弱，而是洞察万物规律和自身条件之后的理性选择，也是另外一种坚守。放手和坚守一样，对一个生命来说都是不可或缺的，它闪耀着理性和智慧的光芒。

　　当我们在人生之路上探索之时，会遇到岔道，若是在岔道前有太多的犹豫和不舍，则会停滞不前。很多看起来不能放手的东西，只不过是生命中的一个瞬间，是一个过渡。并不是所有人在任何时候都有放手的勇气，对曾经迷恋的果实放手，才能体验到豁达人生的独有境界。

一个人站在过渡的跳板上，在犹豫是不是该放弃之时，才是最痛苦的。因为你始终在分析利害，权衡得失。在决定是不是跳过"放手的跳板"之时，其实并没有那么艰难，只需要鼓起勇气，闭上眼睛，轻轻一跃。放手不是深渊，而是一尺之水，一带而过。对于内心的修行而言，这简简单单的一带而过就是一次飞跃。

固执地认为不能放手的东西，未必真的不能放手，不能放下的仅仅是我们内心中的挣扎和犹豫。当我们放下手中那片瑰丽的云彩之时，得到的将是蔚蓝的天空。放手是解开心灵枷锁的钥匙，经历过一次，便是一次人生的升华。放手，是大智慧，需要大勇气。

接受无常的考验

　　人生最大的勇气不是不惧怕死亡，而是坚强地活着，勇敢地面对生活带来的压力和考验！谁也没有能力去改写历史，我们要做的就是把握当下，接受生活带给我们的种种考验。时间会毫不留情地把一切毫无痕迹地带走，留给我们的只是回忆！我们无法留住自己想要的，赶走不喜欢的，我们只有学会珍惜、满足和面对。

不分别过去，
不执着未来，
不戏论现在。

　　舅舅是个修行的人，给我讲过很多修行者和菩萨的故事，并且要我不多想过去，不担心未来，要我学会把握住当下。后来我遇到了很多人，尤其是一些年轻人，很多都是被过去的种种所困扰，对未来很迷茫。对此，我总是笑而不语，等他们说完，我会问他们：你打算怎么办？

人生长夜，宇宙黑暗，三界火宅，众苦煎迫。我们没有能力去改变过去预知未来，所能够做到的仅仅是把握住当下。人这一生，最大的勇气不是无惧死亡，而是坚强而又坚韧地面对各种各样的压力和考验。过去的已经过去，来不及懊悔和挽留，时间会把一切都带走。未来还没有到来，我们无法预知，更不能强求。

活在当下的人们可以缅怀过去，却始终要和过去分别；可以憧憬未来，却不能执着于未来，因为只有当下才是最真实的，又是最难以把握的，看似唾手可得，却又稍纵即逝。

"活在当下"不仅是一句禅语，更是一种心态，是一种无悔、无忧的平和。不对未来"高瞻远瞩"地做无谓的猜测，不对还没有发生的事情做无意义的担忧；不把过去的痛苦和苦涩再品尝一次，而把过去当作昨日留下的幻影，能让我们在当下的压力和考验中更加自在。

珍惜过往，满足当下，面对未来。美好和幸福会在触手可及之处等你。

看远、看透与看淡

看远，才能览物于胸，只看眼前美景，难见山外之山；看透，天下熙熙，皆为名来，天下攘攘，皆为利往；看淡，不是不求进取，也不是无所作为，更不是没有追求，而是平和与宁静，坦然和安详，不以物喜，不以己悲，离尘嚣远一点，离自然近一点，淡泊就在其中。年轻时看远，中年时看透，年老时看淡！

上师曾经不止一次地告诉我，与世无争才是大境界、大智慧。可总有人觉得"等我有了金钱、地位"之后也可以做到与世无争，现在的我正在努力拼搏，还放不下，其实这是错误的。名利是人生必然要遇到的关口，肆意追逐者众，淡泊对待者少。那些绞尽脑汁不择手段追名逐利的人，他们的一生注定都无法摆脱担忧和惊惧、浮躁与烦恼。普通人虽然难以拥有上师那样的大境界，但可以活得坦然平和。

　　面对名缰利锁，年轻人更需要往远处看，看过山外的山、天外的天，就不会那么急功近利地抱定功利之心，自己才能活得更加自在宽博。在经历了岁月的洗礼之后，人到中年就会看得更加通透，懂得顺势而为，变得温良恭谦、仁厚大度。到了老年则应该看淡，甘于寂寞，不求闻达。

　　淡泊不仅是一种良好的心境，更是超脱尘世的豁达，是领悟人生、参透世界之后的一种从容，是辛苦修行之后的大彻大悟。

　　不以物喜，不以己悲，可以让自己不再虚伪，也不需要圆滑，还原一个真实的自我，达到平静宁和的境界。面对万事万物，坦然安详，才不会被俗世繁华中的浮躁和纷扰所诱惑，才可以心境清明，不染尘埃。

即便置身风雨，
也要内心明媚

　　当我们明白人生和自我都不是用来战胜而是用来相处的时候，我们就会明白：有些东西并不合理，但是必须相信；有些东西并不牢固，但是必须依靠。学会驾驭自己的生活，即使困难重重，也要满怀信心地向前。不自怜、不自卑、不哀怨，一日一日过，一步一步走，那份柳暗花明的喜悦和必然的抵达，在于我们自己的修持。

　　人生是一匹马，
　　轻快而健壮。
　　人，要像骑手那样大胆而细心。

　　人生并非完美，众生每日德业兼修，就是在力求尽善尽美。在逐渐完善自我的过程中明白人生和自我不是用来战胜的，而是要学会与之相处。

一切苦痛皆源自执着，但无执并不是一下子就能够做到的，需要经过长时间的修行。无执之人，不会有一定要放弃什么或者战胜什么的想法，他们能够与世间的一切和平相处。很多事物的存在是不是合理，都无须介怀，只有学会驾驭生活，才不会随波逐流。

剔透的美玉，需要经过自然界长期而又持久的孕育，同样，只有被不断雕琢与磨砺，心才会更加纯净。领悟到这一点，我们才能正确对待我们所受的苦，明白苦难存在的意义，从而不再自怜自卑、怨天尤人。

驾驭自己，驾驭生活，即便面对重重艰难，也要一步一个脚印地继续前行，这如同鸟儿若不能牢牢控制翅膀，就飞不上高空。哪怕生活波涛汹涌，也应牢牢驾驭，满怀信心地走下去。真正掌握了、驾驭了，才会有一颗强大的内心。就算置身风雨，内心也必是一片明媚；反之，就算晴空万里，内心也早就湿透了。

宽容是佛性的光辉

选择将什么装进自己心里，是人生的一门学问。心里装着别人的错误，就会用放大镜到处挑毛病，一再地折磨他人，也无利于自己；心里装着善良、宽容、感恩，生命就会充满阳光，他人的一切不好，会在你博大的胸怀中瓦解冰消。所以，人生是苦是乐，关键看你喜欢与什么相伴。

小时候，智慧的姨妈曾经说："天之所以无边无际，是因为宽；地之所以承载万物，是因为容。"这是宽容给我比较早的印象。我的上师曾经不止一次地对我说，佛是宽容的，佛法也是宽容的，人人都可以学习，哪怕根本不是用佛教的名义，也可以学习。对此，我深信不疑。

天是宽容的，地是宽容的，佛也是宽容的。放大别人的缺陷和错误，不能以欣赏的目光看待他人，这不仅无利于自己，也是在折磨他人。宽容，本身是一种美丽而祥和的境界，容忍别人也是对自己的大度。

只看到别人的错误，除了证明自己的狭隘之外，并没有任何益处。内心充满宽容的光辉，用善良的目光去对待他人的不足，不仅仅可以收获他人的感恩，更是对生命本身的敬畏。

容忍那些不足的、不完美的，对那些自己认为不好的人和事宽容，会让胸襟变得宽广，可以让心灵充满阳光，一切狭隘的、短视的东西都会消失，人性中的弱点也会在宽广的胸怀中得到净化。

人，并不完美，人生也不总是喜悦。是用挑剔的眼神死死盯着别人的缺陷，还是以宽容的心态理解他人的短处，是对自我心灵的一次检验。人生的美好与否，关键取决于我们用什么样的眼光去看待。

宽容是智慧的体现，是佛性的光辉。

强大的自我
是一切修持的根本

　　这一生，除了自己，谁也不能对我们负责，所以，我们一定要将自己修炼得强大。要对自己有信心，相信自己能做出好的决定。养成自己思考的习惯，不要随意附和别人，大胆地承担失败的后果。其实，凡事只要我们认真做了，只要我们今天做得比昨天好，我们就应该为自己喝彩，为自己鼓掌加油！

我们不应贪执犹如闪电般的此生安乐，
否则到自己衰老时就会后悔没有修持善法。
以上师的言教去依教奉行，将来就会获得安乐。
若我们现在没有精进修持，就跟疯狂的人没有多大的差别，这真是非常遗憾。

　　法王如意宝的话不仅教导世人要精进修行，还给人们指明了人生方向。在这个世界上，在我们的一生当中，只有自己对自己负责，才是最可靠的，别人的天空我们也撑不起。把自己修炼得强大，即使微不足道，我们的人生也不会变得苍白单调。我们不是人生的观众，切莫在别人的世界里旅行。

要对自己有信心，相信自己就是人生最好的编导，相信自己可以自由地安排生活，只有这样，才能演绎出最辉煌的灿烂。此外，要养成独立思考的习惯，即便是面对失意和挫折，也不要盲目附和别人，要始终保持心灵和精神上的独立。我们要有主见和信念，时时刻刻都知道自己需要什么。坚持恪守这种需要，胜而不骄，败亦不馁。无论成功或者是失败，都要勇敢地承担。

始终如一地相信自己，相信自己足够强大，失意便不可怕，挫折也不会让人忧伤。精神上的强大，可以让我们面带微笑，步履坚定，生命不同凡响。

当失意和苦难如烟尘一般飘散之时，你会豁然发现，不论是人还是事，只要认认真真做过了，一切都不会太难。也许我们的人生并不宏大，微如草芥，但只要生机勃勃，总有一天可以冲破顽石，自由生长。拥有了强大的内心，即便是写满了悲欢离合的人生之旅，没有江河的奔腾，也可以一点一滴汇集起来，水滴石穿。

努力奋斗就是自我修行

　　人生一定要努力，努力是人生的一种精神状态。与其要求自己一定要成为一个什么样的人物，获得什么样的成就，不如磨炼自己做一个努力的人。只有努力了才可能拥有，就算是最终没能实现梦想，也不会有太多的遗憾。往往最美的不是成功的那一刻，而是那段努力奋斗的过程。

　　人生就是从生到死的一个存在过程，这种看法虽然没有错，但也不是完全正确，人生是以生为初始，却不是以死为终结。人归于净土之后，还可以留下很多东西，还可以继续影响他人，比如说我们的精神。

　　面对纷纭的事物，面对飞逝的时光，人们往往会生出无助、迷茫甚至壮志难酬的负面情绪。与其这样感慨，还不如抓住宝贵光阴，凭努力积极进取。

努力是把人生从理想化为现实的关键。无论是入世还是出世，只有努力磨炼自己，才能让生命更加富足。努力，是一种面对人生的精神状态，不论我们的人生是平凡的还是伟大的，不论我们的生活是失意的还是苦闷的，如果连努力实现想法的愿望都没有了，纵然活着，又有什么意义呢？生命难得完美，总会有各种遗憾，但这并不意味着失败，也不是一无所得，因为在追求生命完美的过程中我们收获了成熟，收获了坚韧和理智，这是仅属于自己的宝贵财富，我们应该心存感激。

努力，可以把不满变成进取，把失败化为坚强，可以把一时的失意酝酿成前行的动力。不必要求自己一定要达到某种高度，也不必要求自己一定要做到某种成就，但我们却可以用努力来证明自己并没有被惊涛骇浪吞没，而是一直在抗争，一直发出不屈的呐喊。这个时候，我们就会发现，整个人生旅途，最亮丽的风景不是实现梦想获得成功时那一刻的闪光，而是努力奋斗过程中留下的那一道道风华。

随性而存，知命无忧

　　我们少年时渴望成年的自由，中年时却怀念童年的纯真。很多时候，我们并不满足自己的现状，而又无力去改变。不管这个世界给了我们怎样的深奥和滋味，但每一天也都要真实地度过。内心的反抗、言行的顺从、纠结的矛盾与明智的决定，所做的一切都是在为追求人生的完美而自我挽救。人生有穷达，知命则无忧。

　　时间的威严就在于从不为任何人、任何事做丝毫的停留，它从不为我们的成功而微笑，更不为我们的失败而叹息，只是匆匆地走过。在时光悄无声息地流逝中，我们也被无形的大手推着向前，从渴望成年的少年，到了回想童年的中年。我们的人生就在这时光中颠簸、踌躇，在高峰低谷、山高水长中挣扎、取舍。人们的内心极力想要反抗这个世界带来的风雨，却随着自己年龄的增长而渐渐顺从。很多时候，常人并不能按照自己的意愿去生活、去存在，不得不在纠结和理智中做出选择、做出决定。

今天经历的一切，必然成为明天的回忆。当青丝被时光染白，当岁月在我们的脸上留下深深的痕迹，我们也就渐渐醒悟了，原来我们所做的一切都是为了让并不完美的人生更加完美。虽然有时候这种努力是徒劳的，但我们依然在做，因为这是唯一的自我挽救。

不再纠结于有穷尽的人生，知命则无忧。

执着是一种负担

　　如何面对人生中的得与失，这是很多人纠结的难题。该得到的，不要错过；该失去的，洒脱地放弃。过多的在乎会将人生的乐趣减半，看淡了，一切也就释然了。执着其实是一种负担，甚至是一种苦楚，计较太多，得失就成了一种羁绊，迷失得太久，便成了一种痛苦。放弃，不是放弃追求，而是让我们以豁达的心去面对生活。

在人生旅途中，
最宝贵的东西不是"得不到的"和"已失去的"，
而是和得失无关被你紧握在手中的美好。

　　人生中的得失是让很多人纠结的难题。世界上有无数的牢笼，而真正让我们困于其中的正是自己的心，以得失为牢把自己羁绊住了。

在意得越多，越会被外界的浮光掠影所迷惑，以至于乱了心神，把得与失编织成一团乱麻，让自己走不出来。得失很简单，该得到的就要抓住，该失去的就应该潇洒地放手。总是在患得患失之间徘徊，反而让人成了得失的俘虏，生活也会被得失的权衡所占据。看淡一些，做到"心无增减，得失随缘"，一切也就释然了。

人生路上，失去从来就不是穷途末路，而是该转弯了。过分地执着于得失，只能让我们背负起难以承受的包袱，带着这些上路，再强壮的人也很难走得太远。能够做到断、舍、离，生命的空间会更加宽阔。

看淡得失，并非是麻木不仁，也不是以消极的态度遁世而出，而是以豁达、洒脱的心态面向更加宽广的生活。不管怎样的生活，都值得原谅，我们终将与这个世界握手言和。

只有把桨朝后划，
船才会往前行

　　人生需要沉淀，要有足够的时间去反思，才能让自己变得更完美；人生需要积累，只有常回头看看，才能在品味得失和甘苦中升华。向前看是梦想，是目标；向后看是结果，是修正。有多少事，如果当初回头看看，就会做得更好；有多少人，如果能回头一看，就可以拥有自己想要的。回头，身后其实也写着前进的路。

手把青秧插满田，
低头便见水中天。
心地清净方为道，
退步原来是向前。

这是布袋和尚的一首诗。几句简单而又直白的生活话语，就把佛性淋漓尽致地展现在眼前。上师也曾经对我说起过同样的道理，也是用了很浅显的例子。

上师问："水盆中有什么？"

我答："水盆中有月亮。"

上师说："既然水中有明月，又何必抬头看天空？"

梦想与目标确实是在前方，但有很多人和事，需要我们停下匆匆的脚步回头多看几眼。境地不同、时间不同，回顾曾经走过的路途，别是一番滋味。反思让人沉淀，让人变得更加厚重，是一种让人觉醒的最佳途径，修行就是在不断的反思中调整方向，休整身心。

只有把桨朝后划，船才会往前行。人生当中，要有足够的时间回首。回头看，不是放弃前进，也不是不思进取，而是为了更好更快地前行。因为在我们身后，也写着前进的路。慢即是快，退则是进！

给灵魂照镜子，
给心灵做体检

　　人生，最大的遗憾是站不到远处去审视自己，最大的困难是无法战胜自己。成就往往喜欢眷顾那些虚怀若谷并能时常审视自己的人。审视自己，就是把自己放在旁观者的角度，打量自己、纠正自己、反思自己，这样才能扬长避短，才能在生活、工作中做到有的放矢。所以，请时常审视自己，调整心态，努力做好当下！

一只眼睛观察世界，
一只眼睛审视自己。

　　世上最大的险阻从来都不是高山险峰，而是自我。阿育王最终皈依佛门，能够从一个暴君、一个征服者化为虔诚的佛门弟子，源于他见到了自己曾被权欲所蒙蔽的佛心。正确地审视自己，审视自己所经历的一切，是修行之人每天必备的功课。

自我审视，就是对自己的重新认识，把自己全面铺开，从灵魂深处做一次检查，看到自己的本源和本性，看到自己的虚妄、卑劣，并且勇敢地将之抛弃，用挑剔的眼光重新定义自己，给自我一次照镜子的机会，审视自我的言行，审视自我的心态……在审视中一次次打量自己，纠正自己。

每一次自我审视，都是一次心灵的体检，都是一次自我沉淀的积累。在审视的过程中，堆积在心灵上的尘埃会被扫除，心境更加清澈通透。失意时审视自我,会发现灵魂上的沉沦;昂扬时审视自我,会看到人性中的骄狂。

不放纵自己，去除掉沉渣，才能生出更加透明的结晶。

不受伤不足以谈成长

　　我们都有过这样的幻想：如果时光可以倒流，将所有的遗憾一一弥补，这样的人生该多完美呀！可是没有经历过失去的遗憾，又怎么懂得珍惜呢？许多事只有亲身经历才会懂，也只有经历过许多的人才明白该以一颗平常心应对无常的人生。不要计较这一路走来的苦与痛，要感恩昨天的经历，追逐明天的幸福。

　　很多人提及逝去的时光，总会想起许许多多曾经的遗憾，并且期待可以回到过去，将曾经的经历再经历一次，以修正不足，达到完美的境地。这种想法是痴妄的，与其这样想，不如去考虑未来该如何做才能避免这种情形再次出现。而且过去的那些你现在觉得不堪的经历未必就没有价值，反而正是因为有了它，今日的你才得以知晓自己的过失与短板在何处。

很多人和事，只有失去了，只有遗憾了，才会懂得其宝贵之处。所以不必刻意强求如何弥补，只要它的存在能够让我们为鉴，让我们成长，这就足够了。

生活的真谛，就是不断吐故纳新、不断完善的过程。不再执着于昨天经历的苦痛和哀伤，不仅仅是大胸怀，也是大境界，是修养心灵之后得来的坦然，是佛性对人性的滋养。

所以，对昨日经历的种种应心怀感恩，而不是常执痴怨。感恩昨天的风和雨，感恩曾经的坎坷和磨难，这一切让今天的我们变得成熟，让我们体验到了最真切的成长。

第六章

智慧源于生命的起伏

知错能改，善莫大焉

　　生命原本艰难，我们却常常雪上加霜。如果你相信因果，仁慈、友善地对待每个人，放开消极，拥抱积极，那你就找到了生活的正确方式。我们拼命想要快乐，但又常在错误的地方寻找快乐。如果真错了，就要立即做出正确的选择。可最困难的是承认自己有错。如果能认错并愿意改变，慢慢地就会在修行的路上精进。

　　承认错误的意义在于避免错误。如果我们还没有做好认错的准备，那就必须做好一错再错的准备。

　　犯错是一种常态，不值得纠结。关键是要在错误中反省，在错误中总结，在错误的人和事上找到正确的方向，找到生活的正确方式。生活中每个人都有诸多的不如意，智者会将这些挫折与困难当作一次历练，勇于面对，用个人的努力及不服输的精神逐一战胜，从而在今后的生活中不断鞭策自己、敲打自己，使个人能力及素质不断提升；愚者则会抱怨不堪、怨声载道，甚者逃避、一蹶不振，从此再不触碰这令他头疼、烦恼的"地域"。

其实，在困难面前，你强它则弱，你弱它则强。当我们勇敢、积极面对时，困难就会变得很渺小，为何要惧怕一个还没有努力克服就放弃的小困难？生活本就是一些好事与坏事的结合体，在享受顺利的同时就应该接受困难与阻隔。就算失败，就算充满荆棘，也要保持同样的热情与态度。

随缘并非安于命运

随缘，常常被一些人理解为不需要有所作为，听天由命，由此也成为逃避问题和困难的理由。殊不知，随缘不是放弃追求，而是让人以豁达的心态去面对生活。随缘是一种智慧，可以让人在狂热的环境中，依然拥有恬静的心态、冷静的头脑。缘，需要很多条件才能成立，若是随顺因缘，不违背真理，这才叫随缘。

万事万物因缘而生又因缘而灭，众生万象都是缘聚缘散的结果。包括人生，也是一种因缘。"既然一切都是因缘的结果，那还有什么值得努力的呢？听天由命去吧！"有些人逃避生活，回避人生，所用的借口是出奇地一致：随缘。这是对因缘的误解，甚至可以说是无知。佛说随缘，其实是依法而存。

随缘，从来就不是放弃追求，也不是什么都不做，任凭随波逐流地漂荡。缘的本质是不由前定，更不可预知，随缘是要充分发挥人的主观能动性，以智慧的眼光和顽强的毅力，尽可能地促成因缘，而不是坐等空守。

缘首先是尽人事，然后才听天命，一切成败的关键，在于自身的奋斗和努力。面对不成熟的东西，不要轻举妄动，更不可以强行为之，否则就会适得其反。而当机会成熟时，就应该紧紧抓住，奋发图强，一切成功就会是水到渠成了。

随缘不是逃避的借口，而是要你以"入世"的积极心态去努力追求，刻苦耕耘，以"出世"的从容心态去面对收获，做到不为物喜、不以己悲的淡泊，收获清静，收获本心，这才是随缘的真正境界。

不争才能得到

　　我们常常被一个"争"字所纷扰，争到最后，原本阔大渺远的尘世，只剩下一颗自私的心了。其实在生活中，可以有无数个不争的理由：心胸开阔一些，得失看轻一些，为别人多考虑一些……哪怕只是少争一点，把看似要紧的东西淡然地放一放，你会发现，人心会一下子变宽，世界会一下子变大。不争，人生至境！

　　学校里论排名，年长后论名誉、地位……攀比心让人陷入"争"的烦恼。可争来争去谁也不会得到最初想要的东西，就只剩下那颗自私自利的心了，这又何必呢？处心积虑所争来的名誉、地位，无非是加重内心空虚与不安的毒药。就像食物吃得越多，便越难以消化，最后还可能伤害自己的身体。得到并不意味着拥有，如果不适用，反而会成为一种累赘，除了加重人生的负担之外，毫无意义。

　　与其在伤人伤己的喧嚣和吵闹中争来争去，争得头破血流，还不如放手。让心里的欲望冷却，消解掉累赘的功利之心，看淡得失，胸襟才能宽广，我们与他人、与世界才能更好地和平相处。如果我们目前做不到，那么就暂时把想得到的东西放一下，或许一切问题就能迎刃而解了。

　　一定要分出高下胜负是最没有意义的事情，为了争而争，更是人性的悲哀。上天给予每个人的东西是等量的，你把属于别人的东西抢来了，可能会让别人的生命因此失去平衡，这是任何一个有慈悲心的人都不会去做的事情。

糊
涂
的
人
未
必
不
聪
明

　　谁都希望自己是一个非常聪明的人，都希望得到人们的认可，于是很多人会用各种方式在众人面前展示自己的聪明才智，结果往往是自作聪明。我们在很多时候是需要糊涂点的，糊涂不是昏庸，而是为人处世豁达大度，拿得起，放得下。凡事不要太执着，轮回的路上要想得开、看得开，该糊涂的时候就糊涂，难得糊涂。

　　很多人喜欢竭尽全力在他人面前展露自己的聪明才智，可惜结果往往适得其反。面对他人时既不自卑低头也不狂妄自大，不计较不抱怨，做一个"聪明的糊涂人"，人生未必会活得那么累。其实希望得到别人的认可和羡慕，这并非完全是因为虚荣心，而是心灵需要得到满足的一种外在表象。世间的诸多过往都证明了一个浅显却很实用的道理：吃亏是福。

　　难得糊涂，是一种境界，是斤斤计较的人无法拥有的。它就像一面铜镜，映照着我们的酸甜苦辣。从来都不糊涂的人，不见得就会聪明，事事都精明的人是难以成就人生真正的大业的。我们要做拿得起、放得下的人，遇事随缘，凡事随心，不强求。乐在糊涂，才能成就智慧。

　　聪明的做人方式是小事愚、大事明，这是一种很高的修养。小事不影响大局，无须斤斤计较、患得患失。小聪明能聪明一时，但不能聪明一世。水至清则无鱼，人至察则无徒；静坐常思己过，闲谈莫论人非；大事守原则，小事学变通，方是智者本色。

理由是弱者的借口

　　总有那么一些人，喜欢把自己平庸的人生归咎于条件不好，可条件都好了，我们还用奋斗吗？成功不能一味苛求条件，如果一味苛求条件，再好的条件也只能成为你捆绑在翅膀上的黄金，它不仅无助于你成功，反而会拖累你前进的步伐。弱者等待条件，强者创造条件，真正的成功者就应善于在没有条件时创造条件。

　　有很多人总习惯于把自己的平庸和失意归咎于客观条件，在他们看来，"条件不好""条件太少"等都可以作为失败的原因，却往往忽视了自身努力不足这个事实，甚至是故意强调客观条件，而完全无视自身的懈怠和懒惰。这是推脱，是对自己人生的不负责任。

　　理由只是弱者的借口，把平庸的人生和失意的生活推给外在，是一种软弱。试想一下，如果条件已经全部满足，我们的奋斗岂不是失去了意义？始终把目光锁定在诸多的条件身上，又怎么看得到原本的初衷？又怎能坚定地走好以后的路？

　　看不清自己，不管有多好的条件都会成为负累与束缚。在通往成功的路上，弱者始终在原地踏步的抱怨中等待着条件降落在自己头上；而强大的人，从不做这种无谓也没有结果的等候，他们会始终坚定地向前，用自己的坚持与智慧突破诸多阻碍。成败的关键永远都不是条件，而是我们对成功的向往和所付出的努力。

人生需要平衡

　　我们来到这个世上，每人都背着一个空篓子，而人的一生，就是不断地往自己的篓子里放东西的过程。如果有了，就想更多，贪得无厌，欲壑难填。只做加法的人生是很悲哀的，远离名利、看淡成败、安于淡泊就是做减法，减去多余的物质，减去奢侈的欲望，减去心灵的负担。加减法并用，人生之旅才会风光无限。

　　在繁杂纷扰的大千世界行走，心里不要一开始便装载太多的东西，虽然人的一生是在不断累积的过程中不断丰盈，然而，承载总是有限度的，人生需要做加法，也需要做减法。人的一生和四季更迭很像，既有生机蓬勃的春季，也有万物凋零的深秋，有所收获就必然会有所丢舍。

　　舍去奢侈和不切实际的欲望，升华出淡泊坦然的心境；减去提防算计，增加慈悲关爱，才不会被过于膨胀的欲望和野心拖累。人生中的减法，不仅仅体现在对那些负面事物的舍弃，更主要还在于对于自我的完善，这是一个淘去泥沙，让本心闪耀出金色光芒的过程。人生有舍才有得，丢掉应该丢掉的，保存应该保存的，唯有如此，才能到达更壮丽的境界。放下那些让我们迟疑困惑的东西，人生需要更多的是平衡。

不管是加法还是减法，生命的运算法则都要尊重大自然的规律、情感的规律、人性的规律。用减法去面对生活中的不如意，用加法去丰盈自己的内心，不失为一种让内在力量更加强大的法则。

命运是一种选择

　　人与人交往，更多的不是改变对方，而是接受对方。如果光想着改变对方，那不是生活，那是战争。命运不是一个机遇的问题，而是一个选择的问题；它不是我们要等待的东西，而是我们要实现的东西。把弯路走直的人是聪明的，因为找到了捷径；把直路走弯的人是豁达的，因为可多看几道风景。路不在脚下，在心里。

　　人们总是试图去影响、改变身边的人，其实这是非常费力而又效果甚微的举动。每一个人都与众不同，用自己的标准要求别人，矛盾便会滋生，这显然不是我们想要的，最合适的办法是接受对方，接受这世界的种种光明与阴暗。

　　人们习惯于等待命运的降临，期待着"命中注定"的某种改变。其实早在你等待的时候，命运已经改变过无数次了，但这些改变并不是直接改变了我们的命运，而是改变了我们自身，而我们身上的所有变数本身就是命运的一部分。除了变化，没有什么是"命中注定"的。人所要面对的不是等待命运把改变降临到人生中，而是要在诸多的改变中选择最适合自己的那一个。

对于理想，有些人会径直前行，而有些人则迂回前进，区别仅仅是选择的不同。选择两点之间最短的直线，用时最短；那些迂回前进的人虽然走了弯路，却能看到更多别样的风景，得到不同的收获。是以最快的速度到达，还是不紧不慢地在沿途中安然欣赏，要听从我们内心的声音，遵从心的选择。

理想会在等待中变老

　　常常有朋友说：等我老了，就要去环游世界；等我退休了，就要去做想做的事情；等孩子长大了，我就可以轻松了。我们总误以为自己有无限的时间与体力，为什么不现在就一步一步靠近梦想呢？别老是期望等有空时再接近它，否则我们会在活了半生后，却发现自己成了理想中最不想变成的那种人。

　　很多年轻人都曾谋划过去远方进行一次放松的旅行，不过却少有人能真正落实到行动上，似乎生活中有很多的无奈，让我们的理想搁浅。其实，真正阻挡人们享受生活、放松心境的不是那些我们口中的理由和状况，而是自己。有时候，我们并不需要把时间、地点和事项一一计划出来，一步步去实现。其实，只需一个背包、一个记录旅程的工具即可。

　　行动起来，跟着自己的感觉走，让自己成为时间的支配者，那么，我们才能逃离现在的自己。工作固然重要，但是比起自己的身体和心灵的舒畅，无疑是需要让步的。不要等走不动了才想起，自己有很多想去的地方没有去成；不要等老得牙都掉光了，才恍然想起，有很多想要做的事情没有及时去做。理想中的自己是什么样子的，如果你还记得，那么你现在就应该好好反思一下了，是不是你距离它已经太远？从现在开始改变，一切都来得及。

遗憾，让我们懂得完美

通常想象总是美过现实，当现实的发展偏离了想象的画面，就有了遗憾。懂了遗憾，就懂了人生，因为，人生没有完美，遗憾和残缺始终都会存在，美好的东西太多，我们不可能全都得到。对于那些已经不属于自己的东西，就别再奢望什么了！有过遗憾会更懂珍惜，没有过遗憾，就算给你再多美好，你也不会感受到幸福。

天上的月亮，一旦圆满了，马上就会复亏；树上的果子，一旦熟透了，马上就要坠落。人所需要的，不应是十全十美的外在事物，而是内心对十全十美的追求。

我曾听到一个年轻人说："如果我有了几百万，就不会像现在这么拼命。"说这话时，一副很理直气壮的样子，可当他真有了几百万，真的会如他所说的那样吗？如果把身旁的事物想象得太美好，当现实的发展偏离了脑海中想象的画面时，就有了遗憾，有了失望。

生活在这个压力很大、节奏很快的时代，很多人的内心会有一种不确定感。有时候，人们会期望生活能对自己好一些，可自己又不去努力。这个社会，没有不劳而获的果实，付出不一定收获成功，可不付出一定不会收获成功。遗憾不是人生中的某种缺失，而是让我们更加珍惜现在的成果。没有过遗憾，就算给你再多的美好，你也不会感受到幸福。就和你没吃过苦，便不会懂得甜的可贵道理是一样的。人世间的完美，不是没有瑕疵，而是对缺陷的清醒认识，只有拥有这种认识，才会产生对美的追求之心。

简单是一种伟大

　　生活的本相是简单的，但要掌握这真正的本相，却总要在经过无数历练之后。所以，我们所说的简单并不是如婴孩般的无知傻乐。更多的时候，只有在我们看惯那种种人生险境、领略过各种绮丽风景后，才会明白一个最简单的道理：远方的景色走近了，就是自己现在的生活；现在的生活放远了，就是别人眼中的风景。

　　很多伟大的真理通常都很简单，同样，最简单的人通常也很伟大。生活原本很简单，却被很多人想得太过复杂。

　　净土不在脚下，而在我们的心中。也许现在的你还在思考脚下的路该如何走，未来的希望又该如何去诠释，未来的人生又在何方。有时候，想着想着，你会哭；哭着哭着，又笑了。这就是成长。当你感觉到自己的成长轨迹越来越明显时，也许你就能感觉到自己越来越成熟了。未来的路很长，偶尔停下来，想想曾经所经历的种种，想想自己曾经规划的未来，与现实又相差多少？也许我们错过一些人、一些事，有过遗憾、伤感，也曾失去过，痛哭过，但这一切终将成为过去。能在经历过这些之后，明白一个简单的道理：远方的景色走近了，就是自己现在的生活；现在的生活放远了，就是别人眼中的风景。简单生活，不是要人去过贫苦、简陋的生活。简单是能有一颗平静的心，接受这个世间不可改变的一些现实。看透，看开，看淡；不念，不争，不惧。

纠结得失是对生命的浪费

　　失即是得，是一种痛苦，也是幸福。因为只有失去，空下的双手才能拾起新的幸福。放不下自己是没有智慧，放不下别人是没有慈悲，每一个人都要懂得放自己一马，也要放别人一马，不要把生命浪费在钻牛角尖上。因为，每个人的一生其实只有两万天。

　　把个人的得与失记挂心间，就不会有平和之气，更不能冷静地对待利益。得与失是事物的两个面，就好像白天和黑夜一样，是最自然不过的事情。纠结于得失，就是放不下，被功利之心迷乱了心智。每个人的生命或许有长短之别，但终究是有限度的。若人与人还要无休止地争斗，则是浪费生命，相当于作恶。

　　时间是世间最公正的分配师，它对富人和穷人、智者和愚者都一样，不偏袒分毫。寸金难买寸光阴，学会自己寻找快乐，在放过自己的同时也放过别人，不在得失的权衡和计算间荒废生命，就是没有虚度年华。生命何其宝贵，不要总把那些个人的得与失记在心头，更不必为此纠结不休。当我们在得与失之间徘徊难抉的时候，只要还有抉择的权利，那么，就应当以自己的心灵是否能得到安宁为原则。只要我们能在得失之间做出明智的选择，人生就不会被世俗所淹没。

得意何尝不是失意之因？失意又何尝不是得意之果？

能作茧自缚，
就要能破茧成蝶

　　有些束缚，是我们自找的；有些压力，是我们自给的；有些痛苦，是我们自愿的。没有如影相随的不幸，只有死不放手的执着。不要把目光盯在别处，只有坚持做好自己，才能看到下一秒的路。不要把某些人和事看得太重，陪伴你到终点的，只会是你的影子！相信自己，我们能作茧自缚，我们就能破茧成蝶！

　　总有些人错误地认为佛法就是神通，可以帮他们避免失意和不顺利。持这种想法的人，对佛法缺少最基本的了解，对于佛的认识也是完全错误的。现实生活中的不顺和失意，和佛没有丝毫牵连，多是个人的种种欲望交织所致，所以人才会被困在里边。

　　从来就没有伴随终生的不幸，有的只是抓住不放、死不松手的执着。除非自己主动解脱，否则谁也帮不了你。在通往彼岸的道路上，除了你的影子之外，没有谁会真正陪你走到最后，所以不要把别人看作是不可或缺的部分，因为那和你无关。

要始终坚定地相信自己，用智慧和勇气走出属于自己的路，不要在得失成败间作茧自缚，要勇于认清自我，知道自己的方向在哪里。当我们朝着明确的方向勇敢迈出第一步时，就是破茧成蝶的开始，接下来才是阳光与风雨的考验。能够帮助我们从苦闷志忑中走出来的，永远是我们自己。

人生要选对位置

　　人生的空虚不在于人的孤独，而在于心的寂寞；人生的智慧不在于善于观察，而在于善于辨别；人生的寻找不在于千山万水，而在于咫尺之间；人生的境界不在于盲目跟随，而在于自我探求；人生的档次不在于外在的包装，而在于内在的品质；人生的成败不在于环境的优劣，而在于你是否选对了自己的位置。

　　世界变得越来越小，人与人之间的距离也被缩小，可人与人之间却树起了无形的壁垒，每个人都活得很寂寞。我想之所以这样，大概是因为人们把自己封闭了，没有用心去感受他人，为了保有安全感，一味地将别人拒于千里之外。

　　面对纷繁交错的人和事，或许我们一直都在以旁观者的目光审视，但若看透，则需要智慧。辨别世间万物，需要一个标准，而这个标准才是本质。人生是优质的还是低劣的，并不在于金钱、财富……所有的外物都只是一层华丽的包装纸，退去外在的包装才能看到人生的内核。过分地追求外在包装，而忽略了内在品质的提高，就犯了舍本逐末的错误。为了包装而包装，是很可悲的。

寒冷中的梅花分外芳香，外在环境的恶劣很大程度上淬炼着品质的绽放，人生能不能最终到达彼岸，完全在于是不是选对了自己所处的角度和位置，并且持之恒之。人生艰涩博大，却又简单明了，可以浓缩成一个简单的"心"字存于方寸之间。有什么样的心境，就有什么样的人生。

机
会
需
要
自
己
留
给
自
己

　　机会对每个人都是公平的，它出现时，并非以花枝招展的形象示人，而是默默地、不起眼地。通常看起来耀眼的机会很多时候都只是空壳，也或许是陷阱；真正的机会起初都是不经意的、渺小的。只有经过主动、睿智的捕捉与积极、持续的努力，它才会变得格外绚烂。机会，从来都是留给有准备的你！

　　机会是漆黑夜空中的一道闪电。如果它到来时，我们恰好睁着眼睛在黑夜中守候，那么就可以借着闪电的亮光看清楚四周的环境，看清楚远方的路；如果闪电亮起时我们还在沉睡之中，那么对于我们而言，就等于什么都没有发生，黑夜依旧是黑夜。

　　任何人随时随地都可能与机会相遇，它到来的时候并不会事先通知我们，所以总是让人猝不及防。机会本身并不华丽，甚至简朴明了到了极致，它总是静悄悄地以最微不可察的形式降临。要做好迎接它的准备，除了需要一双慧眼之外，还需要一颗敏感的心。

　　曾经在大雾中行走过的人都知道，远远望去，前面是蒙蒙一片，辨不出方向和状况，于是，便有人因为缺乏安全感而迟疑、驻足。可当这些人最终鼓起勇气，放下恐惧和疑虑，一步一步向前走时，会发现，其实每走一步，他们都有能力将下一步的方向及目标锁定。所以，请大胆地走，别停在远远的地方观望。向前，目标自然就会出现。

　　也许，下一刻闪电就会亮起。而你，准备好了吗？

心宽了，
人生才不会自乱方寸

　　心小了，小事就大了；心大了，大事就小了。看淡世间沧桑，内心安然无恙。大其心，容天下之物；虚其心，爱天下之善；平其心，论天下之事；定其心，应天下之变。大事难事看担当，逆境顺境看胸襟，有舍有得看智慧，是成是败看坚持。

　　佛教对于事物的划分讲究内外，却不区分大小，在佛的眼中，大小只是形式，并不是事物的本质。大小都是相对的，心若小了，小事可变大；心若大了，大事也能化小。胸怀宽广的人，可以承载生命；心胸狭窄之人，一粒豆子可能也接纳不了。

　　经历了沧桑变故的心，往往是安然的，所以很多经历坎坷的人能够接受很多自己不能改变的事物，而且不会将之推给命运，更不会喋喋不休地怨天尤人。内心平静，才能够更好地控制自己的心绪与理智，对影响自己的事物做出准确的判断，找到心的出路……

　　一个人的胸怀并非朝夕之间就可以修炼出来，而是要经历很多磨难，经历无数取舍，经历许许多多的成败，然后才能以真诚和智慧去接受这个世界的人和事，才可以摒弃一切阻碍自己前景的私心杂念。心开阔了，才能容纳下更多好的品行，人生才不会自乱方寸。心宽，天地就宽。

心态决定你是骑师还是坐骑

　　人与人之间本身并无太大的区别，真正的区别在于心态，"要么你去驾驭生命，要么生命驾驭你，心态决定了谁是骑师"。在面对人生低谷时，有的人向现实妥协，放弃了自己的理想和追求；有的人不低头认输，他们不停地审视自己的人生，分析自己的错误，勇于面对，从而走出困境，追逐自己的梦想。一切由心控！

　　两个饥渴难耐的旅人在沙漠中得到一杯水。悲观者哀叹："仅仅是一杯水罢了，能做什么？"乐观者却很欢喜："我们终于有了一杯水！"人与人本身并没有太过悬殊的差异，真正的差异在于心态。心态不同，人生不同。要么去驾驭生命，要么被生命驾驭。是成为骑师还是成为坐骑，我们的心说了算。物随心转，境由心造，一个人内心有什么样的状态，就会遇到什么样的现实。

　　面对失意、困苦、人生低潮的时候，心态的决定性作用才会凸显。心态乐观、态度积极的人，依靠后天积累的坚韧，能够直面自己犯下的错误，勇敢地进行修正，从而拥有前进的动力。而消极悲观的人，只会在怨天尤人中用"机会没有到来""环境不好"等借口来安慰自己。或许我们还不能控制人生道路上的阴晴，但可以自由地掌握自己的心态，迎接阳光，把影子留在身后。

第七章

生活需要一种姿态

困难越大，
你所存在的意义就越大

生活中的历练，让我们理解了责任，理解了这个社会能给我们的所有尊重。于艰难中，懂得了承受，懂得了坚定，慢慢地丰满我们自己。人生，没有永远的悲伤，也没有永远的欢心。能使我们坚强的，往往不是顺境，而是逆境；能让我们醒悟的，往往不是开心，而是伤心。学会忍受，懂得艰辛，于曲折中前进。

命运总是在不经意间跟我们开玩笑，甚至在很多看起来重要的时刻设置障碍，这没有什么好奇怪的，因为人生之旅本就是风雨兼程，成功与失败并存，苦难与希冀同在。

生活中的艰难逆境，在绝大多数情况下，其实只是对我们的历练。拥有能够承受的肩膀，才能收获心的坚定，这是一个逐步丰满我们自己的过程。

生活中的艰辛，会让脆弱的人猝不及防，遍体鳞伤，但这何尝不是一种磨炼？人在某些时候没有做过蠢事，那他就不会做成聪明的事。逆境中醒悟，会让生命更加通透。把艰难和困苦看作是一本沉重厚实的词典，时时躬下身子去翻阅，你会从中找到解读人生、醒悟心灵的另外一种方式。

前几年遇到过一个信徒，当初踌躇满志、野心勃勃，本以为会功成名就，结果却一败再败，经历了无数荆棘坎坷，但每次都未被压倒。如今对他来说，最大的收获不是事业的成功，而是这些年内心不断积聚起来的力量。用他的话说，就是"逆境如潮，我若礁石，磨难才是人生最大的本钱"。

酸涩苦楚，带给我们的不只是无尽的悲伤，也是催人奋进的磨炼，恰如彩虹从来都是出现在风雨之后。生活中的逆境和艰辛更不是洪水猛兽，而是对自己的磨砺，经过更多更彻底的洗礼，我们的血肉才会更加丰满而健壮。

要知道，苦难从来都是顿悟的灵光。

放下包袱，方能坦荡

　　每个人都有被他人所牵累、自己负累的时候，只不过有些人会及时调整，有些人却深陷其中。在这个充满压力的社会里，生活有太多的难题和烦恼，要活得一点不累也不大可能。身体累不可怕，怕的是心累。凡事不要钻牛角尖，让自己背负着沉重的思想包袱；也不要想得过多，这会让我们活得更累。

人若无心，心自无事。
心若无求，人自平安。
为善不执，老死不惧。
是为清净心。

牧区的生活相对来说是比较艰苦的，尤其是在我小时候，除了放牧之外，还要做些收取木材、挖虫草之类的活。妈妈总是说："身体的累只是一种感觉，只要心不累，就是真的不累。"

是的，身体的疲劳，睡一觉就过去了，第二天依旧会生机焕发；可心一旦累了，便将是一个不容易轻易消解的负担。或是被他人所累，或是被自己所累，生活总会有太多的难题与烦恼。很多人往往深陷其中而不自知。所谓的累，其实只是一种感觉，是我们认为背负的东西太多而感觉到的疲惫。

佛曰：清净如水，清净心即为平常心。

身体上的累并不可怕，把它当作一年四季中总会出现的严寒或者酷热，当作一种自然，当作最平常不过的事情，就不会钻进牛角尖而出不来。心中清净，凡事保持平常之心，成功了无须沾沾自喜，这只不过是人生路上的一个小小驿站；失败了也不要灰心沮丧，因为还可以改变方向从头再来。

生活不是演戏，不需要太多的装扮。放下包袱轻轻松松，生活自然坦坦荡荡。

活着，是一种修行

　　老天是公平的，它一边给你苦难，一边让你快乐，生活的苦与乐总在更迭，没有谁的命运是完美的，有时残缺也是一种美。快乐是精华，能让我们信心十足；痛苦是良药，能让我们顽强支撑。别为难自己，别苛求自己，放宽心，让它包容伤害和痛苦。心宽了，烦恼自然就少了，日子自然就顺了，人生也就圆融自在了。

人生，
是道场。
活着，
就是一种修行。

每个人从呱呱落地的那一刻起，就注定要经受世间的考验。在或漫长或短暂的生命之旅上，和苦难的相遇不可避免，有些人选择勇敢面对，有些人选择仓皇逃离。不管我们是强者还是弱者，老天在让我们得到一些东西的同时，也会让我们失去一些东西，人生本就如此。但那些看不开的人往往因此患得患失，在痛苦中不断挣扎。

佛怜悯世人的苦多乐少。虽然很多人可能达不到佛的境界，但这并不妨碍他们知足常乐。能够在痛苦中寻找到快乐，才是人生智慧的起点。

在追寻佛陀的足迹之时，我到过印度，在宁静的恒河边上，看到了一对情侣。一个红衣女子围绕着轮椅上的爱人翩翩起舞，欢快的舞姿和甜美的微笑至今令我难忘。我当时心中莫名感动，为女子和残疾情侣能够相爱相随而感动。外在的缺憾并不能说明什么，也不能代表什么。这是一个在尘世中遗世而立、内心坚定的女子，心怀爱与慈悲，觉得众生皆是动人的景致。很多事，既然我们在尽力之后也无法改变，那就接受吧。这并非刻意标榜洒脱，而是我们渐渐成熟的标志。在修行的路上，要学会如何爱别人，要学会如何更好地去生活，随时准备接受无法改变的命运，平静地面对失去与分离。不管在生活中，还是在感情上，保持乐观从容的心态，智慧的莲花就会在心头绽放。

我们所经历的每一件事，无论苦乐，都是磨炼，都是成长。活着，就是一种修行。

微笑，是艰难中的从容

　　因为生活，一些人消极地选择了哭泣；因为生活，一些人却积极地选择了微笑。其实生活本身充满苦涩，隐藏着不同的酸甜苦辣，但生活并没有亏欠我们什么，至少，它给了我们生命，给了我们生存的空间。所以，没有必要总苦着脸。只有懂得微笑的人，才能紧紧"牵住"生活的"手"。

辣甜咸苦、酸涩腥冲，此为人生八味。

　　人的一生当中，每一种滋味都会品尝得到。甘甜让人欢喜，苦涩让人厌恶。看到别人咀嚼甜美而自己却品尝苦涩，总认为这是生活的不公。其实生活从来就没有亏欠过我们什么，自然界给予我们的空气与水，皆是天地至大的恩赐，有了这些就已经足够了，剩下的需要我们去发现、去感悟。

　　微笑着面对失意，这是坦然；微笑着接受挫折，则是一种境界，而生活所需要的就是这种豁达与随缘。

地震过后，有个灾民在自己房屋的废墟上流泪，无助地哭泣着："我什么都没有了，还怎么生活？"而他的母亲却搂着他的肩膀微笑着："至少我们还活着，生活还能继续！"

面对灾难，哭泣者看到的是苦难和挫折，是一无所有的绝望；而微笑的人则看到了希望，看到了风雨过后明媚的天空。

生活总是会有苦难和不如意，遭受重挫之后的一丝微笑就是一份自我宽慰的勇气，就是一种坦荡客观的态度。微笑的时候，其实已经满怀信心地走在争取成功的路上了，就像地平线上升起的炊烟，总能给人一种生机与美好。

把哭泣与悲观的沉郁瓦解，带着微笑去面对生活，就算是在黑夜之中，也可以看到天际点点繁星的光亮。那些乐观的人，会在微笑中积蓄力量，以此给予智慧更好的发挥空间。

人生，归根到底，最需要的是面对生活的智慧。

别让心太累

　　常常有朋友感叹活得累，他们的人生往往是这样的：一是期待过甚，预期与现实脱节，条件与结果相悖；二是设想过高，总以为攀高无须坚韧，涉远不用艰辛，对困难估量不足；三是强求过多，与己无关、无缘、无用的，皆想统统据为己有，攫取欲望太深，攀比心态太重。结果，乱了心神，迷了人生。

　　很多人感叹活得太累，其原因大多是内心没有明确的方向，进而觉得自己没有更好的前途，无论如何努力，总是缺少一种踏实感，不知道自己最终的需求是什么。时间久了，这样的感叹就会变成习惯性的抱怨，只会让自己的内心变得泥泞不堪。

　　每个人都希望能拥有更好的生活、远大的前程、光明的未来，并把那些看起来比自己好的人当作参照物。这种需求本身并没有错，只是在实施的过程中需要给自己定一个能够分解的切合实际的目标，不要高不可攀，否则，脱离自身实际，再美好的理想都会变成一种无意义的强求。不切实际的期望、脱离现实的理想终究是镜花水月虚空一场，比上比下，比着比着心就乱了。

人生，往往不在于最终的理想有多么高远，而在于看清楚起点，在于能不能脚踏实地地去对待。对未来的期许，就像是天上的风筝，而现实状况则是风筝线。一根只有五十米的线，再好的风筝也达不到百米的高度。

很多人并不缺少大理想大目标，而是缺少对自身情形正确的认识和坚韧不拔的努力。我们需要的是静下心来，脚踏实地地自省，既不要好高骛远，也无须妄自菲薄，认认真真地对待每一件事情、每一个人，做到智者不惑、勇者不惧，这样内心就会淡然从容，也就不会为物欲所迷。沿着自己想要的方向去努力，这才是真正的求取。

放下喧嚣、妖冶和肤浅的聒噪，还自己一个平实朴素的本来面目，这一切，都要从心开始。勇于舍弃无用无缘的东西，才能明心见性，自在圆满。

勇气是高贵的信仰

　　有些事情现在不做，一辈子都不会做。有人说，我害怕看到结果，可你都有勇气走完那段过程，一个小小的结果又怕什么？有人说，我害怕过程会很疼，可你还没看到结果，你怎么就认定结果不会出乎你的意料呢？退缩，是可能让人后悔一辈子的事！没有经历过主动的人生是不完整的，没有经历过勇往的青春是不深刻的。

　　在寺庙的时候，我喜欢坐在顶楼的平台，看楼下院子里的孩子们疯闹玩耍。有时候看到他们因为一点小的不合对抗得很激烈，一副不是你死就是我亡的架势，可是没过多久，刚刚势不两立的对头就勾肩搭背地在一起玩耍了！我常想，成人之间一旦出现矛盾，为何就那么难复合呢？其实，很多时候都是因为我们想得太多了，又缺乏担当的勇气。

　　成年人总是有太多的顾虑：向刚刚吵过架的朋友示好甚至主动讲和，会不会很没有面子？会不会被对方接受？要是朋友正在气头上，不接受我的歉意，又该怎么办？

　　就这样，怯懦的想法占据了心灵，顾虑的余烟挡住了视线，宝贵的机会便因内心的踟蹰而消逝。酝积于心的想法不应该想想就算了，最重要的是行动。就像修行一样，靠空想是不行的，我们必须要靠自己的行为证明自己的心以及我们在这个世界存在的意义。

　　担心被拒绝，畏惧失败，会让人退缩，进而失去更多宝贵的东西。勇气的缺失，往往会酿成追悔一辈子的错事。害怕在过程中受到伤害，这是怯懦的一种最直接表现。在没有看到结果的时候，就下了一个悲观的定论，臆断出一个最凄惨的结局。所有的这一切，都是退缩的借口。

　　没有勇气面对，就只能躲在主观的背后。世间的人与事并没有我们想的那么悲观，悲观的是自己没有底气，悲观的是我们的内心充满恐惧。如果有勇气走完全部过程，一个小小的结果又有什么好怕的呢？不主动的人生是残缺的，经历过勇往直前才会更加深刻。

　　即使人生淡然，也仍需把勇气当成信仰。

失去，是为了更好地迎接

　　人生就是如此，当你在某方面拥有太多的时候，在另一方面可能就要失去；当你在某方面选择放弃的时候，也许在另一方面你将获得更多。去除那些对于我们来说冗繁、多余的外在物质，将这些外在物质给予那些更需要的人。这对于我们来说不是失去，而是更大的收获，因为我们的内心也会因此得到真正的丰盈。

　　失去和得到永远是生活天平上的两个砝码。

　　得与失，绝非针对一事一物，而是关乎德行与心性的修正。
　　我们在凡尘之中很难做到豁达与开阔，得之欣然，失去就会生惶惶之心，这是人的通病。
　　得与失本就是一而二、二而一的共生体，就好像阳光下的形和影，从来就没有分开过。失去了灿烂的星月，就会得到一轮更加蓬勃的朝阳；失去了青春的单纯，就会得到成熟后的丰盈。

有时候，失败的风雨还未散尽，阳光已经普照了。

得到和失去就是跷跷板的两端，当其中的一端轻飘飘地扬起时，必然有一端沉甸甸地落下。因此，得到了一些东西的时候，必然也会失去一部分。只要失去得有意义，又何必忧伤呢？

离别的背后就是下一次相聚，去旧而迎新也是轮回上的收获。

无论得失，都是生命中一点一滴的凝聚。我们的失去如果能变成他人的得到，我们也就得到了。

得失常在，贵在心态。

开阔的人生不张狂

　　有时，生活就是一种妥协、一种忍让、一种迁就。并不是所有的事情都适宜针锋相对、唇枪舌剑，多彩的生活，既有阳光明媚，也有倾盆大雨。强硬有强硬的好处，忍让有忍让的优势，任何时候，都需要我们审时度势，适宜而为。妥协不一定全是软弱，忍让不一定就是无能，和为贵。有时，迁就忍让也是一种智慧。

　　在我六七岁的时候，经常跟随舅舅出去放牦牛，在属于那段时光的记忆当中，背诵《普贤行愿品》和看牦牛打架就成了我最深刻的记忆。

　　互相顶撞的牦牛非常凶悍，舅舅总是要耗费很大的力气才能把愤怒的牦牛赶开。当时舅舅的原话已经记不大清楚了，只记得那个从舅舅口中说出的浅显道理："针锋相对、互不相让只能头破血流，要是都退一步，就可以和平相处……"

忍让不是软弱，而是一种崇高的修养。从另外一种角度来说，忍让力的大小其实表明了人生能量的高低。世间事物越宽阔，接纳力便越广。同样，一个人的忍耐力越大，便越能从容应对世间的诸多无常。忍让不仅仅是美德，更是产生和平氛围的必要条件，是剑拔弩张人际关系的调节器。一个内心不能平和的人，他的生活必然是急躁而慌张的。暴躁、莽撞、冲动，只会把自在拒之门外，无法圆满。

忍让一些、迁就一些、大度一些，远比互不相让的争执更有效果，更能把狂风暴雨变成细雨春风。强硬虽然有它的好处，用在自己身上是一种坚持与自律，但用在别人身上则可能会变成对他人的伤害。避免剧烈的碰撞，化干戈为玉帛，不仅是为人处世的方法，也是个人修养的提升。它让我们的人生境界更加广阔，一次宽容也许就能打开一扇封闭已久的大门。

忍让是智慧，不是怯弱，是为了让心灵上的闸门挡住奔流的污泥浊水。

愈是不能留下足迹的地方，愈要走得坚定

　　对于生活，我们应该从容地面对与接受，无论结果是获得还是失去。很多时候我们会觉得前路茫茫，不知道路在何方。其实路一直就在脚下，一切的过去都是以现在为归宿，一切的将来都是以现在为起点！不管过去多么暗淡，也不管未来多么辉煌，往前走吧！正如，我们不应害怕生命会结束，而应担心它从未开始。

路上虽没有我的足迹，
但我已经走过！

　　阿妈在农场的那些日子里，我每个月都要骑马去看她一次。虽然路途遥远，要穿过树林和荒原，还有可能会遇到狼，但我并不害怕。我不害怕自己会迷路，也不害怕天会黑，因为我知道恐惧只是一种虚无，人不能自己给自己设下陷阱。不管是白天还是黑夜，路一直都在脚下，只要我们勇敢地往前走，就可以到达。

生活中的路如此，人生之路也是如此。

很多人年少时，因为冲动或者是其他什么原因，屡次改变自己的航标和目的地，虽然及时醒悟，还是走了很多弯路。甚至在刚才，他可能还不知道属于自己的那条路究竟在何方，又会通向何处。但这并不可怕，只是心还没有被安顿好而已。不经历无数的悲喜，没走过生活的戈壁和绿洲，又怎会体验到生命的另一种滋味？在没有抵达之前，每个人的人生都是出发的状态。

人在迷茫困惑之时，即便走在路上，也会深感归期无望，不知道应该是掉头转向还是该奋勇向前。这时候不妨停下来看看、想想，等我们幡然醒悟之后，就会明白，这只不过是人生的一个弯道。黯然神伤也好，欣然愉悦也罢，都要空下心性从容面对。不管这条路是宽广无阻，还是偏僻坎坷，它总是在向前延伸，而我们也必定要走过，心怀勇敢，一直向前！

愈是不能留下足迹的地方，愈要走得坚定。

安于当下，才能笃定未来

　　不是谁都明白活着的价值与意义，不是谁都懂得人性与人心之间的渺小和伟大，更不是谁都能理解生命与生活中，得到与失去之间的缺失与差异。珍惜生命的人，他会明白自强不息中的云淡风轻；抛弃生活的人，在荼毒自己生命的同时，又在荼毒自己。只有走好我们生命中的每一步，才有可能迈向生活的彼岸。

　　从呱呱落地，到在静寂中离去，悲喜、成败、爱恨……构成了人从生到死的全过程。时间如行云流水划过，永不停歇，而生命终究要归还，如何行走就备加重要。

　　每个生命的存在都是一种持续的修行，我们不仅要追求活着的事实，也要认真对待活过的每一个瞬间、每一个片段。人有差异，命有不同，但在悔恨和错误中挥霍，则是对生命的浪费，是对自己的荼毒。我们的目光可以不去触及最遥远处的风景，但不能不明白这一生应该怎么活。把每一天都当作崭新的一天，把每一天都当作生命中的最后一天，安于当下，才能走好未来的路。

每一天的工作和生活，哪怕是平淡无奇地度过，也要以最热情的态度去拥抱它，去热爱它。只有这样，我们才会对每一个充满了希望的明天心怀期待。

我们的一生，或者伟大，或者渺小，或者根本认识不到这种大或小，但这不妨碍我们对生命、对生活的珍惜。若生命是在虚度和沉沦中苦苦煎熬，纵有千万个希望，也会成为泡影，最后什么都不会剩下。

如果珍惜生命，就要从珍惜每一天开始；如果珍爱生活，就要从珍爱每一个人、每一件事开始。踏踏实实地走过每一步，认认真真地留下每一个足迹，才会活得不彷徨。

切莫好心办了坏事

　　我们总是自以为是，总是用我们觉得正确的去告诉别人：你错了；总是用爱的名义，去安排、去侵入别人的生活，然后告诉他：我真的是为你好；总是毫无缘由地去批判，用不屑的眼光去蔑视一些所谓"无能"的人。殊不知，对与错不是我们一句话就能判定的，生活对于不同的人来说不尽相同，或者我就爱这样的生活，那就是好的。

人之所以犯错，

不是因为他们什么都不懂，

而是因为他们自以为什么都懂。

很多小孩子，都不喜欢大人对他们指指点点，更不喜欢大人告诉自己这些应该怎么做、那些应该怎么做。他们有他们的天性，虽然大人们总是以爱的名义去规整他们的错误，但绝大多数情况下，他们并不觉得自己真的错了。一件事对不同的人来说，对与错其实并不会统一。

生活中的人们，尤其是那些到了一定年龄的人，总是认为已经拥有了太多的经历和经验，习惯于凭借固有的经验做出判断。他们总是想告诉别人怎样才是对的，怎样才是错的，而且会对别人说："你那样做是不对的，按照我说的去做吧，这是为了你好。"

类似的自以为是或者自以为非在生活中屡见不鲜，本意或许是好的，是为了让别人少走一点点弯路，少碰几回南墙，用最少的努力得到最好的效果，但这样也会带来坏处，因为对与错不是谁一句话就能决定的。历史总是重复上演，过来人曾经失败了的方法被年轻人再次尝试，或许就会成功。

时常鄙视别人愚笨的人，他自己未必真的聪明。生活或者生命中的每一个命题，都值得用各种方法去反复尝试，因为生活本身对于每一个人都不尽相同。即便是同样一个人，面对同样的问题，哪怕因为时机的不同，也会出现不同的情况。生活是多样的，在我们用各种各样的名义去侵入别人生活的时候，就是在犯自以为是的错误。

量力而行才能自在

　　我们的生活中不外乎有三件事：一件是自己的事，就是自己能安排的事情；一件是别人的事，就是别人主导的事情；一件是老天爷的事，就是我们能力范围以外的事情。人的烦恼往往来自忘了自己的事，爱管别人的事，担心老天爷的事。要轻松自在不难，只要管好自己的事，少管别人的事，不操心老天爷的事！

　　老穆是个来自川西的工匠，已经在扎嘎寺很长时间了。他是个热心肠，总是帮着大家办些大大小小的事情。有次闲谈，老穆深有感触地对我说道："给人帮忙，真的很累！为了给别人帮忙，我连自己的事情都耽误了，可别人的事情还是没有做好。"

　　我告诉他："解决好自己的问题，才能更好地帮助别人，不要强迫自己做为难的事情，就没有那么多烦恼了。"

　　热心帮助别人是每个人都应该做的好事，但不是说什么事情我们都能够用上力。超出自己能力范围的强为，不但结果可能适得其反，自己也可能会身心俱疲。不要因一时之喜而轻易承诺，也不要刻意标榜自己出众的能力，否则善意的帮助则会变成一种个人的炫耀，致使初心与结果适得其反。

　　不同的人有不同的处世方法，或者是方，或者是圆，帮助别人也要张弛有度。先管好自己，做好自己能做的事，再去帮助别人。但对于那些自己完全无法做到的事情，还是交给老天爷好了。谁也不能主宰谁的世界，总有一个门槛是我们跨不过去的，与其一头撞在门楣上，还不如不跨过这个门槛呢。

　　人生最美丽的风景，是内心的淡定从容。世人都期待得到别人的认可，可到了最后他们就会明白，生活是自己的，在没做好自己的前提下，去帮助别人，于人于己都是一种不负责任的行为。

别做低头走路的人

对于生活，我们往往是在度过，往往将最美好的愿望寄予终极。仿佛最美好的风景只在彼岸，而此岸只是一种过渡，因此我们对沿途的风景常常忽视。其实，生命中的绝大部分风景都是在途中。活着是为了经历，经历就是修行。也许它是平凡的、琐碎的、漫长的，要学会安于途中。

只顾低头走路的人，
领略不到沿途的风光。
生命不在于结果，而在于历程！

生活当中，大多数人总是把所有的期望都寄托于最终的结果，企盼着那个恢宏壮丽、波澜壮阔的结果到来，好像生活的意义就是踏上彼岸，而非过程本身。

如果所有的目光都盯着那个"结果"，就会忽略了通往结果的"旅程"。活着不是为了得到或者失去，更不是为了成功或者失败，而是为了体验这个过程，欣赏这个过程。过程与结果，一个是要走的路，一个是所选择的方向，只有方向选对了，认定了，走好了，才是最重要的。

就好像登山一样，你选择哪条线路，决定了进程的长短与快慢，终点终将抵达。登顶固然可喜，但最美丽的风景不一定真的在顶端，途中的鸟语花香、虫鸣声声、风雨艰辛更值得品味。

不注重经历的人，就算到了彼岸也会忘记沿途的风光，不能为生命增色。

安于过程，潜心体会。相对于结果的辉煌或暗淡，追求的过程才是最好的修行。

生活需要一些意外

　　生活中很多时候很多事情，我们原本计划得很好，想象得很美，可往往走着走着，一切就慢慢变了，变得不那么美好，有时甚至变成了一个任务、一个包袱。如同旅行，本是一件轻松快乐的事，结果往往成了在路上奔波，只为了那一个个景点的"到此一游"，却错过了走走停停旅行的意义。

　　很多事情的发展并不会遵照人们的预期，即便我们早就制订了严谨的计划，无常依旧随时可能发生。比如，明天你准备外出游玩，但转瞬间阳光明媚的天气变成了阴风细雨，以至于游玩的计划成为泡影；比如说准备与老友相聚，却因为临时有事给牵绊住了，不得不把朋友间的相聚延期。

　　很多人在没有做一件事之前往往习惯于把它想象得十分美好，等真正去做的时候，才发现希冀和现实之间并不能画等号。原本的美好计划，时常会变成一个沉重的包袱，好像赶任务一样驱赶着自己去做，即便是完成了这个任务，也早失去了想象中的愉悦与自在。

这就好像我们满怀期待地筹备了一次旅行，本以为整个过程会充满欢声笑语，看到的也肯定是山清水秀，但真正开始旅行的那一刻，你可能突然感觉很心烦。即便是已经上路了，但在一个又一个景点之间匆忙奔波，除了筋疲力尽的劳累之外，恐怕不会对你的心灵产生任何深远的影响。意外总是会存在的，我们需要随时做好应对的准备，最为关键的是要修好自己的心，学会与无常共处，平和不惊。

不要担心错过什么，只要记住在路过的时候收获了什么就可以了，千万不要为了走而走，更不要为了行而行。

放下沉重，
你需要手持鲜花而行

　　快乐与痛苦、拥有与失去、成功与失败……都是来了又去。万物皆有开始和结束，不管你愿意或不愿意，这一切都是人生须经历的东西。无须回避，勇敢面对，坦然地去接受现实。然后，努力甩掉心灵的包袱，相信有些祸福只是一念之差。我们原谅生活的同时，也是为了更好地生活。面对，放下，自会多一份自在！

　　疲惫的旅人问菩萨："我走过了太过漫长的旅程，实在是太累了，能让我不那么累吗？"

　　菩萨看了看旅人肩上的大包袱，笑问道："你的包袱里装的是什么？"

　　"包袱里装着这一路的艰难困苦，装着我所经历过的风风雨雨和这一路上的汗水。"

"你背负着这么多东西，怎能轻松？"

世人就好像求佛的旅人，在人生的道路上经历了太多，牵绊也就多了起来。很多人觉得累，那是因为还没有学会放下。放下并不意味着舍弃，而是一种选择与面对。放下的前提首先是接纳，并且在我们做这种选择的时候，我们要确定自己的心是平和而愉悦的，不是因为被逼无奈而心有不甘。放下，不仅是一种面对生活的气度，也是一种得到解脱的智慧，更是一种求自在的精神。

世间苦乐的界限并不明显，往往只有一步之遥。是苦是乐，完全取决于我们的心会偏向何方。一个人能走多远，与所背负的包袱的大小有关系。

万事万物皆有始终，无论得失成败，都是人生的经历。面对，接受，然后放下。在清晨感受生活和生命，在黄昏安然入梦。轻轻松松何尝不是一种自在？

放下沉重，我们需要手持鲜花而行。

生活值得原谅

　　每个人都有选择自己生活的权利，旁人不该过多地去评判。很多事情本来就无所谓对错，因为我们每个人在看待同一件事情时的角度不同、情感不同，得出的结果也是不同的。人都有追逐幸福的向往，有的人勇敢，敢于抛开一切去拥抱幸福，为什么不祝福他们呢？尊重、宽容地对待一切真实的情感吧！

要尊重每一个人，
无论你认为他是何等卑微与可笑。
要记住，
活在每一个人身上的是和你我一样的性灵！

不要轻言己是，更不要轻言人非。是非对错，谁又能分得清呢？因为世间本就没有永恒的标准。

　　有的人总是习惯于用自己的眼光和固有的角度去看待人和事物，并对此做出或褒或贬的评判，其实这是错误的。生活中的每一个人，都有属于他自己的生活方式；生活中的每一件事，都没有绝对的对和错，只不过是因为角度和立场不同，因为看待的眼光不同。

　　人，都有选择生活的权利，而我们要做的则是尊重这种权利。只有尊重，才能理解，才能在坦诚和宽容中化解分歧。佛说一花一世界，就是指每个人、每件事都有独属的性质，不能用单一的眼光去看待。理解了这些，人会变得更加宽容，也会更加豁达。

　　以宽容的心态去理解别人的生活方式，这是发自心底的真诚，是一种自我升华。

　　对于那些抛开牵绊去追求幸福的勇者，世人应该给他们更多的理解和更多的祝福，因为这本就是一种靠修行得来的品格与修养。

第八章

爱是人生最好的营养

别等有能力了再去爱别人

　　不要等被爱了才想到要去爱，不要等寂寞了才明白朋友的价值，不要等拥有许多后才开始去帮助需要帮助的人，不要等犯错了才记起朋友的忠告，不要等伤了别人才去乞求原谅，不要等分开了才想到去挽回……不要等待，因为我们不知道等待要花费多少时间。而且，人生并没有那么多时间去等待。

　　人生并没有想象的那么漫长，当很多人懂得这个道理的时候，回头望去，人生之路已经走过大半，在惆怅中学会的珍惜，势必会浪费太多的曾经。

　　在风雨中与我们相随的人，都是无数的前因才换来的善缘，比世间所有的黄金都宝贵。也许他们身上有诸多缺点和瑕疵，但这丝毫都不影响他们对我们的爱和帮助。我们要学会的是宽容，而不是争吵，主动去爱他们，而不是等到感受到诸多的被爱之后才想起去爱。"等我有能力了就去帮助别人"，这是一种不负责任的懒惰，因为帮助和能力无关。一句宽慰的话语，一个相互理解的微笑，都将是莫大的帮助。

我们的人生并非无限，环绕在你我身边的，除了所剩无几的时间之外，还有很多无私的关爱。所以，千万不要等到要说分手的时候才想起挽回，不要等到他们已经感受不到你的爱的时候才想起去关爱。趁着还有能力去珍惜，趁着还有机会去珍惜，就从现在这一刻开始，付诸行动吧。如果连这点你都做不到，再多的期盼与渴望也会变成一厢情愿的胡思乱想。

与你相伴的人是人生的珍宝

　　轮回的路上，很难得有人能陪着我们一直走下去，不同的旅程总有不同的人相伴。走着走着，也许在某个岔路口，挥挥手，各自就转入了不同的旅程。所以，相伴的时候一定要珍惜，牵手的时候一定要紧握，因为，一旦分开了，一旦松了手，再见就不知会是在哪一世。世人都知道要珍惜，可是真正做到的又有几人？

　　与我们相伴相随的人，是人生中最值得怜爱的珍宝。

　　人生路上，总有不同的人在下一个路口加入旅程，也总会有人在我们转弯的一个瞬间离去，有时候，这种离去甚至来不及告别。一起走过平淡，走过坎坷，到了岔路口，却要挥手说再见了，真的是人生最大的无奈。

　　如果有一天，你突如其来的关爱让他受宠若惊，那肯定是你平日的关心太少的缘故。给陪伴你的人多一些关心吧，因为你们相互扶持、相互陪伴的时间不是无限的。也许在下一个路口，你和他就只能分开。人生道路上的一次松手、一次分开，再见之时已不知会是哪一次轮回。当那些陪伴我们走过很长路途的人开始变老，当他们啰啰唆唆地重复着一些老掉牙的故事之时，你不要烦恼，仔细倾听他们的每一句话，让他们感受到你的温暖和关爱。也许下一个瞬间就是分离，也许下一个路口，你将不得不和他们道别。

岁月是人心最好的证明

　　伤害可以让一个人成长，时间可以让一个人坚强，终结的友情可以让两个人一夜之间学会看透。当我们流连于伤感时，千万不要攻击、不要诋毁，因为人生何处不相逢。时间会是最美的答案，多年后，我们发现，其实分开以后还是可以做朋友。没有什么事是过不去的，唯有自己跟自己过不去。

　　有生就有死，有始就有终，万事万物都脱不开这个最根本的循环，友情也不能例外。或是因为一次争吵，或是一次意见相左，与朋友之间深厚的友谊就在不知不觉间走到了尽头。和朋友的交往，就如两条斜线，在相聚之后又要分离，这个时候，我们只需要把美好留在心底，剩下的就交给岁月去处理吧，它是人心最好的证明。

　　沉溺在伤感中的时候，万万不能攻击、诋毁曾经的友谊，你们曾经是一个整体，对他的攻击就是对自己的否定。人生何处不相逢？

你和他还会再次相遇，备好祝福与微笑以待用到。

时间是最完美的仲裁者，在岁月面前，没有什么事是过不去的，只有你自己和自己过不去而已。

分离，还可以珍惜。在上一次分离的过程中，在你挥手而去的时候，记住留下一份关爱。前路漫漫，道一声珍重，也许只要一个转身的机会，时间就会让我们再一次相聚。

爱自己，才有能力爱人

　　不要把所有的快乐与幸福托付在一个人身上。一辈子爱一个人是可以的，但没有人愿意挑着一个担子走一辈子的路。爱别人之前要先学会爱自己。怎样爱自己呢？珍惜自己的生命，尊重自己的原则，保护自己的身体，珍爱自己的生活，有自己的爱好。世上没有十全十美的人，不要勉强自己，更不要伤害自己的心！

　　可以用一生一世来爱一个人，但不能把所有的快乐和幸福放在一个人身上，这样的爱会变成一种负担。别让我们所爱的人如此沉重。

　　如果我们想更好地爱一个人，首先要学会爱自己，这是你能够更好地爱别人的前提与能力。

　　爱自己，首先要珍惜自己的健康，时刻关注自己的身体，吃干

净的食物，努力锻炼，远离疾病的困扰。在快节奏生活中适时地放
松一下，让自己的心灵得到休息。遇到不愉快的事情不烦也不恼，
宽容对待别人的错误，及时改正自己的过失。看一看蓝天白云，听
一听鸟唱虫鸣，做一些自己喜欢做的事情。不要让太多的欲望占据
自己的心灵，要用感恩的心态面对生活、接受生活，知道哪些该做、
哪些不应该做。要让精神保持舒畅，无论面对什么样的得失成败，
始终坚守自己的原则和底线。

　　每一个人都有属于自己的优点和缺陷，接受一个并不完美的自
己，并在修行中逐步改善。只有成为一个健康豁达的人，才能付出
更多的爱心。

慈悲与智慧需要共生

一个人只有慈悲，却无智慧，这种慈悲就是迷信，只能徒增自己的盲目愚痴；一个人只有智慧，却无慈悲，这种智慧会成为自己傲慢的资本，最终只能增长无边的邪见。所以，慈悲与智慧犹如人的双足，缺少一个的话，在解脱的道路上就走不了多远！

怜悯即慈悲，世情即智慧。

弘化利生救助一切众生，这是慈悲，而为了避免"怀揣好心却做了错事"，在布施的时候就需要智慧。世情通达，才能明白缘起性空的道理，才能明白"因缘"二字，才知道应该怎么去做。

随着社会的发展，物质极大丰富，而精神却一再萎缩，如战争、灾难、环境的破坏等诸多悲剧一再上演。人们无法控制自己无限膨胀的欲望，不择手段地相斗相争，自以为已经掌握了一切力量，在傲慢和不知反省中增添了无边的邪见，智慧用错地方，便会产生悲剧。

慈悲从来就不是空想，还需要我们去做。心有慈悲，行动如果跟不上，慈悲的力量便得不到发挥，便帮助不了别人。而且慈悲也不可以乱用，对恶的慈悲就是对善的扼杀。

慈悲与智慧，有如人的双足，相辅相成，缺少了任意一个，都会因为失去平衡而栽倒，只有互相扶持、互相调和，才能在求解脱、得自在的道路上走得更快更远。

理解是爱的前提

　　没有理解的爱不是真爱。我们不理解的人，是不可能去爱的；如果不理解却爱上了一个人，那它就不是真正的爱。我们要明白、理解自己所爱的人的需要、渴望及痛苦。想要理解和真正爱一个人，就应把自己放到"他的立场"上，与他成为一体，许多因不理解而生出的矛盾也就容易释然了，也就会幸福地爱了！

　　爱，不应是华丽而又空泛的名词，而应是朴实而又具体的动词。这个动词首先要有一个对象和前提：我们爱谁？爱他的什么？如果失去了这个前提，爱就会变得空泛而盲目。爱一个人，必须要理解对方。如果爱是一朵美丽的鲜花，理解就是广袤的土壤，没有理解的爱只是空中楼阁、水中幻影，爱根本就无从谈起。

　　爱在对他人的身体、情感的关心、体贴、呵护上得到体现，而理解是将对方洞察之后的释然。知道对方在想什么，想做什么，希望得到些什么，才能真正去爱。如果失去了理解，爱就很容易变成一种强硬的躯壳，会变成一种剥夺，陷入"爱之深，恨之切"的尴尬境地，结果往往会出现爱人分手、朋友反目等一些我们不希望发生的意外。

爱一个人，处理好一段关系，要把自己置于对方的角度，站在对方的立场上思考，不主观臆断，只有这样才能避免"好心做错事""帮忙帮倒忙"的糟糕情况出现。充分考虑对方，理解对方，才能和对方结为一个密切而又不可分割的整体。生活需要爱心，而爱心需要理解。理解越多，爱也就越多。

经营好自己，
爱才不会荒芜

　　生活中很多事情是无法经营的。例如，时间不能经营，它会在我们的珍惜、发呆、挥霍中慢慢流逝；情感不能经营，利益会让激情褪色、爱情枯萎；微笑不能经营，它是不求回报的天使，是根植在我们心中的春天。我们可以做的，是好好地经营我们自己，经营好自己的心灵空间，不要让爱在我们心的淡漠中渐渐荒芜。

　　湮没在泥沙中的金子必须在一次次淘洗中才能闪耀光芒，人生也是需要磨炼才能流光溢彩。

　　经营自己不是伪装，更不是掩饰，而是不断修正自身的缺陷，调整自己的不足，充分发扬自身的长处和优点，最终达到超越自我、完善自我的目的。

　　经营需要勇气和自信，要始终坚定地认为自己是独一无二的个

体，有着还没有被发掘出来的闪光点和长处，从实际出发，实事求
是地审视自己、探索自己，挖掘出自己更大的潜能。这是一个克服
自身缺陷、勇于面对挑战的过程，需要持之以恒，需要顽强的意志
去消灭人性中固有的懒惰和懈怠。

经营自己的过程，就是让生命的种子生根发芽，从一株孱弱的
幼苗成长为参天耸立的大树的过程。经营了，生命才能茁壮，爱才
不会荒芜。

爱与心都需要适合的距离

　　生活中许多情感都是败在距离上，远了生出不满，近了又生出矛盾。距离其实是彼此的一种尊重。在爱中需要距离，没有距离的相处是自私的，不能只想着自己，而不顾及别人的感受。爱不是枷锁，况且，给对方空间的同时也给了自己空间。不必靠太近，我们还有各自的生活；不必离太远，只需要一个转身的距离。

　　有人说距离产生美，也有人说距离拉开了，美就没有了。距离太远的话，会生出很多思念，但也会让人遗忘；距离过近，虽可以亲密无间，也最容易产生摩擦。如何准确把握距离的远近，是生命在历练中留给我们的智慧。

　　距离，一方面是空间与时间上的，另一方面则是心与心的间隔。适当的距离，可以给对方腾出一个合适的空间，同时也等于是给了自己空间。只有足够的空间，你和他才能从容地面对，才能有互相审视对方的机会，于是就有了自我反省、自我调整的余地。如果靠得太近，相互之间的距离全部被挤压，想动弹一下都变得十分艰难，无论做错了什么，都已经没有了改正的机会。零距离反而容易让心生出距离。

　　每个人都需要最起码的生活空间，每颗心都需要审视、反省、调整的余地，相互之间保持一点距离，给对方留出一点点空间吧。不过心与心不要离得太远，拉长的距离会让你和他始终处于紧绷的状态。或许人与人、人与世界只要一个转身的距离就已足够了。

只有真爱才经得起平淡

　　我们常常看到的是，感情经得起风雨，却经不起平淡。很多伴侣携手走过人生最艰难的日子，却在生活安逸的时候分开了。当各自进入下一程感情轮回时，转了一个圈，却发现结果原来都一样。我们可以不断追求美好的事物，但感情是需要经历与沉淀才能长久的，不可能永远都波澜壮阔。真爱一定经得起平淡的流年！

　　我听过一则小寓言，说的是无论狂风怎么样努力，都不会吹跑行人的衣服，每当狂风吹过的时候，人们都会把衣服裹紧；而太阳根本就不需要做什么，只是暖暖地照耀着，人们就会自己把衣服脱下来。这和很多伴侣在艰难险阻中能够携手同行，反而在生活变得安逸的时候分开的道理是一样的。

　　感情可以经受起狂风暴雨的洗礼，是因为在洗礼中会越来越深厚，而生活一旦安稳下来，感情反而容易被平淡所消磨。

湍急的溪流冲下高山，冲刷溪谷时往往是清冽的，但流进池塘平静下来之后，往往会变得浑浊，甚至生出一些杂质，这就需要适时地沉淀一下了。感情也只有经过沉淀，才能滤掉杂质重归清澈透明。

生活不可能一直轰轰烈烈，人生也不会永远都波澜壮阔。进入到平静缓和期的时候，就到了该反思生活的时刻。反思过后，才能雨过天晴，清浊分明。

越亲近，越要谨慎承诺

　　我们常常会忽略自己身边最亲近的人，忽略了他们的感受，总以这样那样的借口要求他们理解，却未想到很多的理解都是相互的。对自己的老人、爱人、孩子不要轻易地许下诺言，你就是他们全部的希望，一旦你忘记了自己曾许的诺言，或者你轻许了一个自己根本实现不了的诺言，带给他们的可能是更大的失落与伤心！

　　一个人，不管外人看来多么坚强，也总有脆弱的时候。能够帮助我们的，从来都是离我们最近的人。他们可能平时看似普通，但在我们最无助的时候，却能够以最快的速度、以最无私的心态给我们雪中送炭，以温热的情感让我们从无助的寒冷中脱离出来。

　　理解总是相互的，在我们要求亲人理解自己的时候，自己是否对他们也付出了同样多的理解呢？对于自己的爱人、孩子和老人来说，你才是最重要的那一部分，你就是他们的整个世界，也是他们全部的希望。如果你做得到，就不要让他们的目光中出现失望的忧伤；如果你做不到，就不要轻易许下诺言。

有时一句不假思索、脱口而出的诺言，你可能自己都不曾在意，或者只是随便一说，但对那些关爱和期待着你的亲人而言，这就是他们光明的未来，就是充满了希望的明天。你的轻率和随意，可能会毁掉他们的希望和明天，这比有些事情你做不好更让他们伤心。

越亲近，越要谨慎承诺！

爱是一种慢性循环

　　爱，是一种循环。爱，给予他人，不见得立即有直接的回报，但最终也会循环到自己的身上。如果你在爱护自己的同时，也考虑爱护他人，你就会得到更多的爱；如果你愿意帮助其他人获得他们需要的事物，你就会因此而得到你想要的事物。给予的越多，得到的也越多。学会爱和给予，带给我们的将是一生的财富。

　　爱发自内心，加持于众人，最神奇之处就在于，在经历了岁月漫长的冲刷之后，绝不会有一丝一毫削减，反而历久弥新，再次回到自己的身上，这就是爱的循环。

　　父母曾经花费很多时间和精力教会子女吃饭、穿衣这些最简单的事情，并且给子女带来了最初始的智慧启蒙，教会子女做人的道理。随着时光的流逝，当初连走路都跌跌撞撞的孩子已经长大，而健壮的父母已经垂垂老矣，我们更愿意把充满了爱心的碗筷送到老人的手边。我们用温暖的目光看着父母，就如同当年他们用同样的目光注视着我们一样。渐渐地我们也会老去，我们对子女付出的爱心会再次出现在自己的身上。

当你把爱给予他人，在很多时候并不能立刻就得到回报，但最终会回到你的身上。在学会呵护自己的时候，也要学会爱护他人。爱与被爱，并没有泾渭分明的界限，很多时候，爱与被爱是同时出现的。给予他人的越多，你收获的也就越多，虽然不一定现在就能得到回报，但回报终究会在未来的某个时刻出现。学会爱，学会给予，懂得爱别人就是爱你自己，必将收获安宁和满足。

父爱是人生的阶梯

　　小的时候，是父亲把我们驮在肩上，让我们能看得更高、更远；长大后，我们可能比父亲还高了，见识得比他还多了，可父亲永远是我们心中的大树。

　　在藏地有一句关于父爱的俗语："父亲是梯子。"这句话是如此贴切而又传神，把父爱的高大和无私表现得淋漓尽致。小时候很多人都还无法懂得这句话所蕴含的深邃含义，但当我们长大渐渐读懂的时候，很多人都会忍不住泪流满面。

　　小时候，父亲把我们放在肩膀上，并不是让我们感受他的高大，而是为了让我们比他站得更高、看得更远。当有一天我们超越了父亲的时候，他依然会是我们脚下的梯子，梯子存在的意义并非让我们仰望，让我们赞叹，而是让我们攀登。为此，父亲一点都不介意垫在我们的脚下，这正是父爱的伟大之处。

　　终有一天，我们的肩膀会比父亲的更加宽阔坚实，但留在儿时
记忆中的那个肩膀依然如山一般坚毅。父亲给予孩子的爱大多是深
沉而又含蓄的，只有在岁月的流逝中仔细品味，才能体会其中的甘
甜与醇厚。父亲教会我们勤奋，让我们懂得什么是责任，让我们知
道什么是尊严。当我们面对艰难时，父亲会大声提醒我们挺起胸膛，
勇敢面对风雨。

爱不是占有

　　当我们爱一个人的时候，通常会产生控制和占有的倾向，通常会要求爱的人这样或那样，却很少有人在要求别人的同时要求自己，所以矛盾就有了，争执也起了。轮回的路上，不管是做亲人、爱人、朋友，能同行已经很不容易了，在信任与宽容中快乐地走吧。争执或猜疑时，多想想对方的好，一切也就释然了。

　　有一位信徒因为和爱人的关系很不和睦，彼此之间经常争吵，问我如何才能改变这种局面，我告诉他："宽容、信任。"
　　两个人相处的时候，无论关系如何亲密，终究是两个不同的个体，而且都拥有独立的思想和观点，有属于自己的为人处世的方式和不同的想法。而很多情况下，我们和所爱的人在人生旅途中同行的时候，往往会试图控制并占有对方，而且这种占有通常都是以爱的名义进行的。一些人会要求对方这样那样，或者是不要这样不要那样。真正能够做到严于律己、宽以待人的人却很少，大多数人不能够以要求别人的标准来严格要求自己，这样的状态下，矛盾和争执就会以最自然而然的形式出现了。

我们要多想着对方的好，想着对方给予自己的帮助和温暖，并以感恩的心态对待与我们同行的亲人、爱人和朋友。许多事总是在经历后才会明白，就像感情，痛过了才懂得如何保护自己，傻过了才懂得如何坚持与放弃，在得与失中才会慢慢明白自己想要的是什么。

看己要看短，

看人要看长。

平淡是爱的保鲜剂

　　我们都需要爱。像空气一样，爱很自然地为我们带来喜悦和幸福，而真正的幸福是充满平和与满足的喜悦。如果在爱中我们没有办法让自己开心，老是纠结于各种烦恼，老是纠结于各种不满足，那这份爱终究会变淡。在爱的时候一定要往好的方面想，平和、满足的心态才会拥有幸福、长久的真爱！

　　如同鱼儿离不开水一样，人离不开爱。可一些被爱包围的人，却总是纠结于那些波澜壮阔、轰轰烈烈的感受，殊不知爱终究会褪色、会变淡。

　　生活不总是高低起伏、雄壮热烈，更多的还是各种各样的琐碎和平凡。如果总是向往一些刺激的感受，那会偏离了生活的方向。如果爱所表现出来的更多的是激情而不是温情，这个时候你就需要调整自己的心态了。

激烈的碰撞不是生活的常态，高峰和低谷的巨大落差也不是生命的主旋律。更多时候，生活是平平淡淡、普普通通的，而我们则在平和与宁静中度过生命的大部分，辉煌和灿烂只是短暂的闪光。不必为朴实平淡而烦恼，要有知足常乐之心，满足于已经拥有的幸福和喜乐，接受并且习惯这份平淡，就不会有那么多无谓的烦恼。

朴实而又平凡的爱才会天长地久。

亲情是爱的最高境界

　　爱通常是因欣赏而开始，两个人因心动而相恋，因离不开而结婚，但更需要宽容、习惯和适应才能携手一生。当爱情到了一定程度的时候，便会不知不觉转变为亲情，两个人便会逐渐视对方为自己生命中的一部分。也只有亲情才是我们从生下来开始就注定的，别无选择，并且赋予责任。激情虽美丽却短暂，唯有亲情长久、安然！

越走越长的是远方，
越走越短的是人生。

　　因为相互欣赏而吸引，因为吸引而心动，然后相恋，当感觉已经不能分离的时候就会结婚，这是我所见到的婚姻的流程，但这并不等于爱情的全部。因为爱情还有一次最华丽的转身：亲情。

充满了浪漫色彩的爱情，本身就具有华丽璀璨的特性，但这种华丽如同流星，虽然光彩夺目，却很难持久，并且会受到外界因素的影响。亲情和爱情不同，亲情本身更具朴实无华的特色，在相濡以沫地长久生活中所诞生的爱情，是将对方视为自己生命的一部分，而不是只把对方看作美丽的花朵。花朵只是生命周期中一个阶段，所以爱情远没有亲情更加稳固持久。爱情是后天因缘在交互作用下的产物，而亲情才是生命中注定不可改变的重要组成部分，不能放下也无从选择，这是一个必须接受、必须真诚相对的存在。亲情的背后，往往是生活的积累沉淀和生命的责任。

亲情是温暖的太阳，虽然没有流星那么灿烂夺目，却永远照耀我们的人生。它会随着岁月的流逝而越来越稳固，越来越深厚，无法割舍，所以情到深处，便会升华。

学会割舍才能重新开始

当一份相知相守已失去意义，就不如立即斩断那残存的希望，重新去选择新的未来。其实，生活并不需要无谓的执着，没有什么是不能割舍的。学会放弃，生活会更容易！

世间从来就没有一成不变的东西，当所追求的失去了意义，当昔日的追求在变化中成为一种负累、一种痛苦，就应该果断决绝、毫不犹豫地割舍掉，比如看不到未来的生活或者一段痛苦的回忆……世界一直都在变，没有割舍，就没有崭新的追求。

然而，割舍过程中最纠结、最难以舍弃的就是感情，有些感情对一个人的影响太深太久，割舍需要莫大的勇气，需要快刀斩乱麻，不允许后悔。

生命中有很多东西都不是必需的，所以也不必无谓的执着，顺其自然地放下一部分，生活才会更简单、更有意义。

　　快乐的秘诀不在于获得更多，而在于珍惜既有。其实人人都承蒙恩宠，享有莫大的福气。而真正最幸福、最快乐的人，了然于人生的不完美，却又能在这不完美中感恩并珍惜自己所拥有的一切。

别等到一切都来不及

　　遇到真爱的人时，要努力争取和他相伴一生，因为当他离去时，一切都来不及了；遇到可信的朋友时，要好好和他相处下去，因为在人的一生中，遇到知己不容易；遇到曾经背叛你的人时，要宽容地对待，因为他也是你人生路上的教科书；遇到曾经和你有误会的人时，要趁机解除误会，因为能解释清楚的机会并不多！

　　在纷纷扰扰的喧嚣中，我们曾与无数人相聚，又和无数人分离，一次又一次上演着红尘中的悲喜苦乐。在多如恒河之沙的相遇中，能遇到一个真爱的人，是何等不易！哪怕只是一次错过，都有可能让我们的生命发生转折。也许你还会遇到很多人，但是生命中的真爱只有一次，千万不要等到失去了才知道后悔。

　　如果你能遇到一个理解你的人，并且你也能够理解他，就不要太在乎得失。世俗的标准越多，牵绊就越大。把心彻底放下，坦诚相处，如同呵护自己心灵那样呵护这份缘分，即使有一天遍体鳞伤也在所不惜。

不要惧怕受伤害，他人的错误会成为你未来最好的借鉴。珍惜一切可以消除误解的机会，真诚主动地把曾经的误解和不愉快解释清楚，这样做并不会被人看低，这恰恰说明你的人生达到了一定的高度。

第九章

信念是菩提

在别人的质疑中坚强

　　当我们犹豫的时候，这个世界就很大；当我们勇敢迈出第一步的时候，这个世界就很小。等到有一天我们变成自己喜欢的样子时，谁还会质疑我们当初的选择？而那时，我们已经变得更好了，也就一定会遇到更好的人。其实，人生像一截木头，或者选择熊熊燃烧，或者选择慢慢腐朽。风雨人生，淡然在心。

　　无论做人还是做事，总会面对不可胜数的艰难和阻挠。当我们因为外界或者是他人的困扰裹足不前的时候，这个世界就变得很大，大得超出我们内心所能够想象到的一切；当我们突破了重重阻碍，在他人惊愕和不解的目光中毅然前行的时候，就会豁然发现，世界原来很小，小到可以直接装进心里。

　　迈出关键的第一步，需要勇气，而勇气正是直面外界困扰之时的气魄，是面对未知的胆识和对失败的担当。在修行当中，要勇于精进，勇于发现自己的不足，不要因为对于失败的恐惧而走上迷途。要感觉到内心当中无穷的力量，怀着对大境界的向往，坚定地修持自我。

不要总是希望得到别人的认可，这是对自己的怀疑。如果没有充分相信自我的勇气，你将必败无疑。当我们在修持中精进，当我们在生活中成功，当所有的一切都变成我们希望的那个样子，就不会有谁还会质疑我们当初的选择和执着。所有好的改变，都是因为当初那至关重要的第一步。

不要因为别人的质疑而暗淡了自己的星空。

奇迹是条少有人走的路

　　奇迹，是不会在容易的路上绽放的。也许，在所有不被看好、无人尝试的选择背后，会有不曾见到的可能，不曾设计的未知。未知让人恐惧，引人好奇，也因此证明你的勇气，成就你的自信。在每个死胡同的尽头，都有另外一个希望的天空，在无路可走时迫使你腾空而起，那就是奇迹。

　　当你被一层又一层的困扰所束缚的时候，不要灰心丧气，旧有的框架、禁锢就是为了让我们去突破的。勇敢地冲出去，冲向崭新的境界，我们就完成了破茧成蝶的华丽变身，因为这本就是生命的奇迹。

　　人生几十年的轮回辗转，乐此不疲地追名逐利，如不能遇到佛法的指引，会很难真正认识自己的本心，打破执念。奇迹从来不会出现在坦途之中，只有当我们走遍了所有的道路，试过了所有的选择，在艰难险阻中依旧充满自信、怀着最大的勇气做一次创新的尝试之时，奇迹才会以峰回路转、柳暗花明的方式降临到我们的身上。所谓的奇迹，大多是别人不愿意去走的路，是别人没有尝试过的方法，是别人不看好的选择。正因为如此，通往奇迹的路上才充满了许许多多的未知和不明确，也正因为莫测的前途和未知的风险，才孕育出不可能之中的最大可能。

奇迹，不是上天的恩赐，它是勇气和信心在长时间淬炼中升华出的顿悟。

信念会越用越多

我们通常会成为自己相信的那种人。如果我们不停地对自己说"我做不了这件事"，很可能最终就真的失败了；相反，如果我们抱着我一定要做到的信念，那么相信自己就一定会有能力完成它，即便开始时我们不能。所以，任何时候都不要失去信心，也不要放弃希望，人生就是一个不断圆满的过程。

深窥自己的内心，你将发现一切奇迹都诞生于信念之上。

一个人被塑造成现在既有的状态，有时间、空间和环境的因素所在，但更多的是来自主观，也就是我们的内心。当你相信自己不是某种人的时候，就会不停地做出十分强烈的自我暗示：我肯定不行，我做不了。这样的想法和执念会在潜移默化中改变自身，直到最终真的不行，真的做不了。而人往往会把这一切看成是自身缺陷导致的必然结果，其实早在不知不觉间就已经把因果颠倒了。

　　自信是一种强大的力量，可以化渺小为伟大，变平庸为神奇。记得在我小时候，一场白灾让牧区受到了很大的损失，但我的家人和乡邻都认为人定胜天。没想到第二年遭遇了旱情，情况更加恶化，可我发现似乎人们战胜苦难的信心却更足了，大家都在一种强大力量的驱使下力争将损失降到最低，而事实也最终证明，不畏艰险勇往直前一定会换来柳暗花明。

　　信念虽然无形，却可以让接触到它的人保持积极向上的心态。它并不能让我们得到什么，也不是直达成功的捷径，它只是让我们的内心更加坚定。信念不像碗里的水，会越喝越少，信念会越用越多。

　　相信自己，没有什么事情是做不好的！

心不死，一切都能变好

最使人颓废的往往不是前途的坎坷，而是你自信的丧失；最使人痛苦的往往不是生活的不幸，而是你希望的破灭；最使人绝望的往往不是挫折的打击，而是你心灵的死亡……所以，充满自信、满怀希望、心中有爱地去拥抱生活，就是再糟糕，一切也都会慢慢变好的。

在几年前的大地震中，我们曾为灾区的人们祈愿，并且送去了一些帮助，但我们所做的这些，都比不上灾区人们心中希望的重建重要。心存希望，人就不会颓废。灾难只能停留一时，而希望则能贯穿整个人生。

在困苦和灾难面前，能够让人们颓废的绝非坎坷的前途和莫测的命运，而是希望的破灭。当一个人绝望的时候，他的心也就死了。很多时候，我们正是依靠希望的力量才能走出阴霾。人生路上的伤与痛不可避免，但只要我们还没有放弃希望，还拥有自信，成功或许会迟到，但绝对不会不到。

困境不是绝境，不要常常觉得自己很不幸，因为还有很多比我们更不如意的人，要能乐天知命，随遇而安。把失败作为一堂必修功课，遇挫折时不要灰心丧志，不是路已到尽头，只是该为自己换个跑道罢了。若能将失败当成教训引以为鉴，通过检讨，学习不再重蹈覆辙，便是人生的精进！

挫折就像是一块石头，

对于弱者，它是绊脚石，

对于强者，它是垫脚石。

借口是修行的大忌

　　我们做某件事总喜欢找些理由，我们总以为今天的打拼是为了明天的快乐。可是，快乐不在路的终点，它就在我们走着的路上。所以，理由有时只是一个错误的借口，它让我们原本轻快的心慢慢变得疲惫和麻木。还原事物的本质，就是在还原我们自己。有些事情不是看到希望才坚持，而是坚持了才会看到希望。

因为无论多么完美的借口，
都无法改变事物的本质。

　　在我修行的过程当中，一直都十分强调"精进"二字，上师也曾反复对我提及。精进，要先发愿，然后次第去修行。但是在具体的修行实践当中，发愿的人很多，他们却没有完成目标，基本上什么都不曾做过，并且总是可以找到这样那样的理由。

"没有时间""近期太忙"……其实都是借口，只能说明没有努力去完成已经发下的愿心。修行如此，生活更是如此。借口从来都是懒惰和懈怠的代言人，与它为友就是修行停滞的开始。

借口会让人原本轻快的内心变得沉重，不仅会耽误修行，还会让人走上岔路。

直面过失，勇敢地纠正它们，才是真正的精进。

人生或苦短或漫长，世事都依旧纷呈。选择成千上万，虽然都在追求既定的目标，但最终都会奔向各自的宿命，因为这就是人生。无论心境如何，无论我们以什么样的方式活着，都是我们与这个世界的因缘。缘分各异，深浅有别，无须强求。

不要因为和别人之间的差异而改变自己。对自己的选择负责，每一天都充实饱满，整个人生又怎会黯淡无光？

人在顺境中是看不破人生的

轮回的路上，并非都是鲜花坦途，常常会有不如意的事发生，令我们纠结于心，叹息不已。逆境是成长必经的过程，不要把情况看得那么坏，要勇于接受逆境。当困难克服了，困境过去了，才会尝到人生的真味，生命也会因此而日渐灿烂。在顺境中修行，永远不能成佛，我们要感谢给我们逆境的众生。

轮回的路上，并非全都是一帆风顺，还有荆棘和坎坷。生命历程之中，时常会有些令人不如意的事情发生，这些并不美好的事情，总是令人徒然叹息形成心结，通常情况下，我们称这种情形为逆境。

逆境属于生命的一部分，不必把逆境中的一切看得那么糟糕，也不需要过分排斥疏远它，它是一匹桀骜不驯的烈马，只要驾驭了它，就可以骑乘飞奔。在修行中，逆境是最好的导师，可以指引我们勇敢无畏地迈步前行。在我们的生命里，它是一座燃烧着熊熊火焰的熔炉，可以剔除我们性格中的杂质，淬炼出更加坚韧的品性。

佛会给俗世中的人们准备好一条渡过苦海的小舟，以使人们可以到达光明宁静的彼岸。在每一条生命之舟上，都悬挂着用挫折编织成的帆。

挫折之所以称为挫折，就是遇挫而折的意思。如果我们能够在挫折中奋起，在困境中成长，挫折也就不算是挫折了。对于有些人而言，困境就是绝境，就是沉沦到底的无底深渊；而有些人则把横亘在面前的阻碍当作是更上一层楼的台阶。

每一次跌倒，都是收获经验的时刻。哪有不碰壁的人生？穷途末路并不可怕，拒绝面对失败，也就意味着远离成功。如何面对这些生命中的景观，是人们必须要学习的重要课程。人生苦海，广大无边，每一朵浪花都要勇敢面对。

成功是在艰难中成长

　　所谓成功的人，一定是比别人努力，比别人付出得多，经历了更多的磨难。凤凰涅槃，正是因为经历了强烈的痛苦，才会有震撼人心的美丽。一个人的成功并不是偶然的，他是踩着无数的失败和痛苦走过来的。别人看到的只是他今天的光辉和荣耀，只有他自己知道，在他通往成功的路上，有着怎样的艰难与辛酸。

一个人越成功，
他所经历的磨难就越多。

　　羡慕别人所取得的成功之时，一定不能忘记，别人之所以能够成功，是因为他付出了很多。

　　成功来源于辛勤的劳作，当我们还在享受着阳光、清茶之时，成功的人已在默默低头做事。不断地付出并不一定就可以获得成功，但不付出则全无成功的可能。

失败或许存在偶然的因素，但每一个成功都绝非偶然。没有走过充满坎坷和曲折的成功之路，就无法体会成功的来之不易。

人们往往只看到成功者所得到的鲜花和掌声，看到他们的辉煌和荣耀，却不知荣耀的花环是用荆棘编织而成的，每一个成功者都是遍体鳞伤的勇士。坚定地朝着成功的方向奋勇向前，在别人不理解的否定和嘲讽中坚守自己的本心，战胜一切艰险，走过一路坎坷，这本身就是生命的壮举。

如果你拥有成功者的勇气和决心，拥有他们的智慧和坚韧，并且愿意付诸行动，能在屡屡失败面前百折不挠，那么，你也一定不会失败。

苦难是人生的台阶

　　要时常对自己说，做一个谦虚而知足的人吧，把生活中所有的苦难都当作上天赐予的礼物。感谢磨难给予我们坚强，感谢挫折给予我们勇气，感谢欺骗给予我们智慧，感谢藐视给予我们自尊。经历寒冷，才知道温暖；体验艰辛，才知道甘甜。把所有的痛苦和不快都藏在心底，当作生活的历练，然后笑着去面对世界。

　　感谢天地容纳了我们，感谢父母养育了我们，感谢上师把知识和智慧传授给我们……生活给了我们太多太多的东西，需要我们感恩的也太多。当我们以谦卑的态度心存感激之时，别忘记感谢那些曾经降临在我们身上的艰难和困苦。

　　一帆风顺的人生不会精彩，但生活带给人们的苦难却是美好的催化剂，它让人变得成熟，让人躬身自省，懂得坚强，不再畏惧。

这些接踵而至的苦难，历练了我们的心性，它在我们的脚下铺垫成一个又一个进步的阶梯，让我们距离成功越来越近。

人生路上的曲折磨难、顺畅快乐即是命运。不要畏惧它的无常，虽然有时它来去无踪，也不要因为它怪诞就俯首听命，听任摆布。它一半在我们手中，另一半在老天手中。我们越努力，手中握的那一半就越强大，获得就越丰硕。绝望的时候，别忘了自己拥有一半的命运；得意忘形的时候，别忘了老天手中还握着另一半。

给
沉
重
的
心
情
松
绑

　　压力是一种无形的东西，看不见摸不着，它可以促人成长，也可以压得人喘不过气来。每个人或多或少都有一定的压力。然而，压力并不可怕，可怕的是面对压力时颓废不堪的样子。面对压力，我们要学会合理地释放。压力更多的还是来自自己，适当地放下，给沉重的心情松绑，快乐并健康地活着就是最好的。

　　很多人对我说："仁波切，压力像山一样沉重，我该怎么办？"

　　每次面对这种问题，我总是笑答："我也有压力，你看我不是很轻松吗？"

　　压力就像是空气，无所不在而又无孔不入，无论是入世的众生还是出世的佛陀，都会遇到，只不过对待压力的态度不同而已。想明白了这一点，就不会再对压力抱有畏惧的心理了。

　　就如同生命和空气的密切关系一样，人始终生存在各种压力的包围当中。压力不可怕，可怕的是面对压力时的脆弱心态。有的人曾被压垮过，心灵难免会被惶恐占据，变得纷乱芜杂，时间久了，就会逐渐迟钝、麻木，于是新的压力就在旧压力的基础上形成了。

压力，时时刻刻都在考验着人们对生活的态度，如果我们选择了退缩，无穷无尽的烦恼就会随之而来。适时地调整自己，给沉重的内心松绑、减负，从容面对，我们会明白压力和动力的相互转换关系。把压力当作生命中最为本质的那部分内容，而不是当作突如其来的不速之客，就不会在重压下颓废、迟钝。

在修行的路上拥抱自己

　　我们最痛苦的孤独不是身边没有知己，而是心中遗弃了自己；我们需要的帮助不是来自别人的关怀，而是实在而顽强的自助。连自己都不肯接纳自己，便无法要求这个世界给你一个位置；连自己都不敢正视自己，便无法在红尘中找到理解。我们需要常常坐在对面审视自己，要学会爱自己，并时常给自己一个拥抱。

如果我是我所拥有的，
如果我失去我所拥有的，
那我是谁呢？

　　佛教所针对的标物只有两个：人和我。对于刚刚接触佛法灵光的初学者，只要能达到度我的境地，就已经算是入门了。

不仅要认识到自我存在的意义，而且要参透这种存在。在整个生命过程中，只要没有遗弃自己，就不会感觉到孑然一身的孤独。

在遭遇艰难困惑的时候，我们需要的往往不是来自自我以外的关怀，也不是他人对自己进行注释，而是在肯定自己的基础上顽强地自助，在内心中一遍又一遍地审视自我，弄清楚自我所处的位置。

佛说，物随心转，境由心造，烦恼由心生。对于来去无踪、去留无痕的命运，我们不要因为它的诡异而放弃，更不能任由它摆布自己，我们要用自身的优秀与坚持挣断命运的绳索，用毅力和恒心来强化自己的内心。

在试图求助于佛之前，请先求助于自己。认识并且理解内在的真实自我，看清楚了核心和根源，才能做到心中有数。随着内观修行的精进，便可以逐渐认清自我、净化身心、体验无常，从中感受到安详、满足与愉悦。

理想是闯出来的

你想过普通的生活，就会遇到普通的挫折；你想过上最好的生活，就一定会遇上最强的阻碍。这世界很公平，能闯过去，你就是赢家；闯不过去，那就乖乖退回去过你原本的生活吧。能否成就梦想，并不是看你有多聪明，而是看你能否笑着渡过难关。我们最先衰老的从来都不是容貌，而是那份不顾一切的闯劲。

你攀上了什么样的山峰，
就有什么样的高度。
这是世间最显而易见的因果。

世界始终是公平的。我们能得到多少，取决于我们曾经付出了多少；我们可以拥有什么样的生活，取决于我们曾经突破了多大的障碍。在你羡慕别人的财富、地位之时，应该把更多的目光投向他们曾经付出的努力，而不是他人最后的收获。

有些人跨不过横亘在机会和收获之间的障碍，以致功败垂成，在困难面前乖乖地退回去，继续原本的生活；而有些人则在艰难困苦中审慎思考，以果断的魄力奋勇前进，最后成了赢家。决定收获多寡的因素，不是这个世界给了我们多少，而是我们面对机会时投入的勇气和智慧的大小。所以说，能否将梦想化为现实，更主要的还是看我们在机会面前是畏首畏尾、抱残守缺，还是在风口浪尖上力挽狂澜去战胜困难。

对于那些微笑着面对艰难并且一直笑到最后的人，一切所得都是理所当然。

没有经历半途中的风霜，自然就攀不上顶峰，也就看不到远处的绝美风景，这没有什么好抱怨的。

佛应该是宁静祥和的存在，但佛教中也有威武至刚的金刚，也讲求勇猛精进。人们最先失去的不是青春容颜，而是那份勇往直前、敢于横刀立马的闯劲。而我们的生活会是什么样子，正是取决于此。

在自己手中的才是梦想

　　每个人都应该拥有属于自己的梦想，千万别拥有别人的梦想，因为别人的梦想一旦加于你身上时就成了期待。你可以一辈子不登山，但心中一定要有座山，它使你总往高处爬，使你总有奋斗的方向，使你任何一刻抬起头，都能看到希望。当我们不再需要别人的认可来证明自己的时候，我们就真的强大了。

　　"一花一世界，一木一浮生"，佛用最浅显的语句解释了世界、极乐、净土等这些繁杂浩瀚的大问题。我们可以从迦叶尊者的拈花微笑中读懂这个道理：每一个人都是一个世界。在佛学与现实的融合当中，归结到生活里，就是说每一个人都应该拥有属于自己的梦想。这是最朴实的人生态度，朴实中透着平淡与真切。

　　人的生命是自己的，梦想也是自己的，如果把别人的梦想强行加持在自己的生命中，我们的整个内心将很难平静，或许只能作为别人的希冀而存在。如果只是为了活给别人看，并为此改变自己，是非常悲哀的，也谈不上有意义。

人生当中最好有一个明确而又清晰的梦想，使之成为前进路上的方向。这个梦想可以高不可攀，可以遥不可及，但一定要存在。人生之路到底如何，不需要攀比，更不必在意别人是不是认可，真心走下去，才会充实。当我们不在意他人的认可，也不需要对别人来证明什么的时候，便真正的成熟了、强大了。

在梦想这条路上，没有谁可以给我们做出任何安排。梦想在哪里，梦想应该是什么样子，不问天地，不问他人，只问我们自己！

半途而废，一切皆空

　　常听很多人埋怨说做事情太难，成功是多么不容易。其实，不是困难太多，也不是成功离我们很远，而是我们在前进的过程中遇到困难时很容易就退缩，半途而废。做事情往往不是因为困难而胆怯，而是因为胆怯而困难。困难，困在屋里就难；出路，走出去就是路。当你觉得山穷水尽时，扛过去就又是一片艳阳天！

　　"不怕山高，就怕腿软"，这是在藏区广为流传的俗语，却充满了从生活中积淀出来的智慧之光。很多人总是抱怨世事艰难，抱怨成功太远，在埋怨山峰的高不可攀之前，还是先看看自己有没有失去攀登的勇气。

　　真正让我们远离成功的不是困难本身，而是我们对困难的畏惧以及"知难而退"的心理。人们总是因为困难无法跨越而退却，却不知正是因为我们的退却而使困难加剧。当秋风乍起的时候，最先凋零的总是枯黄的那片树叶；洪水冲刷之时，最先被卷走的总是松软的土壤，而不是坚硬的磐石。所以说，困难之所以成为困难，完全取决于我们面对困难之时的态度。昂首挺胸地迎难而上，再高的山峰也会在我们的脚下，半途而废则一切成空。

没有在泥泞中艰难爬行的经历，没有在层层叠叠的茧里所受的束缚，就永远不会领悟。每一个生命，注定要面对外界赋予的艰险和困难，相对于这些，我们内心中的胆怯才是最大的拦路虎。

别在他人的风景中停留

　　看到别人成功，很多人都只顾着羡慕，而始终把自己当成了旁观者。其实，任何事情只要你去做，并且付出了努力，你也可以做得很好。我们要学会多和自己竞争，事情是不分大与小的，复杂的事情要简单做，简单的事情要认真做，认真的事情要反复做，相信成功会来找你！

与其羡慕他人的光鲜，
不如加快自己的脚步。

别因为在他人的风景中停留，而忘记自己的路。
　　走在自己的路上，遇到要遇到的人，经历要经历的事，这才是我们需要面对的。生命这场戏，我们不能不参与。
　　人生中最大的竞争者是自己，在和自己竞争的过程中，别站错了位置。一旦我们站到了观众席上，就等于是弃权，失去了比赛的资格。

在现实生活中，事情有大小之分，有繁简之分，但每一件事都是一次考验。用简单的心态去面对复杂，拿出"较真"的态度去面对简单，不敷衍，有耐心，认认真真地做好所有的大事小情，不断给自己的人生打高分。

羡慕之心，人皆有之，而如果我们因此认为梦寐以求的东西在别人身上，则是危险的。清楚自己的方向，懂得取舍，即便一意孤行，也胜似茫然无措。

要对得起自己鲜活的生命

　　逆境使人成熟，绝境使人醒悟。稻穗越成熟越懂得弯腰，人越懂得弯腰才会越成熟。不要把别人对自己的放弃，变成自己对自己的放弃。人生的日子都是越过越少，剩下的日子都是越来越重要。所谓顺其自然，并非代表我们可以不努力，而是努力之后我们有勇气接受一切的成败。

落日，我必须告别了。
当西边的云霞，从金黄到微蓝，
那将是我生命的终结。
即使你努力凝视，
即使我不断地回首，
当大地回归沉默，
我依然还是要走。

我们一起学会接受无常吧！

送我们的心灵回到家园。

很多人问我，为什么那么努力地去做一件事情，可结果仍然不尽如人意？是努力不够，还是因为自己根本就不是做这件事的材料？

因为期待一件事情的结果，所以努力拼搏地去做。但是希望越大，失望越大。世间所有的事物都存在着无常，只有无常才是世间的真实。即便如此，也不用悲伤烦恼，因为无常让人成长，并不会让人生倒退。低垂的稻穗才是饱满成熟的，而那些空瘪轻浮的却保持着高昂的姿态。世间的道理也是如此。只有那些真正经历过痛苦，并且在痛苦中成长起来的人，才会弯腰俯首以谦卑的态度面对生命。

人生，如高山之巅的花朵，只有不畏艰难，不怕挫折，敢于正面坎坷和失败，才能拥有坚强的一生。人要在逆境中迎风而上，在痛苦中寻找快乐，在迷茫中辨识希望，不到最后，绝不认输，不为别的，只为能对得起自己鲜活的生命。任何一个生命都有穷尽之时，随着时光的流逝，剩下的日子会越来越少，但也越来越珍贵。勇敢地接受正在遭遇的现实，勇敢地去面对一切不可能，珍惜一切失败和成功，哪怕最终迎接我们的并不是我们当初的希冀。接受无常，才能找到真正的心灵家园。

内心淡定，远离污染

　　世界越是浮躁，我们的内心越应该淡定，因为内心的平静可抵御外界的干扰。浮躁，会使人性失去根基，使清澈纯洁的心灵受到污染，最终导致精神的贫困。只有淡定，才能让我们于浮躁的社会里坚守原则，在物欲横流的社会里保持内心的从容与淡定，让心灵回归清纯。"宁静致远，淡泊明志"，给心灵一片滋润的净土。

　　佛法讲"空性"，其用意在于要人们认清宇宙与人生的真相，以解除身心的束缚，获得解脱和自在。有些人因为不了解"有"的空性本质，把"有"当作一种永恒不变的存在，这种本心是一种贪欲。还有一些人，认为世间万物是虚幻的，于是放纵自己，为所欲为。其实这两种人生态度都是内心浮躁的外现。

　　世界越是浮躁，我们的内心越应该淡定。在奋发前行中坚持，不走捷径，不做无意义的攀比，保持有志者事竟成的决心与恒心，如此才能增加人生的定力，战胜浮躁，淬炼内心。有时候，禁锢我们的，不是环境设下的牢笼，也不是他人施与的压力，而是自己将自己囚禁：看不开尘缘聚散，看不开诸事成败，把自己局限在狭隘的空间里；忘不了身外的爱恨情仇，忘不了繁杂的是非恩怨，把自己尘封在暗黑的记忆里；放不下身外千般烦恼，放不下心头万般纠结。结果，无端中迷失了自我。得失之间，方显境界，守住一颗超然物外的淡定之心，不为外物所羁绊，便能海阔天空。如若急功近利，患得患失，即使活得再累，也难以守住幸福。

做一个心里有光的人

　　我们总以为阳光只是来自太阳，可是在我们心里幽暗的时候，再灿烂的阳光也不能把我们拉出阴影。其实，阳光不只是来自太阳，也来自我们的心。只要我们心里有光，就会感应到世界的光彩；只要我们心里有光，就能与有缘有情的人相互照亮；只要我们心里有光，即便在最寒冷、阴霾的日子，也能感受到温暖！

　　在圣者法王如意宝晋美彭措——我最尊敬的伟大上师离世的时候，我没有办法如同修行很深的僧侣那样，怀着安详和平静去对待，而是心中充满了难过。但那个时候的我已经可以接受这些悲痛，并将之化为修行的力量。

　　伤别离是每个人都会经历的痛苦，从内心的寒冷中走出来，需要内心里有阳光。阳光不只是来自太阳，而且还存在于我们的心中。

当内心被阴暗笼罩的时候，再怎么灿烂的阳光也照耀不到心灵深处。无论这个世界让我们多么不堪，无论生活多么窘迫，只要内心充满阳光，就不会孤单，不会因一时的起落而患得患失，也不会因人情的冷暖而痛心。心灵的阳光，是生命源源不断的动力，它可以是一种勇气，也可以是一种信念。没有哪个心存阴霾的人可以走得很远。让黯然的心变得明亮起来，才可以更加平静地接受现实，坦然领受生命中的考验。让阳光流进心田，与那些同样心有阳光的人互相照亮，才能驱走恐惧，不畏艰辛。

人，一定要在心中升起一个太阳。

THE ZOMBIE CHRONICLES

Book 1 – The Zombie Chronicles

CHRISSY PEEBLES

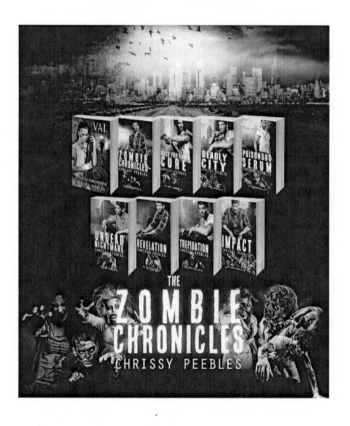

ACKNOWLEDGEMENTS

To: My fantastic editor, Autumn.

Thank you, Kellie Dennis for all of your magic making these covers!

Cover Art by Kellie Dennis at Book Cover by Design
www.bookcoverbydesign.co.uk

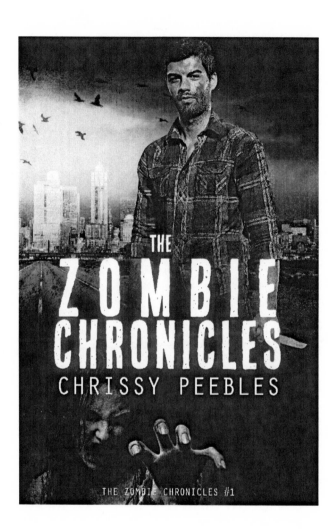

THE ZOMBIE CHRONICLES

CHRISSY PEEBLES

THE ZOMBIE CHRONICLES #1

CHAPTER 1

One year earlier...

It had been a long day in July, with heat waves rampaging throughout South Carolina. Even though nighttime had long fallen and the temperatures had cooled down noticeably, my shirt still stuck to my back. I wondered what good that shower had done that I'd taken before meeting Sherry.

A rush of wind blew through my hair as we rode to the top of the Ferris wheel and then stopped, hovering in midair. I breathed in, relaxed, and listened to the distant screams, music, and laughter echo below us. Sherry set down the stuffed pink pig I'd won for her in the ring toss and folded her hands in her lap, enjoying the silence. I dared a quick look at the stuffed animal, fighting with myself whether to be proud or sink into the ground. The guys back at school surely would've suggested the latter, but I didn't care. Granted, it wasn't the giant teddy bear I'd spent twenty bucks trying to win, but Sherry seemed happy with her little plush pink prize nonetheless. She squeezed my hand, and I smiled.

I rocked the cart back and forth with my legs.

"Hey! Stop it," Sherry said, twining her fingers through my hair.

"But you told me you loved it when somebody shook the cart at the very top. And I do too. Love that adrenaline rush."

She smiled and batted her lashes at me. Her whole demeanor screamed flirty, so I inched closer and wrapped my arm around her to pull her closer. "Do you want to play games or make out?" she whispered suggestively.

Her eyes sparkled like big onyxes as I gazed into them. We had liked each other for months, and we'd been shamelessly stealing glances at each other until I finally plucked up the courage to ask her out. It was our first big date, and I'd been dying to kiss her all night. "What do you think?" I asked with a smile.

She inclined her head as though in thought.

That same moment, a piercing scream echoed from below us. Forgetting our first intimate moment, I peered below into the darkness to the gathering mass.

"What's going on down there?" Sherry asked.

"I dunno." I squinted to get a better view, but the steel rods of the Ferris wheel blocked most of my view from where we were dangling. All I could make out were red and blue lights flashing in the distance, blinking in rhythm to the sound of blaring sirens. I leaned out until I could count five police cars speeding toward the midway.

"What's happening?" Sherry asked again, this time more quietly, as though she was talking to herself.

I paid her no attention as I continued to scan the commotion below. A man tumbled to the ground. The same moment, a group of people pounced on him. From up above, they looked like they were attacking him with their bare arms and legs.

Sherri grabbed my shoulder and gave it a hard squeeze to get my attention. "Oh my gosh, Dean! I think a gang of thugs are attacking the people in line."

I shook my head. *It can't be.* We lived in a family tourist town, its biggest crimes consisting of kids pick-pocketing sweets from the local supermarket and old ladies complaining about Friday night litter on their porches; the crime rate was so low that misdemeanors made the front page. I couldn't even remember the last time there'd been a public beating or any kind of vicious attack. "Maybe it's nothing," I said, my brain trying to justify the picture before my eyes.

"It sure doesn't look like nothing," Sherry said. "You think they're on drugs?"

I shrugged, hesitating. I wasn't naïve enough to think there were no drugs where I lived, but to see their effects creeped me out big time.

Bang! Bang!

Before I could answer, shots echoed from the nearing cars. I wrapped my arm around Sherry and forced her head down the way I had seen on television and in all those action movies. "It looks like the police are firing into the crowd!" I yelled.

"No! They can't be." She clutched her chest. "My sister's down there. I hope she's okay."

The ride jerked forward. As we started to descend, Sherry leaned over me to peer at the blinking lights on the bar that rotated inside the wheel.

I gripped her hand. "We'll find your sister. I promise."

"Thanks, Dean."

A scream tore through the air, followed by growls and hisses.

"What's that noise?" Sherry asked, frantically glancing below us.

Peering past the yellow bulbs twinkling all around me, I tried to see what was happening below. My senses were on full alert because of the danger we were in. I knew a stray bullet could hit us, or one of the drug-crazed people might decide to attack us. We had to get out of there, fast, before something happened. A cold chill rushed through me as the cart stopped at the wooden platform.

I scanned the area for the best possible escape route. Crazed weirdoes were biting and tearing into the flesh of screaming, innocent bystanders, their blood staining their clothes and the asphalt beneath their feet. My stomach protested, ready to hurl up all the greasy hotdogs, funnel cakes, and cotton candy I'd eaten. My mind screamed, *This can't be true! People just don't go around biting each other like cannibals! It has to be a joke.* But I knew from the grotesque salty-metallic smell wafting through the air that the blood was all too real. It wasn't a joke...but the grossest thing I'd ever seen in my life.

"Dean, what's happening?" Sherry asked, shaking my shoulder frantically.

"I have no idea, but we've gotta get out of here."

The possessed people shuffled toward us. My pulse pounding in my ears, I spun quickly in hopes of getting out the other way, but the entrance was blocked with more people flooding in. The silver line dividers dropped to the ground with a loud *clang*.

"We're trapped!" Sherry said, grabbing my arm tight.

"No!" I shook my head vehemently. "Don't even think that. We'll climb up the Ferris wheel."

"And if that doesn't work?"

I hesitated, considering my words. "Then we fight," I said, suppressing a gag at the rotten smell.

Guttural sounds—strange growls—emanated from the group as they stared us down like they wanted to rip through our flesh. They had greenish-looking, cracked skin, torn clothes, and white eyes. *Contacts? A wicked case of cataracts? Liquid latex? Special effects?* I had no idea, but I was ready to take them on.

A girl with long blonde hair inched closer. She looked dead, her head unnaturally askew. Sudden recognition hit me with a jolt: *Sherry's sister!*

"Jenny!" Sherry shouted; her voice overwhelmed with emotion. "Oh my gosh! What happened to you? You're creeping me out."

Jenny suddenly lunged at me, snapping her jaws like a rabid dog. She came within only inches from sinking her teeth into my carotid when a policeman fired shots. Jenny—or whatever she was—crashed down to the ground.

Shocked beyond all belief, Sherry leaned over the cart door, letting loose of her stuffed animal. It fell to the ground, right next to the thing that looked remotely like Jenny. Her gaze darted to the policeman holding the gun. "You shot my sister!"

"I'm sorry, miss, but that's not your sister anymore!" he shouted back. "She would have killed and eaten the both of you!"

More of the possessed group shuffled toward us. My heart raced. I clenched my fists, ready to take down anything in my path. I slid my leg over the bar, preparing to jump out of the cart and fight when one of the policemen fumbled with the controls. We took off with a jerk. I fell back into Sherry's arms, and we shot up about five feet in the air.

The beings lunged after us, shaking the bottom of the cart so violently we nearly fell out. Sherry clung onto me with a death grip. The group continued with their guttural chanting, and I swore I was trapped in some kind of lucid nightmare.

"What are they?" Sherry screamed in my ear. "What's going on? What happened to Jenny? Why was she...like that?"

I steadied myself by holding onto the steel bar with one hand and wrapped the other around her as I tried to make sense of what was happening. Below us, the group of possessed people seemed to have multiplied, holding up their arms as if they wanted a ride too. I dared another peek over the edge and regretted it instantly. The whole gathering looked like something out of a horror flick, blood covering their clothes and caking their skin.

Some started to stumble toward the officer, who shot anyone—or anything—who got too close. "Hang on, kids!" the officer said. With another yank, we sped up into the sky, stopping at the very top. This time, shaking the cart for thrills or making out was the last thing on my mind.

"That policeman...he...that cop shot my sister!" Sherry said between gasps. She buried her face into my chest and wept. I pulled her close, not sure what words of comfort to give her. More shots were fired, followed by ear-piercing screams and then...nothing. Panic ensued from other riders still stuck on the wheel at various positions. *Better to be up here than down there,* I figured. We had to be at least 150 feet up in the air, and that made me feel safe from whatever was happening below.

My cell phone rang jolting me out of my stupor. I fumbled in my pocket and answered the call.

"Dean?"

"Dad!" I said. "What's going on?"

"Oh, son, thank God you're alive. There's no time for explanations. Where are you?" he asked, his voice betraying an edge.

"I'm on a date with Sherry. We're stuck on top of the Ferris wheel at the beach. It isn't moving. Dad, I think everybody's dead down there! I-I don't know. It's all just so...it's crazy, Dad, like some kind of horrible movie!"

"We're coming to pick you up, and then we're getting the heck out of town."

"It's too dangerous," I said. "I know this is going to sound absolutely crazy, but you gotta believe me. People are turning into some kind of cannibals...and they're attacking people."

"I know. Don't worry. I'll be armed. I'll get you out of there, I promise. Got it, son?"

"Where are we going?"

"Your brother's flying us to the island with Grams where we'll be safe. These things are attacking everybody in Myrtle Beach. We've gotta get far away from here as fast as we can."

On the other end of the phone, glass shattered with a *crash,* followed by my mom's piercing scream. I gasped as the line went dead. "Dad!" I shouted. "Dad?"

CHAPTER 2

One year ago, a deadly virus decimated the world leaving swarms of brain-eating zombies in its wake. Survivors rushed to the makeshift fortresses, walled-in cities protected by towering concrete walls and a military force to be reckoned with. I managed to make it to one of these safe havens with my brother and parents, and that afforded me the chance to spend the last year sheltered from the gloom that rocked the land. My brother, on the other hand, decided to leave the safe confines and continue fighting with the U.S. Army to fight the onslaught of the undead. He became a top-notch zombie-hunter, but my parents and I didn't see much of him after that. My mother feared he might not come back alive, if at all.

Initially, the virus immediately turned anybody into zombies who had type 0+ or A+ blood. The rest of us seemed safe as long as we didn't get exposed through broken skin. We never knew what really caused the outbreak. And when scientists thought they had it figured out, the rules would change slightly. The virus mutated, and now if somebody was bitten or scratched, it could take up to five days before they turned...unless they died which meant the change came immediately.

I tried to make the best of the situation. It wasn't that bad. Our house had electricity and water, and I led a fairly normal teenage life—right up until I had to leave and jeopardize my safety (and consequently my future) for the sake of a girl I'd only just met. But I really had no option. She was scheduled for a lethal injection, and I could not stand by and watch that happen. I planned on stopping the execution, even though I knew the stakes were high. After all, if I'd have been caught by the authorities, they would have promptly booted me out into Zombie Land. It was a fate I did not want to subject myself or my parents to, but after pondering it and considering my options—and the girl's, which were none—I realized it was a chance worth taking. I had to save her, no matter what, and I could only hope my parents would understand.

My plan was bold, daring, and sneaky, as a proper rescue mission should always be. I knew that getting her out of the clinic fast, before anyone noticed, was the key to success. I smoothed my hands down my crisp white scrubs, smirking beneath my "borrowed" surgical mask as I adjusted it. I knew I would need a good disguise in order to get past the soldiers, and I was proud of myself for so easily snatching the medical uniform from the linen room.

Lucas, a friend of mine, laughed at the sight of me in the baggy cotton get-up. "I thought this was some kind of James Bond mission, not a pajama party."

"Ha-ha. Very funny," I muffled out from beneath the mask.

He eyed me up and down. "Well, you look ridiculous, but you definitely fit the part."

"Well, secret agents have to hide their identity somehow, right?" I punched him in the arm, and he grinned. Lucky for me, Lucas had the security clearance to sneak me into the isolation area of the clinic, and he'd owed me a favor for a while. *It's about time he paid up*, I thought, and I knew I could always count on Lucas. He was a fitness buff with huge arms, and he was the one who fit the part: He made for a perfect soldier with his camouflage uniform, Army boots, and buzzed head.

"This is a huge risk you're taking, but I completely understand." Lucas swiped a card over a control panel, and the door opened with a loud *click*. "Be careful, though, and whatever you do, don't underestimate her. That virus is flooding through her veins. They have good reasons for putting her in quarantine."

"Don't worry. I don't plan on joining Bite Club any time soon, I promise." With a last glance back, I walked in through the heavy steel door. As soon as the door closed behind me, it hit me: *There is no turning back now.* I took a sharp breath and focused my gaze ahead.

The room looked just like any other sickbed, complete with sterile-looking white walls and the strong, bleach-like aroma of a plethora of medicines. On the far right was a huge lamp that cast an unnatural glow on the tiled floor. On the far left, a narrow bed with white sheets that were arranged around a frail woman told me I had the right room. I took a hesitant step forward, then stopped, suddenly unsure of whether or not I really was doing the right thing. What if she's already turned? What if it's too late to help her and I'm risking my safety for nothing? Fighting with myself, I took a step back.

Suddenly, Val rose to her feet. Her fists were clenched, and her eyes were wide with terror.

I pulled down my mask before she got the chance to pound me. "Hey! It's me."

"Dean!" she said. "You know I've been...bitten. But why are you...? Look, you shouldn't be in here. You know being anywhere near me is a death sentence."

I slowly unwrapped the bandages from her arm and cringed. The zombie bite looked worse—far, far worse—than I had anticipated. Green pus drained from the open wound on her lower arm, and it reeked of dead, rotting flesh.

"That bad, huh?" Val asked when she saw my ghastly expression, her voice echoing off the white walls in the confined isolation room. She brushed back her disheveled, long brown hair. "It's funny how fate works. I spent so long trying to find you..." Her voice quivered as tears welled up in her blue eyes. "And now that I have, we won't even get to spend one day together."

I let out a long breath. "Don't talk like that. We'll have plenty of time together—so much time that you'll probably get sick of me."

"How do you figure that? And for the record, I don't think I'd ever...I would never get sick of you."

"Because I have a possible cure?"

She cocked a brow. "You mean the experimental serum?"

"Yeah, I snatched a bag of vials from the lab."

She gasped. "Do you know what woulda happened if you'd been caught?"

"I don't care. I'll do anything to save you." I wasn't lying. I'd barely known the girl a few hours, but there was something about her, something worth saving, even at the risk of imprisonment or death. The funny thing was; I never thought I had that kind of sacrificial savior in me—especially for a girl I wasn't even in love with. But after hearing her story, I knew there wasn't anything I wouldn't do for her. She needed me, and I was going to be there.

"I can't believe you'd go through all this for me, basically a stranger. It's impressive. Thank you." She softly touched my arm. "But those vials haven't been tested, so there's no guarantee."

"Doc was sure this batch would work. He told me they're on the verge of a major breakthrough, so it's worth a shot—no pun intended."

She smiled at my accidental joke. "Okay, if you say so. Give me the medicine. I'd rather be a guinea pig than one of those brain-munching things out there."

"I can't, Val. It's too early. The virus has to be in your system for...well, for a set amount of time before the medicine has a chance to work." I didn't have the heart to tell her that the medicine couldn't be given to her until *after* she turned into a zombie, a process that usually took about five days with the mutation of the virus now. *Yeah, she has a right to know, but just not now.*

"A set amount of time? How long before you can give it to me?" she asked, sounding a bit more panicked and demanding.

"Just a little while more."

"You know I don't have that kind of time." She threw the bandage back on and pressed firmly on the tape. "Be realistic, Dean. You know the rules. I've been compromised. They'll be in any minute to kill me, humanely of course."

Her words pierced my heart, especially since I knew they rang of truth; if I didn't intervene, she was doomed. "That isn't happening! I'm here to break you out." My plan was to sneak Val out, take her to the next sheltered city, and then give her a secret potion that the doc had been working on for months—the supposed cure to the nasty Necrotina

17

virus that had spread across the U.S. and the globe, turning men, women, and children into zombie-like beings with the burning desire to feed on human flesh.

"Really?" She grabbed my arm as if I was kidding.

"Really."

"Well, in that case, what're we waiting for?"

"We can't go until Lucas comes back and gives us the go-ahead. If we run into the general, our plan is screwed. It'll just be a minute."

She nodded and then placed her hands on her hips, her gaze imploring. "Is your brother going to help us?"

"I haven't told Nick anything about you. He'd just flip out, and right now, we need him focused if we want our little plan to work."

"I want to meet him. I *need* to meet him."

"You will. I begged him to take us to the next city, told him we have to deliver some antibiotics for the doc."

"Great. Think your smokin' hot plan will work?"

"Trust me, nobody will suspect a thing."

"So what's the plan?"

"For starters, we're flying." Making it up to the roof was the only way to get past the heavy security. Nevertheless, even though flying was the safest option, in those days, nothing was a safe bet any more.

"Wait...did you say we're flying?"

"Yeah. Didn't I mention that Nick's a pilot?" What I hadn't told my brother was that I'd be hiding a secret stowaway in the back of the helicopter. *Oh well. I'll worry about that later.* I was sure Nick would understand once I told him the entire story.

The door burst open, and Lucas peered in. "You guys ready? There isn't much time."

I motioned her out of the cell and pointed to a gurney. "Hop on!" I helped Val onto the gurney, then threw a sheet over her body up to her neck, mimicking medical protocol for handling the diseased on their way to the morgue.

"You've got to play dead," Lucas said. "So no blinking."

Val blotted the sweat from her brow.

"Are you gonna be okay?" I asked her, ignoring the sudden dread in the pit of my own stomach.

Her jaw clenched. "Don't worry. I'll bring home the Oscar. My life depends on it."

As I wheeled her down the long corridor past a group of soldiers, I was hit with a rush of adrenalin like I'd never felt before. Danger aside, I was having the time of my life. I'd never wanted my parents' version of the "normal teenage life". I had been thrust into the middle of a real live—or dead, if you think about it—zombie apocalypse, the kind people had been joking about and making videogames and movies about for years. Like my brother, who had chosen the military for his own adventure, I lived for that stuff, always seeking a thrill. I craved being where the action was, and finally I was there, immersed in a risky rescue.

When we approached the guards, a chill ran across my spine. We all knew that if we didn't get past that squad, it was all over before we even really got started.

"We're putting her on ice," Lucas said without so much as a nervous quiver in his voice.

The sergeant shook his head. "It just never ends, does it?"

"Nope." Lucas looked at me. "You got this from here?"

I nodded and moved down the corridor fast, my heart thudding against my chest. Once we were around the corner, I bolted. Metal wheels screeched against the tile floor in protest of the speed I was pushing, and I hoped Val didn't fly off the thing as we took the corners. The hall turned right, then a sharp left, and then a right again. "Okay, it's safe," I said, stopping. I started to strip off my white pants. Having Nick see me in scrubs would blow the entire plan, especially if he knew I was up to no good.

She sat up abruptly. "Please tell me you have clothes on under there."

"Of course. Now c'mon!" I helped her down and pointed. "The helicopter pad's this way."

We raced through the corridor and up the stairs and finally reached the helipad, where a healthy gust of wind rushed through my hair. Val jumped into the back of the military helicopter and lay down, and I threw a U.S. Army-issued olive green wool blanket over her.

"I have a little confession to make," I whispered between breaths, just in case Nick made a sudden appearance and caught me off guard.

"You secretly wear women's clothing?"

"Geez, no!" I couldn't stifle a tiny chuckle; the girl was funny, even in the most stressful of situations, and I appreciated that.

Her gaze narrowed. "Well, that's good to know. So what is it?"

"I didn't tell Nick about any of this. He has no idea you're coming whatsoever."

She let out a huff. "Ah. So when you said nobody will suspect a thing, you *really* meant *nobody*. Geez. I don't believe this. I thought he knew a girl was coming, but he hadn't been informed about my identity."

"Nope. Please just keep quiet until we get to the city, okay?"

"Fine," she mumbled, "but you should've told him."

A minute later, Nick jumped into the helicopter and put on his headset. "Ready, bro?"

I jumped into the copilot seat and buckled up. "Yep."

"You got the list of antibiotics we need for the doc?"

"Sure thing." My big brother always played by the rules. That made him perfect for the military, of course, but it was exactly why I didn't tell him about Val. He would've never agreed to sneaking her out of the city; he did nothing against the rules—ever. He lived by the moral code 100 percent. I don't know where he inherited that from, though, because I didn't mind bending the rules when it was appropriate.

He turned over the helicopter engine, and a few minutes later we lifted off and climbed slowly into the sky over Kelleys Island. The island wasn't far from Sandusky, Ohio. That's where Cedar Point was located. I had triumphantly ridden all seventeen roller coasters in that amusement park. Well, before everything happened, but I'll never forget the adrenaline rush I felt.

Kelleys Island was the perfect place to go for refuge because we were completely surrounded by water. Zombies couldn't swim, and as a backup, there were towering walls to keep the undead from penetrating the safe haven. That helped us all sleep easier at night. We had a nice cottage that was owned by my grandma. She lived next door in a spacious bed and breakfast that she ran before the zombie outbreak.

All the Lake Erie islands had become refuges for a multitude of people, and citizens were making lives there, living almost normally, with the exception of knowing that outside those walls, the hungry dead were walking. In order for everyone to maintain such a lifestyle, the city had very strict rules in place. One of those rules stated that if a person was bitten, execution was mandatory—

without exception, whether the victim was the mayor's son or the housekeeper's daughter. The safety of the many could not be compromised for the life of one.

"We should be back before supper," Nick called out.

"Yep!" I yelled over the noise of the helicopter.

Halfway there, I heard a loud *pop,* something like a car backfiring. The floor and walls began to shake and vibrate. My head jerked back and then snapped forward as the helicopter plunged, cutting through the white clouds like a knife. Looking out the window, I noticed a plume of dark smoke swirling outside the copter.

"Wh-what's happening?"

Nick fumbled frantically with the controls. "Malfunction. We're going down!"

"Mal-what?" I asked with a gasp.

CHAPTER 3

The helicopter dropped in altitude at a pace that felt like light speed. A sudden loud banging, like hundreds of baseball bats smacking against us, echoed beneath my feet. Gripping the arm rests tightly; I looked out the window, though I shouldn't have. The copter skidded on its belly and skipped across the treetops. The vibrations shook the floor like an earthquake. I braced for impact, knowing that even if we somehow miraculously survived the crash, we'd still have to live through the flames and/or toxic fumes that were sure to envelop us. I shook away the thought of blackened, tangled, twisting metal burning in the charred trees. My head jerked forward as Nick clipped a row of towering trees on a thirty-foot ridge. The helicopter jerked, forcing the side of my head into the metal wall. In an instant, everything was dark.

I don't know how long I lingered in that quiet darkness, surrounded by nothing but tranquility and carelessness that had become a sure death sentence in the real world. As I hovered in that dark place, unconscious of my body, the softest whiff of fumes assaulted my nostrils, slowly but steadily jolting me back to the grim reality: *We crashed...in Zombie Land.*

With a groan, I opened my eyes and took a deep breath, but the fumes from scorching metal burned my lungs. Nick's big head was staring down at me, and I pushed him away and vomited into the grass. Glancing around, I noticed Nick must have gotten me out and dragged me away from the wreckage. Vines, flowers, and towering trees surrounded us. We must've crashed into a forest.

My brother squatted beside me. "Are you okay?" he asked, his voice wavering.

The blazing sun beat down on my skin. Spots danced in my vision, and my head ached, especially when I rubbed the bump that had formed on the side of it where I'd clunked against the dashboard. I'd never felt so crappy in my entire life, yet I knew we had to get moving. I slowly sat up and rubbed my pounding head. "I'm fine...I think."

"Fine is perfect, especially when we're lucky to be alive." He patted my back. "I tried the radio, but it's dead."

As my mind cleared, I suddenly remembered Val. *Wait...only both of us?* My jaw set as I peered around, frantically searching for her. "Where's Val?" I blurted before I realized what I was saying.

Nick regarded me from under drawn brows. "Val? You must have hit your head pretty hard. We crashed in the middle of freaking nowhere. Don't you remember anything?"

His words barely registered with me. *Of course he couldn't check on Val or pull her from the wreckage. My idiot self didn't even tell him she was onboard.* Ignoring my brother's questioning look, I jumped to my feet and dashed for the pile of burning metal. I twisted my body through a jagged opening and climbed inside, ignoring the shark-like metal teeth tearing at my skin and clothes, then dove through the fire and smoke, searching desperately for Val. My hands dived right in, ignoring the searing pain that ran up my arms from when I'd tried to shield myself against the dashboard during the crash.

"Dean! What are you doing?" my brother yelled after me. "I told you the radio's not working. It's fried, man, just like your brain."

Ignoring him, I kept looking. The black bag of vials rested upside down on the floor; I was relieved they were plastic and not glass, so they hadn't shattered, and there was still hope for Val. Coughing and choking, I continued to stumble through the wreckage.

"I'm not gonna be the one to tell Mom and Dad that your foolish crap got you killed!" Nick shouted again. "Get out now!"

Smoked poured from everywhere, and the crackle of fire unnerved me. Even though I couldn't see a thing, instinct commanded my hands to push through the debris. About halfway through, I thought I felt something warm under my touch. *Val! Crap, she's not moving. Is she even breathing?* "Val! Val!" I choked out. I could hardly breathe myself from the pain and smoke, so I dragged her toward me. I scooped up her seemingly lifeless body and shuffled out as fast as I could. "Oh, Val, I promise everything's going to be okay. Don't you go dying on me."

As I felt for a pulse on her neck, Nick ran up to us. "Who is that, and how'd she get aboard my bird?"

"Oh, thank God," I said.

"What?"

"She has a strong pulse."

Nick's brows drew together, darkening his features. "Dean, what's going on? Who is *she*?"

Shaking my head to signal him that it wasn't the appropriate time for a million questions, I laid her down far from the wreckage, just in case it exploded like crashes always do in the movies. "I'll explain later."

Nick grabbed my shoulder. "No! You'll explain now. Who the heck *is* this girl, and why's she with us?"

I swung around and shot him a venomous look. "Chill out! Her name is Val, and she needs our help."

We held each other's gaze for what seemed like forever.

Then, as if something suddenly clicked, his shoulders finally dropped. "Val, huh? Well, is she okay?" He ran a hand across her forehead. "She's burning up." Then his gaze drifted to the bandage on her arm, and he peeked under it, gasping. "She's been bitten." Nick stared at me in disbelief. "What were you thinking? Sneaking a bitten chick out of the city? This is against protocol, Dean...not to mention you're gonna get us all killed with your knight in shining armor crap!"

"Let me explain..." I hesitated, gathering my words, but he cut me off.

"I don't want to hear it, and I want no part of this. You're helping a zombie victim. What's wrong with you? You know there's no hope for her." He punched the tree as sudden realization hit. "Wait a minute. You lied to me, didn't you? You aren't taking antibiotics to the doc. You were just using me to help you drag *her* out of there! Do you ever use your effing head?"

I looked away. I felt so guilty for landing us all in such a dire situation, such a mess. "No," I whispered.

"No what? No you weren't delivering antibiotics, or no you never use your thick head?"

"Both, I guess."

"I don't believe it. This was nothing more than an elaborate hoax." He ran a hand through his dense hair, his eyes throwing daggers. "Tell me one thing. How long have you even known this girl?" he asked, sounding as if he dared me to tell him an answer he already knew and was disgusted by.

"Less than a day."

His lips pressed into a grim line; he was definitely losing his cool. "I put my neck on the line for you," he shouted. "I got us the special clearance to go, and for what? So you could pull a stunt like this, putting all our lives in danger for someone you don't even know?"

"Yeah, but would you have helped me if I'd told you about Val?"

He said nothing and just continued to stare at me with rage and disbelief storming behind his eyes.

"Well, would you have helped me or not?"

He waved his hands wildly. "No! Never! Not like this. Not in a million years! But still, I have connections. I woulda tried to talk to the general and help you guys out. There is a way to go about things and we have to follow orders. You just—"

"Wait, did you say you would have talked to the general?" I snorted, my gaze fixing on the bare trees in the distance as I conjured the guy's image. He was about as helpful as a sleeping pill and just as dampening on one's hopes and dreams. "If that's the only kind of help you can think of, I'm glad I kept her hidden. We'd be burying her as we speak."

"Better than the fate you just handed to her— and likely to us by association. I don't know her, but I bet she wouldn't want to wake up as a flesh-eating monster."

"And she won't."

"Right. What are you going to do about it?"

"I'm going to save her! You aren't the only one capable of doing something about this zombie nightmare, just because you enlisted."

"Save her? You? Please. We'll be lucky if we can even save ourselves. If we run across a herd of zombies, we're as good as dead. We're all alone out here. We've got no communication, no weapons except my handgun, and we're gonna be lugging an injured woman around—until she decides she wants a taste of us." He shook his head. "You risked my life for a girl you barely know, you idiot."

"I'm sorry," I muttered, irritated. "Seriously. How many times do I have to apologize before you believe me? I really was just trying to do what's right, trying to help someone."

"Apologies don't mean anything if you'd do the same crap over again...and you would."

He was right, and I couldn't argue with that, so I kept quiet.

Nick paced in a circle, his brows drawn. I'd never seen him so mad...or scared. "We're in North Carolina. And our original destination is 600 miles away. I say we head back home which is 500 miles away. It's going to take us three times as long to get back because we can only go certain routes." He shook my shoulder as his voice thundered again. "Do you have any clue how dangerous it is out here? Do you? Well, I guess you never had a reason to think about it, all holed up safe and sound on the other side of those city walls on an island."

I pushed him back as hard as I could. "Death and gore...it's all people have been talking about for months, but—"

His blue eyes were intense, and I knew with one flash of them how pissed he was at me. "But nothing! You have no idea. This land is crawling with zombies that want nothing more than to eat our brains. You've been sheltered in the city since the breakout of the virus. While you're out flirting with girls, going to school, and trying to live a normal life, the other troops and I have been out here in...in hell. I've seen it up close and personal, and I can tell you it ain't pretty. In fact, it's probably worse than those stories you've been hearing."

"You're treating me like a kid," I admonished; I hated when he did that.

"Fine. Well, if you want to grow up, now's the time." He thrust his gun into my hands. "You've always begged me to be part of the action. Here's your chance. You're eighteen now, and I've protected you from all this ugliness long enough."

"I don't need your protection, Nick. I can take care of myself—and of Val if I need to."

"Spoken like a true idiot. But anyway, keep that attitude. Even if it's a load of crap you tell yourself, you're going to need a bit of that cocky nonsense to survive."

"I know it's a hard, cruel world outside the city, but I can handle it. I'm a survivor!"

"Love your attitude. I just hope you're prepared because you're going to have to fight like you've never fought before."

"Fine. You want me to take down some zombies? I'm up for that." It wasn't that I'd had much experience at such a thing, but I was sure it couldn't possibly be that difficult to defeat a mindless army of already-dead freaks who walked around stumbling over everything. I'd been taking lessons at the shooting gallery all year, and I'd pretty much amazed myself.

"You'll have plenty of chances to mow down some zombies later, trust me. Right now, though, you have to get rid of our other little problem."

"What problem?"

"You've gotta kill her. You have to kill the girl and put her out of her misery."

"What the heck are you talking about? I'm not killing anyone unless they're dead already and trying to gnaw on my leg like a drumstick."

"But leaving her to her fate is just...it's cruel."

My heart lurched. "No way."

He rolled his eyes. "You're such a liar. You didn't just meet her. How long have you been hiding your secret girlfriend from us?"

Girlfriend? She's pretty and everything, but that's just wrong. "It's not like that, man. I really did just meet her."

"Here's your chance to be a man, Dean. A real man has to make tough decisions—decisions that will save his own life and the lives of his trusted

32

comrades. This girl—this Val—will kill you in a heartbeat, giving no thought to all your pillow talk or those cute little hearts she scribbled around your name in her diary. Leaving your friend here to face her fate is heartless and cold. If you care about her at all, whether you just met her or have been seeing her for months, please be a man and put a bullet in her head for all our sakes."

I shook my head violently. He would never forgive himself, just like I wouldn't.

"I've had to make hard decisions myself," Nick continued, unfazed. "For goodness sake, I even walked in on my zombie girlfriend devouring a couple of my best friends. Shooting her was the hardest thing I'd ever had to do...but it had to be done, so I pulled the trigger."

I shot him a hard look. "Who *are* you? You're so cold, so heartless—not the big brother I grew up with. Protecting the city and killing zombies has made you a merciless killer."

"We have to face the reality of the situation. I know what she'll become. Except for the first night it happened, you've never seen it outside of television reports, but I have."

"You've changed, Nick. When you suited up for the Army, you became...different. You talk about *her* becoming a monster, but maybe you should take a good look at yourself."

He cocked a brow. "You're calling *me* a monster? Really?"

I nodded. Even though I could see the way he clenched his fists, I kept going. "Just look at you. You're somebody else. I don't even recognize you anymore."

His eyes narrowed into slits, as if he might argue for a moment, and then they softened with the pain of the truth. "Well, yeah. I guess being out here all the time...well, it changes you."

I didn't want to talk about it anymore. I just wanted to get Val and get out of there before the army of the undead showed up. "Val's coming with us, and that's final."

"Dean, come on. Don't you get it? Once she dies..." He threw his hands up in the air to make his point. "Look, I've seen it myself. When they come back—when she comes back—they aren't people anymore. Give me the gun, and I'll do it myself."

"Don't you dare!" I shouted. I wanted to pound the idiot so hard. "Listen—"

Grabbing the gun out of my hands, he cocked it and pointed down at Val's head. "We're doing her a favor. Besides, she'll try to eat us the second we fall asleep. Is that what you want, little brother? I mean, I'm sure you would love her to nibble on your ear and all, but not literally."

Ignoring his attempt at sick humor, I jumped into the path of the gun.

"You're pathetic," he shouted. "Just move out of the way."

I flung up my arms like a madman. "No! Put down the gun! You can't kill her."

Nick shook his head. "You're emotional, not thinking straight. She's as good as dead anyway."

I hadn't gone through all of that just to watch my brother murder the girl before my very own eyes. I lunged at him, but Nick twisted and dodged me; his military training had paid off. I lunged again and shoved him hard, and he threw me full force on to the ground. *Crap!*

Cool, calm, and collected, my brother aimed the gun at Val's head. Obviously, it wasn't his first time, and I was sure it wouldn't be his last.

"You can't do it," I shouted. "She's..."

"What, Dean? Why is this girl so important to you?"

I couldn't believe he was being so cruel, so nasty. "She's...we can't kill her because Val is our sister!" And just like that, I'd played my trump card. Even worse, I'd broken my promise to Mom not to say one word to my brother.

He lowered the gun as confusion washed over him. "What? Our sister? Either you're lying or you hit your head harder than I thought when we crashed."

"It's the truth, I swear." I sat up carefully, but I didn't inch any closer. I didn't want him to flip out and shoot her just because he felt threatened or even more pissed. "You pull that trigger, and you'll be murdering our flesh and blood, our very own sister."

The gun trembled in his hands. "I...I don't believe you."

"I know it's a lot to swallow. I just found out this morning. Mom and Dad have been keeping the entire thing a secret. You just can't—not now that we know who she is."

Nick met my gaze. "How do you know this is true? You got any proof?"

"For starters, look at her. Who else do you know with blue eyes and brown hair in those exact shades?"

He shifted his stance. "There are a lot of blue-eyed brunettes in the world. That doesn't mean we're all related."

"You know what I'm talking about. Look at her! She looks just like us!" I shouted. "Just look! She has Mom's nose and Dad's chin. Take a real good look. Deep down, you can't deny it. Just open your eyes for once and ignore the rules and protocols. Some things aren't so black and white, and you can't just kill your sister because it's in the rule book."

He stared down hard at her, as if taking in every feature. "You're...you're right. She's the spitting image of us. If it's true, why didn't Mom and Dad tell us? Why did they keep her a secret?"

I let out a long sigh. "They gave her away when they were teenagers. She's two years older than you."

"Two years, huh? That makes her twenty-four." He pushed the gun into his waistband and then ran a hand through his hair as emotion overwhelmed him. "You shoulda told me right off the bat."

"Like I said, I just found out. Besides, I promised Mom I wouldn't say anything. She wanted to tell you in her own way...later today."

"So how did you find out?"

"I overheard Val talking to Mom. I couldn't believe it." I pulled out a vial from my black satchel; it contained the precious green serum.

"You stole for her too?"

"She's not just any girl. She's *our* sister. Should we give her some and see if it works? Doc seems to think it will do the trick."

"It could kill her, like the last guy," he snapped. "I don't know what to say, what to do. I do know we'll never make it to a city before she turns into a full-fledged monster. Wouldn't that look great on the front of the family Christmas card? Yeah, she'll make a lovely addition to the family reunion next year."

"We have to do something. Like you said, we can't just leave her to her fate."

He crossed his arms. "You hold the possible formula in your hands, right?"

"Right."

"So why haven't you put it to good use already?"

"Well, Doc says it won't work during the transformation. We can't give it to her until she actually *becomes* a zombie. That's how the formula works. The problem was, General Lofters planned to execute her right away, as soon as he found out she'd been bitten. And you know darn well there're no exceptions."

"So what do you propose? We wait, invite her to lunch, and then hand her a cup of tea? She'll rip our heads off as soon as she turns. I've seen how these things work...and eat. They're almost unstoppable."

"She couldn't wait to meet you," I said. "You're her little brother."

"Yeah, right. You mean she couldn't wait to *eat* me." He shook his head. "Play the guilt card, why don't you?" Then he swiftly picked up Val and cradled her close. "It's not safe out here."

"You think I don't know that?"

"Well, what are you waiting for? I've got sister dearest, so let's go."

I nodded and swung the black bag of vials over my shoulder. "You're going to love her when you meet her."

"Maybe, as long as she doesn't get hungry."

CHAPTER 4

Nick and I took turns carrying Val. My arms clasped beneath her body to hold her in place. I struggled along the woody path, intent to keep up with Nick, even though he didn't seem to want to make it easy on me. Granted, he was still pissed that I hadn't told him about our sister right away, but knowing I had saved her life was my personal redemption and justification. I released a long, settling breath and moved the thicket out of the way; still, the deeper we moved into the woods, the denser the thicket became. To make matters worse, Val's long hair almost trailed down to the ground, and I had to be mindful of it so it wouldn't get caught in anything and hurt her. It seemed to me that she should have woken up already, but as the seconds and minutes ticked by, I began to worry that she might not ever wake up again.

"Are you okay?" Nick asked hesitantly after what seemed like an eternity. I noticed his worry lines straight away as his gaze shifted from Val to me then back to Val, as though he couldn't make up his mind whether to forgive me for the sake of our sister or keep being a jerk about it. "Let me take her," he muttered, grabbing her out of my arms.

I opened my mouth to thank him, but he'd already turned his back on me, leaving me standing in the middle of nowhere while he continued his march.

For the next hour, Nick carried Val without complaint. The bulging veins in his arms and neck told me his muscles were nearly at their point of fatigue.

Unable to watch his struggle any longer, I put my arms under her. "Hey, man. It's my turn again. Take a break and let me carry her for a while."

He jutted out his elbow, and ignored me as if I was nothing more than some pesky fly.

We spotted a trail and decided to follow it. It was a brilliant stroke of luck, because we soon came to a clearing, and our pathway ended at an overgrown dirt road. Nick was hopeful that there was a city nearby, so we started to walk off to the side.

I tried not to worry about Val, but it was difficult to put her failing condition out of my mind. "I wonder when she'll wake up," I said.

"Don't go getting all worked up over it. This is completely normal." He shrugged, as though he'd seen it all before—and he had. "During transformation, she'll have these long sleeping spells."

I nodded and then pointed at a green metal sign. "Next town's just a mile away. We need to get our hands on some emergency supplies."

"Yeah, especially food and water, but also a car and gas, if we can get our hands on any."

"Guns and ammo too," I chimed in.

"Right! A heck of a lot of ammo!"

A smile spread across my lips as my mind began to race, searching for ways we might get out of the predicament we found ourselves in. "If we can't find guns and ammo, there're always chainsaws. We could check garages."

Nick shook his head. "Nah. They're too noisy and might attract more zombies. Besides that, chainsaws weigh around ten pounds, compared to two-pound weapons like machetes, crowbars, trench spikes, or baseball bats. Remember, we're looking for anything that can crush or decapitate a skull in one blow. If it can't, there's no use lugging it around."

I was impressed; Nick sure knew his business. "Great tips, Mr. Zombie Hunter," I said with a laugh.

"This is serious stuff, Dean. Let your guard down once—just once—and you're a dead man. Even worse, you might get others killed in the process. Got it?"

I nodded, even though Nick's back was still turned on me.

We walked as fast as we could, remaining silent. My nerves were on edge, and my ears strained to pick up any unusual sound, but the only noise I could hear was the steady *thump-thump* of my heart, beating like a drum in my ears.

I broke the silence first. "So, we're gonna get ourselves a cool set of wheels? I like that idea."

"It's not exactly a shopping spree. Going into town at all is risky. Our goal has to be to get in, get what we need, and get out—as quickly as possible. You got that?" Nick said without turning.

"Yeah, I got it." His camouflage shirt stuck to his sweaty back. I wished he'd let me take a turn carrying Val.

We walked for another minute or so before footsteps thudded behind us. I swung around, ready to battle whoever it was. As I squinted against the glaring sun, I made out two figures in the distance, running straight toward us. My first thought was to run away, but then I came to my senses. *Zombies can't run that fast. Who could that possibly be?*

"Quick, take Val!" Nick handed our sister to me and whipped out his pistol.

I could only make out long hair, so I figured we were being approached by women. "It looks like a couple of girls, running from something. Put the gun down, Nick!"

Ignoring me, Nick held his weapon steady. "No! One of them has a weapon. Don't you know the first rule of survival out here in Zombie Land?"

"Huh? But—"

"Take no chances!"

"Don't shoot!" a female voice shouted.

"Drop your weapon!" Nick shouted.

She dropped it on the ground and raised her hands in the air. "It's a stun gun."

I craned my neck to get a better glimpse as she inched closer. Fear mirrored in her wide, green eyes. Her dark hair hung over her skinny shoulders in long, disheveled clumps. From the looks of her, she'd fallen in the mud while running. A pair of sandals dangled from her hands, and her bare feet were black and dirty.

"Please don't hurt us!" she yelled again. "We're already being followed by zombies."

The cute brunette with blonde streaks was a teenager about my age. In spite of being sweaty and dirty, she still looked hot in plaid shorts and a black shirt that showed off her tan midriff and navel piercing. I tried not to stare, but she was gorgeous.

Nick refused to put his gun down. "Have you been bitten or scratched in any way?"

She gasped for air. "No! I swear we haven't."

He slowly lowered his arm, but hesitation was clearly written on his face. "C'mon then, we need to keep moving."

The girl sighed relieved. "Thanks." A frown appeared across her forehead as she reached down and picked up her stun gun.

Nick resumed his previous brisk pace.

The girl rushed to keep up. "I'm Jackie."

My brother kept moving but shot her a glance. "Nice to meet you. I'm Nick, and this is my brother Dean."

"Nice to meet you," I said, stepping carefully over a few moss-covered logs. If I took one wrong step, Val would fly right out of my arms.

Jackie stomped down on a large fern in her path. "It's nice to meet you too. And this is my cousin, Claire."

I turned my attention to the redhead standing behind her, wondering how I could've missed her before. The girl was in her early twenties. She wore a sundress with a low V-neck and was pretty cute herself. Though she didn't speak, the look on her pale face told me all I needed to know: She was scared to death.

Nick broke through a patch of vegetation. "I wish we coulda met under better circumstances."

"Yeah, tell me about it," Claire said, pushing aside a dangling branch.

"Don't worry. Everything's going to be okay now," I said trying to ease her nerves.

"Yeah?" she said. "That's what the last group of people told me. You know what? They're all dead now."

"Really?" my brother mocked. He hated being underestimated. "Well, maybe next time, they should consider more powerful weapons than stun guns."

As we walked, Nick turned to meet the redhead's gaze. "How many zombies were on your tail?"

"A bunch—not sure how many, but there were a lot. It sucks so much. We've been safe for months. We had the perfect hideout, a mansion just south of here. We had food, clothes, supplies, everything, but they bombarded it yesterday."

That explained why the girls weren't wearing cargo pants and combat boots like Nick and I. Those sandals wouldn't do them any good if they stepped in a puddle of blood or had to climb over a few dead corpses. They'd made the mistake of getting comfortable, something no one could afford to do in Zombie Land. The only safe place was in a sheltered city, with a military force backing it up— or even better, an island like the one I lived on back in Ohio.

Claire frowned as she peered from me to Val, who was still lying unconscious in my arms. "Who is she?"

"We survived a helicopter crash," I said.

"That's horrible," Claire said. "I'm so sorry. I'm glad you were able to get out before it exploded."

"That was you guys?" Jackie said as she briskly walked along. "We saw the flames and smoke at the bottom of the hill after we hiked up it, and then the helicopter—yours, I guess—burst into flames. We hoped nobody was hurt."

"That crash is nothing compared to what we're about to face," Nick said.

We kept walking for a few minutes, following the road I hoped would lead to somewhere. Eventually, we rounded a bend and stopped to peek at a large, contemporary, two-story glass mansion. It seemed to catch the sunrays from every angle. Who did it belong to?

"We can hide in there, right?" Claire anxiously headed in that direction.

Nick darted after her. "Wait. I need to know exactly how many of those things were after you. 'A bunch' doesn't cut it. Can you give me a more specific number? Five? Fifty? If it's a herd, hiding in that house would turn out to be a suicide mission. We'd be trapped with no way out."

"There were about four or five of them," Jackie called back to him.

"Cool. That's not a problem at all. I can definitely handle four or five," Nick said, sounding sure of himself.

"Good thing we ran into you then." Claire smiled shyly, her eyes taking him in. Clearly, had circumstances been different, she wouldn't have hesitated to make it clear that she liked him, but flirting days were over. In the middle of nowhere, surrounded by the very hungry undead, there was little time for exchanging phone numbers. It was more important to tell each other how to avoid a zombie bite.

If Nick did notice the girl's rising interest in him, he certainly didn't show it. His commanding voice barked at them, "Just in case more come, can you girls fight?"

"Fight? Who do we look like? I'm not going anywhere near those nasty things!" she shouted.

My brother let out a long sigh and then met my gaze. "Wait here. I'll check out the house."

"I'm coming!" I argued.

"No! I need you here to watch Val. She's out cold, in case you didn't notice. Do you want something to start nibbling on her leg like a piece of fried chicken?" He clapped my shoulder. "I'll be right back."

He headed off into the house, and my stomach clenched; I didn't like him going in there alone.

"We can't just wait out here forever," Claire said. "Those things are coming!"

I shot her a look. "Aren't you wondering why that door's not locked? You want to run into a house full of zombies that'll eat your brains?"

I could almost see a light bulb flickering to light above her head as realization struck her. "You're right," she said eventually.

Jackie met my gaze. "Thanks for looking out for us."

"Not a problem." I craned my neck to the left and right, spinning in a circle as much as the added weight of Val weight would allow me; though Val was thin, she was a dead weight. My gaze focused in the distance, taking in every detail that might give away a possible pursuer, but I didn't see anything out of the ordinary. The sky was blue, and the birds chirped away like they didn't have a care in the world. It was hard to believe I could be facing a zombie at any given moment. It all sounded like some bad dream—like something I'd read in my comic books as a kid.

A few minutes passed, and my brother's voice snapped me out of my thoughts. "The house is clear, but there aren't any good weapons. Let's head into the garage."

"Sure," I said.

Nick nodded. "Look, I need you out here to help me fight. You up for it?"

"Sounds like a plan." I'd always wanted to jump into the action, especially when my brother came back and told me all about his zombie-fighting adventures. Finally, I was going to get that hands-on experience I'd been longing for. My heart pounded as realization kicked in.

"Let's get Val inside where it's safe," I said, shuffling into the mansion. I didn't have much time to check the place out, but it was pretty clear that the former residents had been loaded. If the place truly had been abandoned, we'd surely find some useful supplies to take with us.

After setting Val down on a yellow sofa, Nick motioned for us to go.

I turned toward the girls as I set my black bag down beside the couch. "Please watch Val and my stuff...and lock the doors behind us!"

"Got it. And don't worry. I got your girlfriend's back," Jackie said.

Nick yelled for me to hurry, so there was no time to explain who Val really was.

"Wait!" Claire said. "Do you want my stun gun?"

"What good is that going to do?" I just sprinted out the door, calling the girls to make sure they'd lock it behind me, just in case they'd already forgotten or misheard my first instructions. I didn't know them all that well yet, so I naturally didn't feel like I could trust them with my sister's safety. At the moment, all I could think of was protecting her so no one would get to her in the first place.

With one hard yank, Nick opened the sliding garage door. It was as loud as a flippin' freight train, and I only hoped it didn't draw any attention. Once it was open, I dashed into the garage and stumbled over a few bicycles that had fallen backward against some white wicker patio furniture. I caught myself by hanging onto a monster-sized grill.

"You okay, klutz?" My brother rolled his eyes.

"I'm fine. Missed a step, that's all." I took a deep breath to calm my nerves and regained my balance. Tools hung neatly on hooks along a giant pegboard attached to the wall next to a large workbench. Wrenches were hanging in order of size. The owner had certainly been organized, and I felt almost bad even considering messing up his neat little display by taking a wrench, but then something better caught my attention: a sledgehammer, sitting right there on the table, begging to be used. Granted, it wasn't the most lethal weapon, but I figured it was better than a screwdriver.

"Good choice," Nick said, "but remember, a zombie with a broken collar bone is still a zombie. Smash the skull and kill the brain."

"Yeah, I know. Stab, smash, penetrate, crush, or puncture the skull. It's pretty simple if you ask me."

Nick frowned. "Don't you dare get cocky! And never underestimate those freaks. Do you understand? The minute you do…you're dead."

"A little confidence never hurt anybody, Nick. It's worth its weight in gold in any arena."

He glared at me. "Dean!"

I could tell my brother wasn't keen on involving me in an episode of *Man Vs. Zombie*, so I tried to reassure him. "I can do this, Nick. Really, I can."

"If I didn't think you could, little bro, I'd have left you in there with Jackie and Claire who are very ill prepared to live in the world we're now faced to live in."

"Hey, your gun's loaded, right?" I asked.

"Yeah, but we've gotta save our ammo. I'll only use it if I feel it's absolutely necessary. Plus, we don't want to attract the zombies with noisy gunfire. We can handle a few though. No worries."

We left the garage and walked down the long, straight driveway. I spun toward my brother. "I don't see anything."

Just as my brother was trying to assure me that'd we'd have the upper hand, my jaw dropped. Something growled behind me.

CHAPTER 5

An unmistakable menacing growl erupted from behind me. Crap. I held my breath and turned slowly. My hand clutched the sledgehammer more tightly as I mentally prepared myself for the unavoidable.

"Don't try to be a hero," Nick mumbled.

Unfortunately, his words didn't quite register in my brain as I raised my gaze at the disfigured human being before me. The gaping mouth, full of black, putrid, rotting teeth and oozing gums made me want to take a step back, but I had to prove myself—to Nick as well as to my own ego. I stood my ground and forced the bile back down my throat. Ugly blue veins stuck out from a shiny bald head. Where strong, healthy arms had once been, there remained only holes, flesh eaten away by bugs. But what scared me the most were the eyes: human, yet dead. I swallowed hard and shook my head slightly. In that moment, facing that thing, I realized that the naïve confidence I'd had before was not enough. No way was I prepared for a real-life confrontation with the undead. Yes, I'd originally been thrilled about the opportunity to kick some zombie butt, but seeing them in person again was a totally different story. For a minute, I was reminded of the Ferris wheel incident all over again. That was the very first night people had become sick and turned into zombies. I froze in my boots, but not for long.

The creature began lumbering toward us. As it moved, thick, dark blood—something like motor oil—ran down its face, dripping off its rotting chin to the dirty shirt, the result of a recent head wound. The hole in its left cheek looked fresh, and clearly its last victim had fought back with a gun.

With my heart thumping, I zigzagged left, away from the bullet-ridden zombie. I grabbed my weapon, but before I could put it to any use, Nick leapt forward and chopped into the zombie's skull. The left eye socket made a suction sound as the eye propelled onto the ground. The corpse stopped dead and then fell backward onto the ground.

I punched the air. *Yes*! My brother nailed it. He absolutely knew what he was doing, and he'd had plenty of experience. After all, he'd been out there fighting those things for a year now.

Nick raced over to the downed zombie and jerked out his axe; I cringed, hoping the zombie wouldn't spring back to life like they always do in horror movies. "Get ready!" Nick yelled. "More are coming."

"I'm ready." I bolted down to the end of the driveway. As I looked over my shoulder, I saw two more zombies to my left. One was heading toward Nick, and the other had its sights on me. I needed more preparation, more weapons, and more tips from my brother, yet I knew there was no time left; the zombie wasn't about to wait for me to get over my rookie stage fright. I knew I had to fight. Nick's and Val's lives depended on me.

Dragging its right leg, the zombie inched closer and then swung its rotting arms at me. He fought like a small child. I knew I could easily take the monster on, especially since everyone knew zombies had an IQ barely above freezing, and they were slower than constipated turtles.

It was such a grotesque foe. I stared into sunken white eyes with no visible pupils. It had green-tinted skin and dirty blond hair, and the red, exposed muscles around its mouth made me want to gag—or maybe it was the foul stench of dead and rotting flesh. He wore a dirty, ripped mechanic's uniform, and his nametag read "Bob". *Poor Bob,* I thought. *How could this...this thing have been a human?* Had he been in a Halloween costume contest, he might have won for his makeup application and most interesting contacts alone, but I knew it had nothing to do with elaborate Hollywood special effects. It was all too real, and regardless of what he'd been in his life, in his living death, Bob was an enemy, and I had to take him down.

Bob hissed, flashing his black, sticky teeth at me.

I was ready to give the mummified mechanic the biggest headache of his life. The sledgehammer smashed through meat and bones like they were breakfast cereal, sending a pang of pain through my upper arm as it reverberated from the impact. I pulled away and then slammed it into the creature one more time, this time with less thought and more power. The second time did the trick, and he dropped to the ground. Realization didn't kick in straightaway, but as my breathing quickened and my eyes focused on the bloody mess at my feet, I knew I'd have to fight off nightmares for a while.

For a whole second, I breathed out, relieved and thinking it might just be over. But barely had I had time to congratulate myself for surviving before the sound of footsteps thumped behind me, warning me of someone's arrival. I spun around quickly, focusing my gaze on the tall figure hovering over me.

"Your first zombie kill." Nick slapped my back. "You did good, man! If the girls' headcount was right, there're about two left."

Adrenalin pumped through my veins. "Well, what're we waiting for? Let's go take down those slimy suckers!" I glanced around, and my senses went on full alert.

Another goon advanced toward me. This one was missing an eye. Its decomposing leg was covered with thin, blackened and bloodied shreds of rotting flesh, and severed bone was visible through its torn, tattered jeans.

I gagged.

"You got this, bro?" Nick asked.

I held my position. "Bring it on!"

"Good. I'll take the other one—the one coming from the right. The more we can knock out with the first strike, the better."

I wiped my brow with my sleeve. "Don't worry! I got this."

A female zombie stumbled over like a drunken sailor, letting out a gurgling moan as she held out her arms, as though she were a long-lost friend aiming for a hug.

"Sorry, honey, but you're not my type," I muttered. "Besides, I'm pretty sure you like me for my brains and not my looks." Focusing on my target, I charged, running toward the zombie at full speed before I kicked it. As it fell on the ground, I swung my sledgehammer and dealt the final blow, crushing its skull. The zombie slumped into a messy heap at my feet, but I had no time to marvel about how easy it had been. As I glanced up, I noticed another one coming and another one after that. *Crap! Where are they all coming from?* The girls had told us that only a handful of zombies were after them, but there were far more than that. Nick was busy taking down one after the other, which meant I was on my own.

Another rotting corpse headed toward me on unbalanced feet. I struck him, but then another one came right from behind. I swung around and struck him in the nose as I turned my hips into the blow. He stumbled back. I raised my sledgehammer and readied myself to take down the next zombie. Suddenly, something grabbed hold of my ankle and started to pull with a might that didn't seem possible, especially from a dead thing. I fell backward on my butt, sending my weapon flying straight out of my hands. The zombie I thought I had killed wasn't actually dead. *Crap! Nick was right. Never underestimate these things.* I kicked and flailed, trying to smash its face, but it would not release the death grip it had on my boot; I had forgotten that zombies were not capable of feeling—even pain.

I assumed a combat fighting stance and immediately went for the closest zombie with scraggly black hair and a missing left arm. It was shirtless and flat out nasty. I wanted to gag at the missing chunks of skin that were missing from its bulbous stomach, and the ropes of intestine that dangled, dragging behind the man with every lumbering step. I struck it hard in the nose, sending the shattered bone up into the thing's brain. The man slumped to the ground with a gurgling sound in his throat.

Another one came. I swung. The sickening sound of shattering skull seemed to reverberate throughout the air. I watched it tumble forward, and then brought my booted heel down hard on its head.

From a distance, ghouls staggered toward me in every direction. Their zombie moans made the hair on my neck prickle. "Remind me why I wanted to do this again," I muttered. My brother didn't answer. A zombie snapped at my boot like some kind of wild animal and bit me. Luckily, its teeth couldn't penetrate leather. Or so I hoped.

A shot echoed in the crisp morning air, and the zombie suddenly let go of me. Its brains seemed to explode from its head, painting the grass in a fresh coat of gore. Nick fired four consecutive shots and took down the zombies closest to me, but others kept coming.

I jumped to my feet, scanning the grass for my weapon. A glint of light shone off to the left. I scrambled over and picked up the sledgehammer I'd dropped when the zombie had attacked me.

After three more shots cut through the silence, Nick yelled, "I'm out of ammo!"

My heart thundered against my ribs. I wanted to play action hero, but reality set in: I couldn't do it on my own. We were outnumbered. "Nick!" I shouted. A zombie's head flew off its skinny neck as Nick's blade whacked through its throat. My heart almost burst through my chest as I watched a dozen zombies surround him. There was no doubt he was tough, but there was no way even *he* could take on so many at once.

The rotting lady in the red dress sneered and growled as she moved toward me. The left side of her face, from cheek to throat had been ripped away. I had nothing but my wits about me. Well, that and a wicked sledgehammer. The decomposing woman half staggered toward me. I took her down in one quick blow.

My fingers tightly wrapped around my weapon as one of those things growled behind me. I spun around. Black slime oozed from its mouth, and for a split second, I stared into its lifeless eyes. Moaning in a grotesque fashion, it inched closer to me, but I was ready. Before I even got a chance to swing, a loud *crack* sounded in the air, and the zombie collapsed in front of me.

I glanced at the house. Val stood just outside the door, a rifle tucked into her shoulder as she squeezed out one shot after another, taking down the rest of the undead army like some kind of female gunslinger. If Nick had ever doubted her being our sister, she had just proven his doubts wrong. Without hesitation, I started pounding skull after skull.

She smiled at me and then turned her attention to Nick, who looked stunned.

"Camouflage gear and combat boots?" she asked. "You're military all the way, aren't you?"

"You know it."

"I figured as much."

"Where did you find a rifle?" Nick asked.

"There's a false wall in the bedroom closet. It's loaded with guns and ammo."

"That's awesome!" I said.

Nick flashed his famous white smile. "You're as resourceful as me."

Val shrugged. "Well, what can I say? I'm the curious type."

"That was a compliment," Nick said, slapping her shoulder slightly, "because I'm pretty resourceful myself."

A hue of red flushed across her cheeks. "Uh...okay. In that case, thanks."

Never much one for giving out words of praise, Nick rubbed the back of his neck, slightly embarrassed. "Uh...I didn't have too much time to look around. You were passed out, and I was worried for everyone's safety with all those zombies around, and—"

Val grinned. "No need for explanations. We're all on the same team. But if I were you, I'd go upstairs and get some more ammo for your gun." She then reached down and threw me a handgun, which I caught in one swift move.

She regarded me from under lowered brows. "You know how to use one, right?"

"Yep," I said. "I've been training at the shooting gallery for some time now."

"Good."

Nick put his gun away. "Thanks for saving our butts back there."

Her blue eyes twinkled. "Hey, what are long-lost sisters for?"

We both smiled.

"It's nice to finally meet you, Nicholas," she continued.

"Please call me Nick. I-I don't even know where to begin. I have so many questions. This entire thing has totally taken me by surprise."

She grinned.

Nick ran up to her, hugged her tight, and spun her in a circle. "Dean told me a little, but not much."

"We'll catch up later, huh?" she asked.

He nodded, and then motioned around to the dead zombies on the ground. "I didn't know I had such a tough sister."

I laughed and joined in on the reunion.

Val held our hands as tears welled up in her eyes. "I've waited so long for this moment. I've met my biological parents, and now I've met both of my siblings. This is best day of my life! I couldn't possibly let those monsters take that away from me."

My brother tucked his gun away. "Girl, we crashed in the middle of Zombie Land."

"It doesn't matter. We're together, and that's all that counts."

Even though it had barely been a day, I already loved her just as much as I loved Nick. I knew how important it was for us, a family, to stick together through thick and thin. I did have to wonder, however, if humanity would even survive the cruel plague of reanimated cannibals. It wouldn't be easy, but deep down, I felt we'd somehow make it. We had too; failure was absolutely not an option.

"Hey, do you have that cure with you?" Val asked. "Now might be a good time to use it."

She wanted to use it because she was slowly beginning to change; I could see that much in her eyes. I thought about how I could break the news and soften the blow, but it would be like trying to hit someone gently with a battle axe. "I do, but I can't give it to you yet."

Mistrust filled her voice. "Why not?"

I realized I'd have to tell her delicately, so she wouldn't flip.

"You're going to have to let the change occur first, become a zombie," my brother chimed in. "I'm sorry, because it's going to suck, but there's no other choice. As much as I detest it, we'll be there for you. When the time is right, I'll give you the antidote."

Val's jaw dropped, and various emotions crossed her features, from dread to disbelief, then back to dread.

I elbowed my brother. "I was going to tell her in a nicer way than that," I half-whispered.

"There's no way to sugarcoat it, bro. She needs to know the truth."

"But I...I can't...I don't want to turn into one of those things!" Val's eyes brimmed with tears.

"It's the only way," I softly said, rubbing my hand up and down her back, which was about all I could do. As much as I wanted to help, I was helpless. I couldn't even find the right words to soothe her, if soothing was even possible at that point.

I expected a fit or lots of crying. She did neither. She just spun around and headed toward the house, her long hair dangling behind her like a curtain.

"Wait!" I shouted, running after her. "Where're you going?"

"I need to punch something, preferably a wall."

I looked at Nick. "Yep, she definitely has our temper." Of course, if I'd have been faced with the same dilemma, I'd probably have wanted to start punching holes in things too.

"C'mon," Nick said. "Punching a wall will solve nothing. Trust me on that. I've only done it a million times. Some of the holes I've left aren't pretty, and my knuckles weren't either. Like I said, it accomplishes absolutely nothing."

She stopped and turned slowly, her eyes ablaze. "Fine! Then I'm going to give those chicks you picked up a piece of my mind."

"Geez. You should've just let her go hit the wall," I mumbled.

She threw her hands up in the air. "You two left me in the hands of complete and utter idiots. Had I not woken up, we'd all be dead!"

I hated to admit it, but she was right. Even if the girls didn't want to fight, they could've been our eyes and ears and let us know which way the zombies were coming from so we wouldn't have had to worry about sneak attacks. Instead, they just hid inside the house after we risked our lives to help them find shelter.

"You're angry at *us*," Nick yelled, "not them. You're mad at the way the cure works. I understand, because I'd be pissed, too, but you can't take out your anger on them."

"Who in the heck dresses fashionable in the middle of a zombie apocalypse anyway?" she said. "Look at me. I'm wearing blue jeans, a t-shirt, and some great running shoes to get me the heck out of Dodge should the need arise. Really, who are they trying to impress? You can't turn on a freaking zombie, no matter how cute your outfit is!"

"Maybe they have a thing for Bob."

"Bob?"

I pointed down at the dead zombie in the mechanic's work suit. "At least that's what his name tag says."

She rolled her eyes, obviously not finding my joke very funny, and I really couldn't blame her for being in a bad mood. We didn't even know if the cure would work. If I was a nervous wreck myself, since the thought of losing my only sister scared me to death, I knew she had to be even more on edge.

"Those little fashionistas hid in the house like a couple of scared mice," roared Val before she slammed the door, beyond pissed.

I certainly hoped those girls had found some weapons, because it seemed my sister's wrath might be more fatal than any brain-devouring zombie.

CHAPTER 6

Nick and I hung outside for a few minutes, and I listened to his monologue as he went over our game plan. I tried to listen as closely as I could, but after a while, I couldn't help but interrupt his train of thought.

"Those zombies looked like animated corpses, like something out of a horror movie. It's just...unbelievable."

"I think you're still high from all that adrenaline. As you can see, it's not all movie magic getup. It's the real thing. We're fighting against the living dead here."

I shook my head, trying to comprehend his words. "They're pretty easy to take down when they come at ya solo."

"Like I said, never underestimate them. All it takes is one scratch or bite. We lost Martin from just one tiny prick from one of their nasty nails."

I nodded, thinking back to the one guy everyone on our street liked, Martin. We had grown up together and gone to school together, where we'd been trained in combat, since that had become customary. I still couldn't believe he was gone. "I know," I said, eager to change the subject before my emotions got the better of me and I slumped into that depressing dump I always sank into when I thought of poor Martin. "That's why I was freaking out when a zombie bit my boot."

Nick's eyes grew wide. "Why didn't you tell me?" He knelt down and started examining my scuffed-up boots.

I pushed him away, a bit rougher than intended. "Hey, I'm fine. He didn't get through."

Nick stood. "You're pretty lucky. Their teeth can cut right through leather."

"Yeah...lucky."

His gaze pierced mine. "Don't ever let a zombie get that close to you ever again."

I returned his glare, ready to stand my ground if need be. "It wasn't like I planned it."

"Yeah? Well, that's what Martin said too," Nick said dryly.

We had both been through so much personal loss: friends, comrades, and even Nick's girlfriend Darla, whom he was forced to shoot. But while I liked to talk about things to unburden my heart from all the fear and guilt over being alive while others were dead, Nick insisted on bottling up his pain, which consequently grew stronger by the day. "I know Martin was your friend as well," I said slowly. "You've been through a lot. I-I'm sorry I called you a monster back at the crash site. I guess

I overreacted. I just couldn't believe you'd want to kill our sister."

He hesitated a moment before answering. I could see his emotions on his face, playing out like a film, right before my very eyes. He felt guilty, but at the same time he also felt it was his responsibility to take on the lion's share of work. "It's okay. I've never claimed there isn't any blood on my hands. I'm probably everything you said and more, but it's what I've had to do to stay alive and defend the city...to survive."

I cocked a brow. "We're cool then?" I asked, knowing we'd just about reached our limit of sentimental, emotional talk.

He gave me a fist bump. "Yup, little brother. Cool as ice."

As we took a quick walk around the house, I noticed two four-by-four Jeep Wranglers in the back yard. "They're perfect! I love Jeeps, man. It's the perfect go-anywhere, do-anything vehicle."

"No off-roading, Dean," Nick said. "We don't want to give the zombies an advantage over us. We stay on open, paved roads. Got it?"

I nodded.

My brother's gaze darted toward the house. "The first thing we need to do is see if anyone lives here. We're all fighting to survive out here, and we have to learn to respect each other, so no stealing. If the owner has abandoned this place or is, uh...gone, then the trucks are up for grabs."

On first glance, the house had looked abandoned to me. I felt confident that we'd soon have ourselves a set of wheels as I swung the door open. I knew the place had to be unoccupied because dust was caked on the furniture and mirrors. The fireplace wasn't stocked with wood and was ice cold to the touch. The living room was spacious and furnished in ugly yellows, antique furniture, oak floors, and cream-colored walls. A mirror hung over two large yellow sofas. I listened to Val going off on the gals and had absolutely no doubt she was my sister; she acted exactly like Nick—and maybe a little like me too.

Claire ignored Val and kept playing a simple tune on an ebony grand piano sitting in the corner of the room.

"You're a natural," I said.

She closed the lid of the piano as tears welled up in her eyes. "I know now isn't the right time to be playing. I just couldn't help myself. That was the last song my mom and I played before we got separated."

"I'm sorry," I said softly, hoping the words would convey just how much I meant them.

She walked away, and my gaze drifted over to the spiral staircase that led up to the second-floor balcony, which stretched across the room with a glass railing. I glanced around for Jackie, who was sitting on the sofa, sipping on a can of Pepsi. My eyes roamed over her perfect body. I knew Val hated her outfit, but it sure showed off her incredible curves and long, pretty legs. I was mesmerized.

Val stared at me for a while, her mouth pressed into a thin line. For a moment, I thought she wanted to say something, but then she just shook her head, as though she found it a hopeless cause to share what was on her mind. She turned her back on me, hesitating, then poured bottled water over a towel and handed it to me. "Clean that thing off! And don't think I didn't notice your drooling." She pointed down at my sledgehammer.

I wasn't sure whether she meant I should clean it or that she thought she'd seen me drooling over it. My gaze wandered from the damp towel to the sledgehammer, and a smile crossed my lips. "I didn't realize a sledgehammer could be so sexy," I said.

She rolled her eyes. "I'm pretty sure you know what I meant."

"Thanks. I know you mean well." With a nod from her, I started to clean all the zombie guts off the hammer.

Val had calmed down some, but I could tell my sister's theatrics weren't over. "When did you have time to change that dress of yours?" she asked Claire, her voice sweet as honey. "While I was out there saving our butts?"

"It was bloody!" she yelled back with mock disgust.

"If all you care about is looking cute, you'll never survive out here! How far do you think you'll get in flimsy sandals?"

Jackie cut in, "Hey, if we'd have known zombies were about to break in and we'd end up running for our lives, trust me, we would've chosen other shoes."

Val set her bottled water down on the coffee table. "If you're going to hang with us, you darn well better get yourself a decent pair of tennis shoes...and next time, you better have my back."

"We will," Jackie said. "We'll go find some jeans and better shoes upstairs. I think I saw some close to our size."

"Why do I smell perfume?" Nick asked.

Val motioned to the girls. "These geniuses found a bottle upstairs and slathered themselves with it."

"We were trying to get the smell of blood out of our hair and clothes!" Claire whispered, the telltale hue of red covering her cheeks. "We've been through a lot, so please, can you just...?" Her voice trailed off insecurely.

I regarded her intently. The way her gaze shifted across the floor uncomfortably told me she knew she should've been out there helping us instead of cleaning up, but either she couldn't help herself or it was her way of dealing with the prospect of an untimely death. *Who can blame her?*

Val looked at me and shrugged. "Can you believe these girls? How are they still alive? I'll tell ya. They've been riding everyone's coattails and—"

"Val, that's enough," Nick said as he sipped on a can of warm Pepsi from the pantry. "These girls have lost people they've cared about. They're in shock and doing the best they can. Besides, they're the least of our worries right now. Let's scavenge the house for supplies."

I nodded. "Yeah, let's look for any possible weapons, canned food, bottled water, and medical supplies," I suggested, knowing Val's dressing needed to be changed as soon as possible.

"You guys are right." Val stood and walked over to the glass wall. "There're Jeeps outside. Whoever lived here might've tried to make it out alive, but they obviously didn't, which explains why the place is deserted. Let's load the Jeeps up with survival gear and get our butts on the road before the same fate befalls us."

"We need to hurry, people," Nick said. "Lingering in this fancy glass house makes us sitting ducks. The only way to stay safe is to keep moving."

Claire suddenly cleared her throat. "Why can't we all just stay here? You killed the zombies who were chasing us."

Val shot her an irritated look. "You're crazy! You might think you're safe in here, but you're not. You can do whatever you want, but we're not staying here. Come with us if you want, or stay here and play dress-up and die."

"What makes you such an expert? After what we've seen out there, you couldn't pay me to come with you, and surely not if you keep being bossy."

"Bossy? Me?" Val looked at me like she was shocked to be called such a name. "Am I bossy?"

I bit my lip. "Uh...well—"

"Well?"

"Maybe just a tad."

Val blew out a breath and turned back toward Claire. "Trust me, the feelings are mutual. I'll drop you off in a heartbeat at the first safe place we find."

Claire tossed her long red hair over her shoulder. "I'm not hitching up with a new group. I've been there, done that. The last one couldn't protect us, and I doubt you can either. My new game plan is just to stay here." She nudged Jackie's arm. "This is a great hiding place, right?"

Before Jackie could answer, Val cut in. "Suit yourself. It's your funeral. But we're outta here, right, guys?"

Nick carried a case of bottled water. "Definitely. Staying here is like signing your own death certificate, especially with these glass walls. Besides, you girls don't even know how to defend yourselves."

"I packed up all the guns, but I left two out for Claire and Jackie," Val said, pointing to the fireplace mantel. "I also put a bunch of holsters on the table for everyone. Well, I think Nick has his own. But anyway, give Claire and Jackie one, and while you're at it, maybe you should give them some pointers."

Claire rolled her eyes. "I'm really not into violence."

"I don't care what you're into. It's all about survival now," Val said. "'Cause those things will tear you apart. They'll munch on your flesh—gnawing, biting, and chewing—all while you're still alive watching."

Jackie threw a couch pillow at Val. "C'mon! That's gross!"

Val placed her hands on her hips. "No, that's reality. You better get hip with the times, 'cause we're living in a post-apocalyptic world now. This isn't some pretty world filled with colorful daffodils and butterflies. It's do or die."

"Does your sister think she's Lara Croft or something?" Claire asked.

"We're giving you some guns," Val said, turning to face her.

She shook her head. "No!"

Val met her gaze straight on. "Yes. You have the right to defend yourself! If a zombie crosses that line, you're gonna need an equalizer."

Claire rolled her eyes as Val continued.

"Now, we're gonna give you a quick lesson, Glock 101." Val picked up a pistol and handed it to the stubborn girl. "Take it! I'm not leaving you here defenseless, Princess."

"Well, I'm not going to let *you* teach me anything," Claire hissed.

Val motioned toward Nick and me. "Fine. We've got two capable guys here. Pick one to coach you. Let me tell you something, Little Miss Thing, zombies don't discriminate, and they'll..."

I tuned her out, glanced at the sunset, and picked up a Glock 26 Gen4 from the mantel for Jackie. She squeezed past Claire, making her way out into the hall. Through the open door, I watched her enter the kitchen. It was the perfect opportunity to have a minute alone with her.

"They need to take a gun and know how to use it. Best-case scenario, they'll smarten up and come with us. Try to talk some sense into her, Dean," my brother said. "I'll work on Claire."

Claire stepped toward him. "Hey! I'm right here you know! Quit talking about me like I'm not even in the room."

"Claire..." he began as I walked out of the living room.

I needed to convince Jackie somehow to leave with us, but if she refused, I still wanted her to have a weapon so she could take down any of those undead freaks who ventured near the house. I knew we couldn't actually fire off bullets without attracting every zombie within miles, but I needed to teach her the basics. I found her standing near the kitchen counter, her arms pressed against the smooth Formica, her forehead creased with fine lines from anger and worry.

Her eyes lit up the second I walked in, and her forehead smoothed, as though all her worries disappeared the moment she saw me. "Hey," she said.

"Hey."

She held my gaze. "What's up?"

"Can I talk to you for a minute?" I asked.

"I'm not so sure your girlfriend would like that. She might kick my butt and feed it to the zombies."

"Val's not my girlfriend," I said.

"Your brother's?"

"Nope. She's our sister."

"I didn't know that, Dean," she whispered. "What do you have there?" she asked, looking down at my hands.

"If you're going to stay here—which I still don't think you should—you're gonna need this." I handed her the gun.

She bit her lip and ran a hand across the smooth chrome. "Dean, I can't—"

"Humor me."

She nodded.

"Okay, first rule," I said. "Never place your finger on the trigger unless you're about to fire. Pretend the gun is loaded at all times." I took out the magazine and unloaded the gun. Then I showed her how to properly hold the Glock pistol and lock her arms.

Jackie's trembling hands reached for the gun. She wrapped her palm around the grip and secured her hold with her other hand. "It's empty, right?"

"Yes, but it shouldn't be. A zombie can come at any given minute. Always be prepared."

She slammed the magazine in with shaking hands. Cocking the slide back, she successfully chambered a round. She slowly raised the gun and put her finger on the trigger. "I watched those things tear apart a sixty-five-year-old woman right before my eyes." Tears welled up in her eyes. "She was in our group...my friend."

I softly touched her back. "Jackie, I'm so sorry."

"I couldn't do anything to help her. Maybe if I'd have had a gun like this, I could've done something." She inhaled and let it out slowly. "Your sister's right. I don't want to watch a zombie munch on me while I'm still alive, screaming, and I don't want to watch another friend die in front of me. I'll give this gun thing a try."

"That's all I'm asking."

She gripped the gun tightly and pointed straight ahead at the fridge. "You know what?"

"What?"

"The next zombie I meet will die."

I didn't want to point out the irony of her words: Technically, they were dead meat already, but I got her point anyway. She wanted them "dead" as in unmoving, shapeless heaps. We all wanted the same thing. I knew she meant every word because the pain was evident in her voice. I couldn't imagine losing the ones I loved in such a horrible way. "I'm so sorry for your loss," I said.

"She's in a better place, and so are the others. Bless their souls." She paused for a moment and then met my gaze. "Teach me, Dean. I want to learn everything. From this moment on, I refuse to run anymore."

I came from behind and held her arms. I couldn't help noticing her perfume, which smelled so good. "Stand facing the target with your feet shoulder-width apart."

She glanced at me.

I smiled. "Now bend your knees slightly." I inched closer and said in her ear, "Extend the handgun toward the target, keeping your arms straight and locked. Got it?"

"Yeah."

I shot her a grin and continued with the lesson. "Okay. Now, with your shoulders squared, your arms form the perfect position for shooting."

"I can do this," she said with confidence.

"Hold the gun on target," I said in her ear. "If it's a zombie, aim for the brain and shoot. It's the only way to kill it. If that's not comfortable for you, I can teach you another way to hold the gun."

"Show me."

I nodded. "Okay. Stand like you're ready to hit someone."

"Like a boxer?"

"Exactly. Now, angle your support arm shoulder toward your target." My hands moved across her body to help guide her.

"Okay." Her contours smoothed under my touch as she followed my instructions.

"Bend your knees while keeping your body weight slightly forward. Grasp the gun using opposite pressure with both hands. Keep both elbows bent, with your support elbow pointing downward."

She spun around. "I think I can do this."

My eyes drifted down to her flat, toned stomach. I could have sworn she caught me looking at her belly ring, but I tried to change the subject quickly. "Look, I've given you some really good pointers, but I'm afraid it's still not enough to survive out here. Why don't you come with us?"

She set her bottle down. "Why?"

"Because it's dangerous. You know you can't stay here."

She let out a long breath. "Claire's right. Getting together with another group won't guarantee our safety. You could stay here with us."

"There's safety in numbers, and staying here is crazy," I said.

"You don't think we can make it on our own?" she asked.

"Not without concrete walls and an army."

"Do you think we could just stay for the night? I know Claire will see things differently in the morning, and so will I. We're just so tired after everything we've been through."

Nick peeked his head in. "Absolutely not! This place isn't safe. We need to get some supplies and

79

load them and our butts in those Jeeps." He grabbed my shoulder. "Get moving now!"

CHAPTER 7

Val, Nick, and I quickly loaded up the two Jeeps with bottled water, a case of Pepsi, and canned food we found in the pantry. I also packed the black bag holding the precious vials. I started up both Jeeps; they ran great. Val found a few red plastic gas cans in the garage next to the lawnmower, which was great; we didn't want to stop anywhere if we didn't have to. It would be wise to get a head start, with nothing to slow us down.

We were all set to go, but my heart sank. I couldn't imagine leaving Claire and Jackie to their fates. I just hoped I could convince them to change their minds—especially Jackie, who I was really taking a liking to. Nick gave me ten more minutes to try and convince her to go with us. I found her in the humongous master bedroom on the bottom floor. What made the room really neat was that it extended from the house with three glass walls and a glass roof. "Hey," I said, noticing she had cleaned up and changed into new clothes. They were a size too big, but they were much more practical than what she'd been wearing earlier. I was sure Val would be impressed with her blue jeans, white t-shirt, and black tennis shoes. She'd also put her hair up in a long ponytail. "We're getting ready to leave, but I wanted to talk to you first."

"Don't worry. I've got the gun you gave me." Jackie glanced out through the spacious glass wall, watching as the setting sun flooded the sky with brilliant colors. She placed her hand on the clear glass. "It's so beautiful, isn't it?"

"Yep. Something like that could even fool you into thinking the world hasn't gone to hell in a hand basket."

She frowned and sat down on the bed. "I was trying to block all that out, if only for a minute."

I sat next to her. "This is a cool bedroom. It's kind of like a glass cube."

She glanced up. "Yeah. I bet it's neat to see the stars shining at night."

I stared at her black hair with blonde streaks. It was striking, original, and beyond cute. I loved her bold look. "So, what's your story?" I asked.

"My story?"

"Yup. Everyone's got one, right?"

"Right, but I guess right now I'm only concerned about the ending." She sighed. "I just want to live another day. Tell me, Dean, is it really possible to survive in such a hostile, undead world?"

"Yes, and that said, I have to make one last-ditch effort to try and convince you to change your mind and come with us. We're leaving in a few minutes."

She continued to stare off into the sunset. "Give it your best shot."

"Jackie, there are plenty of cities out there that are still safe, like the island in Ohio where Nick and I live. I've been there since the outbreak, with no problems. The zombies aren't immortal beings. They can't bust through brick walls or get through our military. We have machineguns, bombs, and all kinds of ways to stay safe. Supplies are flown in every day to help people survive the battle."

She met my gaze. "If it was so great, so safe, then why'd you leave?"

"I didn't—not on purpose anyway. Our helicopter crashed on a trip for make-believe supplies."

She cocked a curious brow.

I continued, "I know it sounds weird, but it's a long story. I can tell you all about it on our road trip." I was pretty cocky and certain she'd change her mind and come with us. By the twinkle in her eye, I could tell she liked me, at least a little.

"I'm sorry you crashed."

"It was what it was," I said. "I can't cry about it now. I need to stay focused and keep moving."

"Can we ever defeat these things? I mean, do you think our lives will ever be normal again?"

I reached for her hand. "Yes, I believe we will prevail. Zombies will die off, and eventually their bodies will rot away. All we have to do is outlive the infected. Yes, there are overwhelming odds stacked against us, but we can do this. I believe with all my heart that humanity can overcome anything, as long as we don't lose hope."

"So you're heading to a safe haven, one of the walled cities?"

"Yes. We can hold out in the fortresses created around the United States. Zombies will run out of food and die, and we'll get our world back. We just need a little time."

She nodded. "You make a good point."

"Then come with us. I'm sure Claire will cave once she sees you're serious about leaving."

A *thump* on the window drew my attention.

Jackie jumped. "What was that?"

I turned and couldn't believe my eyes. A zombie with rotting flesh and oozing eyeballs was hitting his head against the glass. He shot me a stone-cold, glazed-over look that said in not so many words, *"I want your brains...now!"* The stupid thing seemed stumped as to why he couldn't pass through the transparent glass wall.

Speechless, Jackie pointed to the other glass walls.

I gasped. Crap. Another one stared me straight in the eyes. This one looked like a raccoon, with blackened skin around her eyes; she definitely had that I-just-got-out-of-the-grave look about her. The dead seemed to be coming out of the woodwork like cockroaches, multiplying before our very eyes. Our beautiful view of the sunset had turned into a grotesque nightmare.

I stood, but my sudden movement made them moan and groan even louder. Decaying human hands pounded on the glass walls from all three sides of the bedroom, and my heart raced. Brain-hungry walking corpses staggered around with white, sunken eyes and green, mottled skin. It was downright disturbing. I sucked in a deep gulp of air.

The glass shook, and I wondered if it would shatter. I gasped as bloody handprints streaked across the glass. Windows are notoriously easy to break, but I wondered how well a glass wall would hold up. I sure didn't want to find out.

I backed up slowly, focusing on the zombie who was making the most fuss. Even though he had decayed hands with exposed tendons, he still kept pounding. I cringed at his blue-green veins and the open flesh wounds on his forehead, cheeks, and neck. Through a tear in his shirt, I noticed an exposed ribcage with decaying flesh hanging off of it in grotesque shreds. The right pant leg was also torn to reveal a long white femur. Even a famous horror writer couldn't have invented anything as horrible as the very real monster I was staring at.

"Let's go!" Jackie said, grabbing my shoulder.

"Nick!" I yelled. "We've got to go...NOW!"

CHAPTER 8

With the orange light of the setting sun as a backdrop, the zombie looked like a creature out of a horror movie. His decaying palms pressed against the smooth surface of the glass wall, and his open mouth dripped with spit and blood as his dead gaze focused on me, making me flinch. For a whole second, I could barely breathe, let alone form a coherent thought in my head, and then it dawned on me that we had to get the heck away from there.

I grabbed Jackie's hand and headed down the hallway, calling as loudly as my lungs would allow, "Nick! Val! There's a pack of zombies out there. We need to get going now!"

Our feet pounded the hardwood floor as we passed the hall and rounded the corner into the living room. The door stood ajar, as though no one had bothered to close it behind them. I yanked it open and stopped in my tracks when I took in the two towering guys resembling wild mountain men with their unkempt appearance, greasy hair, and long, thick beards.

"Going somewhere?" one asked.

"What the heck?" I took a step back, unsure whether they were friends or foe. They didn't look like zombies, but for all I knew, they could've been bitten and might turn on us any minute. Even if they weren't part of the undead army yet, they could have still wanted our food and weapons. "Who are you? How did you get in here?" My grip tightened around Jackie's hand as I pushed my body forward to form a shield between her and the wildlings. If they wanted her, they'd have to force their way past me first—not that I could have been much of a safeguard against a pair like that, but I hoped I could at least buy her a few seconds to get away.

The one in the red checkered shirt raised his hand and waved his rifle at Jackie and me. "You two with them?" He pointed behind him, toward my brother and Val, who were lying on the ground, their mouths pressed in a grim line that didn't leave me much hope. With Nick holding the back of his head and Val's bloody lip, I knew they'd been attacked and put up a good fight. The wildlings were clearly after our food and weapons. Whether they'd leave us alive or not wouldn't make much difference with the zombies out there, ready to burst in any minute.

I took a deep breath, and then a step forward while pushing Jackie behind me. "Look, mister, there're zombies out back! We've got to get outta here now!"

The other wildman regarded me for a second, probably considering my words and trying to read my expression, to see if I was telling the truth. He patted Jackie and me down and took our guns.

"You don't trust me?" I spat through gritted teeth. "I wouldn't either in your situation, but if I am telling the truth—which I am—we're all dead. Go and see for yourself."

The red checkered shirt guy motioned the other forward and then aimed his gun a bit higher, right at my face. I didn't even flinch as I watched his companion walk past. The mountain man then forced me and Jackie to stand next to the others. A few seconds ticked by before his friend returned, his face a pale mask of horror. I saw his faint nod, and then the red checkered guy lowered his weapon. "We're gonna have to work together if we wanna make it out alive."

I nodded and heaved a big breath. "Give us back our weapons," I said, pointing at my brother and the girls. "We won't be of much help if we can't shoot."

The red checkered guy nodded and held out his hand. "I'm Earl, and that's my friend Tahoe, like the lake."

I ignored him as I walked past. We had to work together to get out of this mess, but I had no doubt the hillbilly twins would happily shoot our heads off and take all our food and supplies once the zombies were properly dispatched.

"I'm Nick," my brother said. "That's Dean, Val, Jackie, and Claire. Give us back our weapons...*now*!"

Tuning them out, I headed for the side door, pulling Jackie with me. I wanted to see if the zombies were starting to come around to the front of the house. Unfortunately, we didn't get far before a flat, metallic *click* warned me of danger. I turned on my heel slowly, my gaze focusing on Earl's rifle, which was now pointed at me again.

"Stop, or I'll shoot you both dead in your tracks."

My automatic response was to touch my holster, but then I remembered that Tahoe had disarmed me, so I remained frozen to the spot. "I figured that much," I said dryly. "But I thought you said we need to work together."

"We were just trying to get a position on the zombies," Jackie said. "Do you think we'd leave our friends behind?"

My gaze became harder and colder, signaling I wasn't scared of him.

Earl narrowed his gaze. "We *are* working together. You help me ward off any zombie attack, and I'll spare your lives...for the time being. Sure sounds like cooperation to me."

"Right. Sounds like a great deal...for you." I snorted. "What makes you think we'll have your back the moment those zombies barge in here?"

"What makes you think they'll barge in here at all?" Tahoe said, speaking for the first time.

For some reason, the younger gruff one seemed to feel safe, as if the zombies were no threat and couldn't possibly get inside the glass house. I wasn't sure why. It wasn't a military fortress. I marveled how young he seemed. On closer inspection, I realized beneath the facial hair hid a wrinkle-free face.

He stepped closer as he stared at us. "You have yet to answer my question. What are you all doing in our house?"

Val picked up a family portrait and ran a finger across the dust. "Funny. You don't look like these happy people, and pictures like these are plastered all around the house."

Earl's mouth twitched at the corners, as though her sarcasm amused him. "They're all dead. Zombies got 'em. So we figure since they don't need the place anymore, and we were the first ones to get our hands on it, it's our house now—at least as of two days ago."

His eyes sparkled, making me wonder as to the validity of his story. *Did zombies really get the poor inhabitants, or was it these two?* I bit my tongue hard so I wouldn't comment and risk their wrath. After all, they were still the only ones holding weapons.

"We're not monsters," Tahoe said, reading my disgusted expression. "We didn't kill 'em. They were dead long before we arrived. Can't you tell from all the dust in this place? Nobody has been here for ages."

He had a valid point, and I hoped they weren't murderers. Just because they didn't kill the inhabitants of the house didn't mean they wouldn't kill us.

"Fine. You've claimed the house," Val chimed in. "Just let us go, and we'll be on our merry way. You can have your home sweet home all to yourselves." Of course she forgot to mention the part about us loading up all their food and water in their vehicles.

"Sure. You're welcome to go, as soon as the zombie threat is over," Tahoe said. "Don't worry. We got four strong men here. Besides, they'll never break in."

I was almost inclined to believe him when a loud *thud* echoed through the room, startling us. Urban legends about zombies touted their slow reaction time and their inability to form coherent plans, but they were just that: legends. No one knew for sure whether they still had any morsel of humanity in them. For all we knew, their brains retained some ability for reasoning and possibly for their own survival. If they did, which was pretty obvious from their attempts to get in, then we were screwed; it would only be a matter of time before they would double and triple their efforts and succeed.

"We have to go, even if it's on foot," Nick said with a glance toward the hall. "Trapping ourselves in this house is suicide. I don't know about you, but we're leaving."

"And going where?" Claire yelled. "Zombies will rip us to shreds!"

Nick shrugged and shot her a hard look. "I don't care. I'd rather die trying than to sit around in here doing nothing."

"I'm sorry, Claire, but I'm with him. The faster, the better," Jackie whispered.

For a second, I felt like hugging her. I was so proud of her for standing up for herself, even if it meant defying her cousin's wishes.

"You don't know anything for sure," Claire said. "None of you do. Maybe we should hole up here until those things leave. They'll get bored and go eventually, and we can leave in a few hours, once the coast is clear."

Jackie shook her shoulder. "No, Claire. Waiting is a horrible idea!"

"You're safe here," Tahoe said. "There are a lot of them, but they can't bust through these walls. And like Claire said, they'll get bored after a bit and move on for easier prey. I've seen it a million times before."

"I agree," Earl said. "It's best to hide out here until they leave. It's stupid to engage them, but if they break in, of course we'll fight with everything we have." Earl shot me a look. "You owe me for saving your lives."

"What?" I asked. "If you would've let us leave, we would have been long gone already."

Earl gave me a cocky grin. "Wrong, my boy. What you'd be is dead. I'm offering you protection here, and when this is all over and done, I expect to be paid for it."

"Paid? With what? We don't have any money," Claire said. "We only came with the shirts on our backs."

Earl smirked. "Who said anything about money? I just want one of you cute gals to keep me company tonight. Is that so much to ask for the price of saving your lives?"

Nick's hands balled into fists. The vein on his forehead throbbed so hard that I prayed he wouldn't do something stupid, like try to hit the guy. Fortunately, he either came to his senses on his own or the rifle pointed at his face made him reconsider.

I grabbed my brother's arm, just in case, and hissed, "Don't let him rile you up. We gotta leave with our heads still attached to our shoulders."

Claire scowled at Earl. "Our lives are on the line! How can you blackmail us like this?"

"Mmm. Feisty. And I love redheads." Earl looked her up and down, then inched closer. "I bet we could have a lot of fun, you and me."

"You're sick!" Val shouted but didn't inch closer.

I glared at Earl. The man was a disgusting sleaze ball and an absolute idiot. Zombies were literally knocking down our doors, but all he could think about was bedding down with a helpless girl. *Maybe we can find a car in town,* I considered. Zombies were prowling out back, but I was willing to take my chances if it meant keeping all three of the girls as far away from Grizzly Adams as we could.

Nick straightened his stance. "No deal, jerk! Move out of my way because we're leaving."

"Fine. You boys can go," Earl said.

"We boys?"

"Yep, but we're keeping the women. You owe us for all the dead corpses I'll have to clean up in the front yard tomorrow morning."

Jackie gasped.

"What do you need us for, huh?" Val spat. "Let me tell you, mister, if you come anywhere near me, I'll bite just as hard as those zombies will. You might lose something really valuable if you go waving it around at me!"

Tahoe cleared his throat, as if he was trying to stifle a laugh.

Val took a step toward him, her eyes darting in my direction, signaling something. She was trying to get their attention so we could devise a plan.

Nick must've realized it, too, because he nudged Claire. "You still got that stun gun?" he whispered.

She nodded, wide-eyed, and touched her pocket.

Nick bobbed his head slightly. "Good. On the count of three, stun Earl while Dean and I tackle the other guy. Then stun him too."

"And then we run," Jackie said.

I moistened my lips and signaled that I was ready.

Claire wrapped her fingers around the stun gun just as the zombies from the back of the house moved onto the front lawn. They were shuffling everywhere. The scratch of their cracked, yellowed nails raked against the glass. There were so many that I had no idea how we'd get past them without being attacked. We had lost our precious opportunity, thanks to Earl and Tahoe.

Nick grabbed Claire's arm and whispered into her ear, "Wait! Hold off. The house is surrounded now. There's no way can we just walk out the front door." He glanced at me. "If zombies break in, we'll need the mountain men to help us fight them off."

I nodded, and Claire slipped her stun gun into her pocket. Our plan was ruined, and it was too late for us to make an escape. We all knew we should have run the second we saw the zombies entering the back yard, but the two sasquatches had foiled that little plan. We could've been in the Jeeps, long gone before the zombies had come around to the front of the house, but that chance had slipped away. Now Nick was right: We needed the mountain men conscious so they could help us battle the undead. On our own, we might not make it out alive.

"What the..." Earl said, locking the door. "We've never had to fight this many before."

"I tried to tell you!" Jackie said.

Earl rubbed his chin. "I thought there might be a group of them running around, but I never would have imagined anything like this...and it's all your fault!"

"What!?" Val screamed, furious.

"That's right. Y'all brought them here to my doorstep! Look at all those corpses in my front yard. I bet you idiots used a gun, attracting them from everywhere!"

The banging and scratching sounds made my stomach churn. Twigs snapped under their rotting feet as they shuffled around the place, hammering against the glass in various locations with various body parts. Something began to shatter, and for a moment, I wasn't sure whether the sound was coming from the walls or the door. I even heard muffled footsteps somewhere at the back of the house, or maybe it was the basement. They were fighting their way in, and that meant only one thing: We had to fight our way out, and the front door was out of the question.

Out of the corner of my eye, I saw a zombie licking and clawing at the glass in front of me. His decomposed face with black and brown muscle wrinkling over the skull stared at me as though he had already chosen his main course for the evening. I didn't want to be trapped while those monsters fought their way in, but just walking out there and hoping for the best wouldn't work either. I looked out the glass wall of the living room and saw zombies dotting the entire front yard. *Earl's right. I bet the gunshots we fired off earlier attracted the herd. We'll have to be way more careful next time...if there is a next time.* The dead army surrounded the entire house, like some kind of scene straight out of *Night of the Living Dead.* The only thing that kept us safe from them for the time being was a towering sheet of glass. I shuddered and vowed to never set foot inside a glass house again; that was one nightmare I wouldn't soon forget. "I need a weapon!" I shouted.

Earl thrust my gun into my waiting hands, then handed Nick and Jackie their weapons.

"Hey, girl, catch! You look like you know how to use this," Tahoe called out a moment before he tossed Val a rifle.

My sister caught the gun in midair and wore a proud smile.

My rifle was already packed in the Jeep, but I still had my handgun. My grip tightened around it, even though I doubted it'd do any good against an entire herd of zombies.

A *crack* echoed in the air a moment before the door splintered and the hinges burst. I froze in place as countless zombies fought with each other to get first pick.

CHAPTER 9

The penetrating howling noise outside the house grew to ear-splitting levels. My finger found the trigger of my weapon as my gaze steadied on the door. Recklessly determined to sooth their constant hunger, I knew the zombies would find a way in. The fact that we were having such a near encounter with so many in such a confined space wasn't exactly confidence-boosting, but I vowed to fight until my last breath.

My gaze focused on the door a moment before it splintered open from the weight of countless zombies leaning and pushing against it. Some of them fell headfirst on the floor, gnawing and thrashing. Horrible odors of rotting flesh seeped into my nose, making me want to bend over and puke my guts out. Their unearthly moans echoed in the air, and I shivered at the thought of them tearing through my flesh, devouring me little by little.

I waved my arm, beckoning the others to follow me upstairs. "C'mon! This way!" My voice reverberated from the walls, but it didn't quite manage to drown out the zombies' hungry calls. Without waiting for an answer from the others, I bolted up the spiral staircase, jumping two steps at a time, faster and faster. My boot glided on the smooth surface, and I tripped. *Crap! This is not the time to panic and lose your cool or your balance, Dean!* I scrambled to my feet but stumbled again, nearly losing my grip. As I hung on to the railing, I peered down. *No flipping way!* The door had been broken in completely, but the opening was too narrow to fit them all through. The zombies who had managed to squeeze in had gathered in front of the doorway in a messy heap, pushing and pulling and attempting to get up, while the ones coming from behind kept tripping, making any ascent impossible. I gawked at the way they had buried themselves, thankful for the tiny distraction that might just buy us a few minutes to get upstairs and find the safest room.

"Come on, boy! Move!" Earl yelled. "You're in my way. If you don't move your butt, I'll personally shove you down there to get acquainted with those things."

I didn't need to see his face to know he meant every word he said. The edge in his voice betrayed his sincerity. So, my legs rose under me as I pushed up the stairs, focusing on my feet so I wouldn't trip again.

The moment I reached the top step, Earl jammed his elbow into my stomach, making me double over, then made room for Tahoe to hurry past. "Blow the staircase up, Tahoe!" he yelled.

"Blow it up?" I asked. "With what?"

"Don't you worry about that!" Earl said.

Tahoe motioned to his friend, then they took off down the hall and disappeared through one of the doors I hadn't inspected before.

My brother raced past me, shouting over his shoulder, "Dean! Come on, man! Don't just stand there! Move it!"

"Coming!" I yelled, taking off after him. By the time I reached him, Nick was already pushing a large oak dresser toward the door, leaving scuff marks across the shiny wooden floor. "What are you doing?" I asked, stopping in my tracks.

"Help me roll this thing down the stairs," he said.

"Why bother? I thought we were gonna lock ourselves in a room and then climb out the window." I peered at him from under raised brows. Granted, my grand plan seemed a lot more fascinating inside my head, before I spoke it out loud, but it still wasn't as bad as the expression on his face made it seem.

"Right. We're just gonna let those things slither up the stairs after us while we pick a random room, lock ourselves in, hear them bang on the door, and then jump out the window to the million zombies waiting for us below? Sorry, bro, but that's a dumb plan. We'll be even more trapped and screwed than we are now."

"I didn't think of that," I said, but he was right. Creating a blockade gave us extra time to find the perfect window to jump from. It would also help us save ammo, since we'd be out of bullets in no time. Our piddly little arsenal was no match for the number of zombies waiting to devour us.

"Come on, Dean," Nick said, unable to suppress a tiny sneer. "We don't have time for discussing it. Just trust me and do what I say." With that, he dashed past and turned his back on me, signaling the conversation was over.

We hauled the heavy dresser to the top of the landing, and then I kicked it until it tumbled down the stairs. It crashed into some zombies on the way down, knocking them to the ground like bowling pins. When I turned around, the girls were sliding a fancy antique couch toward me. With a last heave, I pushed it down the stairs toward a zombie who was heading toward us. I let out a few choice words. Of course it wasn't the most mature thing I could have done in front of Jackie, but I couldn't help myself. The adrenaline running through my veins was making me say things I wouldn't usually say. Besides, every single triumph—no matter how tiny it was—counted when death was lurking savagely around the corner in the vacant eyes and slimy mouths of those things.

Val had dragged an enormous chest of drawers to the top of the stairs. Jackie and Claire began slipping out the drawers and throwing them down on the zombies, hitting them on their heads.

Finally, the two girls gave the furniture a final shove, and it flew down, taking out a couple more of the hissing creatures. Nick threw a box spring, followed by a mattress tossed by Val. Our furniture onslaught wouldn't last forever, but we hoped it would grant us enough time to find a spot where we could safely jump from a window into a smaller crowd of zombies that we could fight off.

"Watch out!" Earl called from behind. I moved out of his way as he lit up a stick of dynamite and threw it down the stairs.

I watched the fire eat through the cord, slowly but steadily flying through the air in what seemed like slow motion. It all happened so fast, yet I felt as though a million years must have passed.

"Get down!" Earl yelled as it landed with a dull *thud* with uncanny precision, right in the middle of the gathered zombie herd.

I ducked and threw my body over Jackie and Claire as a loud *boom* echoed in my ears and smoke swirled all around me. Raising my head, I coughed and peered through the blanket of fire at the gap between the upper and the lower levels of the house. The stairs had evaporated into a huge mess of wooden splinters, interspersed with blood and gore. My stomach protested at the sight, but I didn't have time to digest the image because the next wave of zombies was already gushing in.

I peeked over the banister. There was absolutely nothing left of the stairs, so our only way back down was gone. I didn't know whether to feel relieved or pissed off that the guy didn't consult us before doing something so bold and irrevocable. *What if Nick's plan fails? What then? He blew up the freaking stairs! We're stuck up here!* "Where did you get the dynamite from?" I asked, miffed.

"That's no concern of yours, boy," Earl spat.

Again I had to bite my tongue hard to keep from lashing out at him. I could only assume he must've hidden a stash somewhere and didn't feel the need to tell us about it. For all we knew, the doomsday mountain dudes probably had a stash of every kind of weapon known to mankind hidden all over the place, so I mentally prepared for more surprises to come along the way. "You should've told us," I muttered under my breath. "We had the situation under control."

"Right, like furniture would've stopped all those things!" Earl said, shooting me and Nick a glare as he bolted down the hallway with Tahoe on his heels.

"It did slow them down some," Val shouted, as if defending our honor.

"Hey, Dean," Nick called out, "now's the time to put that plan of yours to good use."

"Great. I'll go look out the windows for a possible escape route," I said.

"I was talking about myself," he said. "I need you guys to stay here and be a distraction."

"What?" I asked.

"Don't worry," Val said. "We're safe up here. They can't fly."

Nick continued, "If the zombies see food, they'll focus their efforts toward this part of the house. We need as many of them as possible here in the living room and front yard so we can sneak out the back or side window."

"I like it," I said. "Let the freaks gather up here while you find the perfect place for us to sneak out. Then we'll be gone...and they'll still think we're up here, the dummies."

"That's the plan," Nick said. "So stand here so they can see you."

Claire grabbed his arm and gave it a squeeze. "I'm coming with you. There has to be a way out of this place."

"I'll be right back," Nick said.

"Um, okay. Be careful, man!" I said, scrambling to my feet. The idea of splitting up sat in the pit of my stomach like a rock. Especially when I was the distraction...the human bait.

With a nod, he shot off down the hallway, with Claire following after him.

"They'll be right back," Val muttered to no one in particular.

I opened my mouth to tell her everything would be all right, but the sound of shattering glass boomed in my ears, stopping my words from coming out. I peered down at more zombies breaking through the towering glass walls and gasped.

"Oh my gosh!" yelled Jackie. "They're busting through the walls!" Her gaze bore into mine, questioning the meaning of it all.

For once, I was at a loss for words and couldn't give her the answer she wanted to hear. If the walls were coming down, it would be only a matter of time before the upper floor was compromised.

We fell silent for a moment. The *crunch* of dragging feet on broken glass as the zombies flooded into the spacious living room was all we could hear. My stomach lurched when a loud choir of the undead groaned, echoing in my ears. The giant room had filled up with moaning, groaning, and hissing, as though the zombies had multiplied. I'd never seen anything like it. I had only seen such horrific scenes in movies and videogames, but now it was happening right in front of me. I was witnessing a real-live (or dead, as the case was) zombie apocalypse with my very own eyes.

Val clapped my shoulder. "Stay calm, okay? The plan is working perfectly. They're all coming to the front of the house. Nick will be back any minute with the perfect spot to sneak out. And then we'll run to the Jeeps as fast as our feet can carry us."

I nodded and forced the fear that was quickly grabbing hold of me to the back of my mind.

"You still got the keys?" she asked.

I nodded, remaining stunned and silent.

She continued bravely, "Good. We need to be ready to pound the pavement the second Nick comes back."

I felt my pocket, just to make sure the keys were still there, but they weren't. Much to my dismay, I suddenly remembered that I'd left them on the table. I pointed at the living room. "No flippin' way! I left them...they're down there!"

"I can't believe this!" She took a trembling breath as she regarded me. Her face became an impenetrable mask as her mind began to weigh the possibilities.

I breathed in sharply to calm my nerves. With the staircase gone, no zombie could climb up, but we couldn't climb down either. Unfortunately, the keys were down there. Our chances of getting out before the walls collapsed down on us were pretty slim, and I felt it was my fault for stupidly leaving the keys downstairs.

"How are we going to get down there to get them?" Jackie asked, her eyes wide, mirroring my own thoughts.

"We aren't," Val finally said, "but I can hotwire the truck."

Earl and Tahoe came from behind, making me jump.

Earl's eyes shimmered with malice as he looked at me. "We need a big, giant distraction. How about some blood?"

"Yeah," Tahoe said. "You know how predictable the little freaks are."

"One whiff, and we've got ourselves a huge distraction," Earl mumbled, still looking at me, making it impossible to miss his vile and threatening insinuation. "Hmm. Blood. Where can we possibly get any of that? Any suggestions, boy?"

My heart raced. I put my hand on my holster, already determined that if I had to shoot either of the bushy-haired crazies in self-defense, I wouldn't hesitate to use a bullet.

"Do you have any more explosives?" Val asked, unfazed.

"Fresh out," Earl snapped, "but you know what? You reek of death." He suddenly reached for her.

Val let out a scream as he ripped the bandage off her arm, revealing the infected flesh. I couldn't help but stare at the darkening gash and the white bone peeking from beneath.

"I knew it!" Earl yelled. "She's nothing but zombie bait!" His eyes shined, his sneer revealing tobacco-yellowed teeth.

For a moment, I thought he might be talking about himself, because everything about him was far more grotesque and rotting than Val's wound—including his soul, if he even had one.

Val kicked him in the nuts and turned to run, but he grabbed her around the waist and forced her to stay put.

My hand instinctively moved to the gun in my holster, but someone gripped my arms from behind and yanked them hard, sending jolts of pain through my shoulders. *Crap.* My weapon flew out of my hands and clattered to the floor, not far away from my feet. I peered at it and pulled toward it, but the guy was in the more advantageous position, making it impossible for me to twist out of his grip. Earl followed my line of vision and kicked the weapon under the railing. It sailed across the floor and under the banister, landing in the crowd of zombies below.

Glancing over my shoulder, I yelled, "Tahoe, let me go!"

He continued holding me in his iron grasp as he hissed, "I have my instructions. He'll kill me if I don't follow them."

"No!" I shouted. "Then at least let her go!"

"Ain't happenin', boy. You might as well just give up now before the same fate befalls you!" Earl said.

"Take me instead!" I begged.

"You're not infected. She, on the other hand, is. She's one bacteria away from being one of those nasty things!"

Jackie whipped out her gun, her eyes shifting nervously from Earl to Tahoe, then to me. She seemed hesitant about shooting another human being, and I knew we were losing the battle. Before she could even make up her mind, Earl shoved her back, and she crashed helplessly through the glass banister, almost plummeting into the void below. She clung on the second-floor railing as her legs dangled dangerously close to zombies. The way they kept reaching up made it obvious they wanted nothing more than to devour her legs as an appetizer.

My stomach clenched as their mouths started to snap open like hungry piranhas. "Val!" I flailed against Tahoe, but he only tightened his grip on me.

Earl grabbed Val and swung her over the banister, hissing, "Sorry, sweetheart, but you're gonna die soon anyway. Might as well go out like a hero and save our butts in the process."

"Don't do this!" she yelled. "Try and show some compassion. At least put a bullet through my head first so I don't have to feel them...so I won't know they're eating me."

"No!" I squirmed and desperately tried to free myself. I knew Jackie wouldn't be able to hold on much longer, and my sister desperately needed my help. I yelled for Nick down the hall, but I doubted he could hear me over the screams and chaos of the zombie frenzy.

"I can't hold on to him any longer," Tahoe shouted. His grip loosened a bit, and for a moment, I thought he might have done so on purpose, as though he wanted me to escape and save Val, but at the same time he feared for his life.

"Well, goodbye." In one swift motion, Earl hurled Val into the herd of zombies. Her scream chilled my blood, etching the memory into my brain forever.

In disbelief I watched as hands and arms pounced on her like a lion on a piece of raw meat. "Nick!" My own voice sounded alien in my ears, as if it couldn't possibly be coming from me.

Finally, Tahoe let go and stepped back.

I tumbled forward, my arms reaching out to strangle the guy who had killed my sister, but Earl was faster, or maybe he had the advantage of being emotionally unattached to the whole situation. My forehead exploded in pain as he threw me against the wall so hard that I blacked out for a second. When my vision cleared, I saw the two mountain men running off. I crawled to the balcony and grabbed Jackie's hand; I managed to pull her to safety, even though my arms were on fire.

As soon as she stepped over the balustrade, she buried her head into my chest.

"Nick!" I yelled again, almost choking on the sudden nausea in my stomach and the bile in my throat. Tears threatened to spill down my face. "Nick!" I yelled again, but no one answered. I looked for Val below, but I couldn't see any sign of her under the hissing pile that had pounced on her. I'd never seen anything so horrible in my entire life. The images threatened my sanity, yet I couldn't look away. I was suddenly fueled by thoughts of revenge, and I swore to myself I'd avenge my sister's death, no matter what. Even though I had yet to make it out of there alive, I'd already contemplated the different ways I could accomplish that goal. *Earl is gonna pay...and so is every freaking zombie I ever come across!*

CHAPTER 10

Standing on the balcony, I stared at the monsters who had killed Val. In one moment, my sister and I were there, valiantly fighting back to back, stubbornly determined on making it out of there alive, but in the next moment, she was gone, just like that. My mind spun in an endless loop of memories that didn't quite make sense to me. My heart raced, pumping blood through my body. My fingers twitched, and my skin prickled, which made the whole situation even more surreal. She was dead, and I was still alive. The world seemed more unfair than ever before. I was caught in a daze, and not the pleasant kind, until Jackie's words snapped me out of it.

"We have to find Claire and your brother," she said softly, though her voice betrayed a frantic edge.

The sudden urge to get moving didn't go unnoticed. I turned to face her. Her eyes were burning with something: *Pain? Disbelief? Anger?* I couldn't tell because my own pain had numbed me.

My own shock and disbelief wouldn't allow me to comprehend that experiencing a comrade's death couldn't be easy on her either. "I'm—I'll stay," I whispered. "I'm not going anywhere until every single one of them is dead."

"No, Dean. You can't. We need you. Your brother needs you. Think of those who are still around, those who care about you, and the pain you'll cause if you give up now and sacrifice yourself for some impossible try at revenge." She grabbed my arm and yanked hard. "She...Val wouldn't have wanted you to do something so foolish. Your sister would want you to get yourself to safety. That was what she was fighting for."

I didn't budge. Her words registered with me somewhere, somehow in the back of my mind. She was right, of course, but I also felt as though I would be betraying Val if I ran away.

"Please," Jackie continued. "Nick has already lost one sibling. Don't make him lose both."

"Let's go!" Claire's voice called from around the corner a moment before my brother and she appeared in my line of vision.

"Dean," my brother said with a nod, "thanks for holding it together here, man."

I turned away, avoiding his gaze. I couldn't bear to tell him what had happened.

"The bathroom window in the back seems like our best bet," Nick said. "We can make a clean getaway. So c'mon, let's go!"

My brother's gaze sliced through me. A single worry wrinkle creased his otherwise smooth skin. I peered into his blue eyes, begging him to understand; I couldn't dare speak the words that burned a hole in my heart.

"What are you waiting for? Let's go! This place is turning into Zombie Central." His gaze became stubborn, and his hands clenched to his sides, as though he already sensed something was wrong but didn't want to acknowledge it just yet.

I froze and closed my eyes to avoid his probing stare.

"What's wrong with you?" he hissed, grabbing me hard by the shoulders.

I opened my eyes again and saw him scanning the open landing, his mind putting two and two together.

"Where's Val?" his shout echoed in my ears. His arms yanked me around like a ragdoll, forcing me to face him.

"Those men...they..." I stammered, my voice barely snaking its way out of my constricted throat. "Earl... he, uh...Tahoe wouldn't let go, and I couldn't...Earl just threw Val over the balcony! He used our sister as a distraction." I pointed a trembling finger to the pile of zombies where she'd been tossed in. The spot was covered in squirming bodies now, and on the remote chance that she was still alive, there wasn't a thing we could do to save her.

"No!" he screamed as sudden realization set in. "Why didn't you stop them?"

"I tried!" I shouted, shoving him as hard as I could. "Why would you think I didn't try!?"

"Well, you should've tried harder!" he said, pushing me back. "For goodness sake, she was our sister, and you just let those jerks—"

"Hold on now! We both tried everything we could," Jackie interrupted. "They took us by surprise. The older one, Evan or whatever his name is, almost killed me."

"It's Earl," I corrected, for it was a name I would never, ever forget.

"He pushed me over the balcony," Jackie continued, "but I was able to hold on until Dean helped me back up."

"Oh my gosh!" Claire said, throwing her arms around her. "That's horrible. Are you okay?"

"I'm fine," she breathed out.

"Where's Val?" Nick bellowed. "Maybe we can still help her."

I shook my head. "She's dead, Nick, and even if she weren't, she'd be torn into pieces by the time we made it down there. There's nothing you—or anyone, for that matter—can do." The sudden realization that I was right hurt me more than Nick's pained expression. My jaw clenched until I thought my bones might snap.

Claire placed a hand on Nick's back, trying to steady him, but she didn't say a word.

"Don't!" Nick said, violently shrugging her off.

"I'm so, so sorry," she whispered, ignoring his command not to touch him. Even though her words were thin and sparse, I could hear the sincerity in her voice.

Nick nodded and kept his head low, and for a second I thought he was choking back tears. Then, letting out a sudden loud yell, like a war cry, he tore away from Claire and began pounding the wall with his fist, threatening revenge on every single one of those cursed things and on the two men who had done such an awful thing, throwing two helpless women over a banister.

I wanted to stop my brother, but there was no chance. Instead, I fought back the urge to join in his cursing. "I'm sorry, man." My voice trembled, and I felt a tear roll down my face. Even though Jackie wrapped her arm around me to comfort me, I could barely breathe, and the room around me seemed to grow hot.

"There was nothing we could do," Jackie said. "You can't blame anyone for this except Earl and Tahoe."

"We gotta go," Nick whispered, ignoring her. "If we don't get outta here, we'll be next. But first there's something I need to do for Val." He disappeared into one of the bedrooms and reappeared a minute later with a gas can. Leaning forward, he started pouring it down from the balcony, soaking the zombies below.

I wanted to stop him before he set the house on fire and risked our lives in the process, but his grim expression stopped me.

"Fire and explosions are fantastic ways to destroy the walking dead." Grabbing his lighter, he yelled, "Die, you undead suckers! DIE!"

"Dean!? Nick!?"

At the sound of Val's muffled scream, we froze, dead cold.

Claire grabbed Nick's hand. "STOP! Listen...that's her!"

I leaned over and saw Val crawling out from under the pack, unscathed. *What? How is that possible? They didn't even touch her?*

She stumbled through the moaning crowd and over to the table. There, she bravely snatched the keys and held them up high.

I shot Nick a confused look.

He smiled, mirroring my relief that she wasn't dead.

"I hit my head. Must've blacked out for a minute. Meet me out back!" she yelled up.

I nodded and pulled Nick's arm. "How is that possible? She's still alive, but how?"

His eyes widened. "It must be because she carries their scent. That wound of hers means she's turning into one. I've heard they don't eat their own kind, but..." He shook his head. "To tell you the truth, I'm not even sure."

I laughed, relieved. "Yeah, they must have thought she was one of them. Then again, I'm not sure that's a good thing."

"I can't believe it," Claire said. "If you're bitten, then you get reprieve from the zombies."

"It appears that way. And since you haven't been bitten, no reprieve for you." Nick thrust a bat into Claire's hands and motioned her forward.

She let out a shaky breath but didn't protest. The poor girl was terrified; I could tell from the way her eyes darted to and fro, and her knuckles had turned white where she touched the smooth, cold wood. "What am I supposed to do with this?" she whispered.

My brother cupped her cheek. "Well, it isn't for playing baseball, that's for sure. I know you're scared of guns, but you're gonna need a weapon of some sort. Just beat the crap out of anything that tries to bite a chunk out of you."

"I'm sorry, but I just...can't," she said eventually. "I can't hit a—"

"A what? Another person? They aren't people anymore, Claire. They're monsters, animals, waiting to eat you alive."

I felt sorry for the girl to some degree, but my patience was growing as thin as Nick's. "You know what? Just give it to me." I snatched the bat out of her hands. After all, my gun had flown over the balcony, and I was in desperate need of a weapon to protect myself. I knew I'd be okay once I got to the Jeep, because my half-zombie sister had packed plenty of weapons, but in the meantime, I had to make do with anything I could get my hands on. I thought my words might talk some sense into Claire, but she just shrugged and let me have her only weapon without protest. I didn't get the girl, but at that point, with survival on my mind, I didn't even care.

"Ready, Val?" Nick yelled.

"Yep! Let's make them pay, boys and girls!" she replied from somewhere to our right.

I craned my neck until I thought I could distinguish her brown locks from the mess of dead people around her, and I saw her standing near the edge of the house, where the glass wall and the door had been.

"C'mon!" Nick said with a wink. Once Val was safely away from the horde, Nick went to work. He pulled a lighter out of his pocket and threw it onto the gas-drenched crowd, starting a zombie roast. Smoke and fire engulfed the small undead army while Nick yelled for us to run down the hall, then motioned us into a small bathroom with a narrow window that we hoped would be just big enough for us to squeeze through.

"There's a huge tree we can shimmy down," Claire said.

I nodded. Squinting, I could see the Jeeps in the driveway, and it was a relief to see that there weren't any zombies in that general area. It appeared as if they had all headed toward the front of the house, where the glass walls had collapsed. I could only assume the noise from the explosion had attracted them and drawn them in that direction.

"Okay, everyone. No talking until we're safe," he said, sliding the window open.

Without so much as a look back, I threw the bat out the window and watched it land next to a towering bush. I climbed out. Branch by branch, I clambered down the giant oak tree. The moment I jumped down and landed on the bare ground, I saw Val running toward me. "Val! I can't believe you blacked out. How's your head?"

"I'm fine."

"I'm so glad you're alive," I said, burying my face in her hair as I hugged her tight. "I tried to stop him, but I—"

She nodded but didn't reply. A rush of emotions overwhelmed me, choking me. We just stood there, holding each other. In that moment, no words were needed, because I could feel how relieved she was. The other's presence was enough to convey even more than we could possibly say.

Suddenly, our Hallmark moment was interrupted by a rude gurgle echoing from the left. Instinct kicked in, and I reached for my weapon. The smell of decaying flesh assaulted my nostrils. The moonlight served as a spotlight, enhancing every black vein, rotting flesh chunk, and seeping, oozing, smelly wound the zombie had endured. I wound up my bat to hit a homerun, hoping to knock the zombie's head out of the park, but

Jackie yanked the bat out of my hands. I shot her a look, but she just shook her head and replied with a grim expression of her own. I knew she was trying to make up for being hesitant about whipping out her gun to save Val. She wanted to prove to me that she was ready to fight now. I knew she had finished the thing off when a *whack* echoed in the air and the hissing stopped.

"You drive this one." Val pointed to the black Jeep and opened the driver door so I could jump in, then tossed me a set of keys; a second set to the red Jeep dangled from her fingers. I nodded and took the driver spot while I watched her jump into the other vehicle.

Nick grabbed Claire's hand and led her to my Jeep. I looked for Jackie, but she had jumped in with Val. I started the Jeep and threw it into gear. As I backed up, I noticed a handful of zombies to our left. My eyes scanned the area for an escape route, but that was about the only path wide enough for the Jeep to muddle through. "They're blocking our path!"

"Run those slimy numbskulls over!" Nick yelled. "They're already road kill!"

I hit the gas and sped out of the driveway, ignoring the loud *thuds* and *crunches* under my wheels. When a corpse hit the hood, I jumped in my skin; filmy white, glazed-over eyes connected with mine. Clenching my jaw, I threw on the brakes and sent him flying off, then sped up again.

Flames engulfed the giant glass mansion and burned brightly against the night. In the flickering lights to my left, I saw a swarm of zombies eating what looked like a human being. It had to be the mountain men...or what was left of them. The beasts tore at an exposed ribcage, oozing what I took to be intestines. The car Earl and Tahoe had ridden in was still sitting in the driveway. "Look! They didn't make it," I said.

My brother followed my line of vision and shook his head. "Justice served and good riddance. What they did to Val was inhuman."

"Gosh, it's so...awful," Claire said.

I pressed the gas pedal down hard, revving the engine and making my brain hurt from the grinding sound. Blackness covered my vision for a second, and I shook my head until my vision returned. Through the blur before my eyes, I saw Val in the rearview mirror, easily following my lead. The vehicle moved at a fast speed down the narrow driveway and onto the unpaved terrain of the woods. Behind us, the glass building became nothing but a burning spot in the evening sky. We drove in silence for a while, until I could see nothing but trees and the darkening sky. Only then did I let out a long breath that it seemed I'd been holding for hours. We had made it, and we were all alive.

"I'm an idiot!" Claire said. "I can't believe I actually wanted to stay. Had you left without me and Jackie, we'd be dead." Tears streamed down her cheeks as reality set in. "I've never been on my own before. Our group—the group we were with—took care of us. They were like my family." She took a trembling breath.

From the corner of my eye, I watched Nick squeeze her hand, soothing her. "It's okay, Claire. Our world has devolved into one where people have to fight and kill each other just to live another day. The people around you sheltered you because they wanted to take care of you, and they fought to keep you alive and safe. Not all people are bad, but not all of 'em are good either," he said, pondering Earl and Tahoe's cruel fate.

"You're right." She sniffed. "We didn't have to fight before, not until today. I've never even held a gun in my life. It was surreal that you asked that of me today. I just...couldn't."

"I know, but you have to understand those people who looked after you—good as they were—didn't do you any favors by protecting you, by sheltering you too much. Now you're unprepared and ill-equipped for what's waiting out there." Nick's tone was soft, but there was a sharp edge to it, as if he was breaking bad news to someone he didn't want to hurt. I hoped Claire would listen and take his advice at face value. My brother was blunt, but his advice—hard as it was to swallow—would help her stay alive longer. "You won't stand a chance out here if you don't learn how to fight and protect yourself," Nick continued.

I listened intently, his words ringing true in my ear. Somewhere in the back of my mind, I was enraged with his brutal honesty, for much of what he said applied to me as well. I suddenly understood why he'd been so angry with me for smuggling Val inside the helicopter. I, too, had been sheltered, living naïvely on Kelleys Island, having no idea that the rest of the world was crumbling around me. Sure, I'd heard stories and plenty of urban legends, but quite like Claire, it didn't seem real until I was thrown right smack dab in the middle of it. The truth was a painful thing for all of us.

Claire laid her head on my brother's shoulder, and he wrapped an arm around her. I was sure he felt awkward about it and was only trying to be nice, for Claire was definitely not his type. He usually liked girls who took on the action, not the ones who ran away from it, squealing about chipping their nails or breaking their expensive heels. *But then again, who knows? Maybe he needs a girly kind of girl right now to balance out all this blood and nastiness. Opposites still attract, right? Or maybe it's just a bad case of nerves.* I knew whatever it was; we had no time for soap operas. We had more important fish to fry, like finding the freeway, for starters.

***

Once we were finally on the highway, I felt a bit safer. Val's Jeep now led the way and we drove for a few hours in absolute silence. I would've loved to

125

have thrown some tunes on, but I was sure all the DJs had been gobbled up by zombies.

Then, out of nowhere, I noticed my sister slowing down, and her brake lights flashed as she pulled over to the side of the road.

"What the heck?" I yelled to my brother.

He jolted awake when I stopped behind her and cut the engine.

"It's Val. She's pulling over."

"Why?" Claire asked. "It's dark outside. Stopping isn't a good idea, right?"

I shrugged. "Who knows? Maybe she needs a potty break or has a flat or something."

My brother jumped out of the car and dashed toward her Jeep, yelling, "Are you mad? No stopping unless I deem it safe!"

Claire and I rushed over to the other Jeep, then stopped the moment we reached Val.

She was on the side of the road by a sign, puking into the bushes.

Jackie's hand rested on her back. She shot us an apologetic look, then went about rubbing Val's back.

"Are you okay?" I asked softly the moment the heaving stopped.

She nodded but didn't seem to want to move from the spot.

My brother and I scanned the area as we waited for her to finish. The long stretch of deserted highway posed no imminent threat, or so it seemed. Nick tapped his gun, signaling that we should get a move-on; I was glad for that, because I didn't want to stick around either. The full moon reminded me of werewolves, and a chill pricked my spine. *Get it together. Werewolves are fake, just something for teenage girls to giggle over, unless they prefer sparkly vampires.* But zombies were real, and my sister was about to turn into one.

"Sorry, guys," Val eventually said, standing.

"It's okay," Nick said. "I'm the one who should be sorry for yelling at you."

Claire touched Val's shoulder. "Is there anything I can do?"

She straightened and flipped her hair out of her eyes. "I'm fine, guys. Thanks for asking. Let's just get outta here. Sorry for stopping."

"Wait," I said, holding a hand up to stop her. "You shouldn't be driving in your condition." I knew she needed rest.

Val motioned for Jackie to get back in. Once Jackie did, Val jumped in the Jeep and slammed the door in my face. Her behavior was moody and sporadic, and it went beyond the normal female oddities. Turning the key, the engine cranked but refused to turn over.

"Why won't this thing start?" she asked. She tried a few more times and the engine finally fired.

Nick peeked his head in the open window. "Dean's right. You're in no condition to drive. Also, we need to re-wrap that nasty wound of yours."

She smiled. "I'm fine, baby brother."

"That's for me to decide," he said.

"Listen, each Jeep is stocked with a first aid kit," Val said. "I made sure of that. So don't worry. I'll have Jackie wrap it up as soon as possible."

"Let me slap on a dressing from the medical kit, and then Dean's driving while you get some sleep." He motioned to the back seat.

"Are you worried I might hurt Jackie?" Val asked. Before Nick could answer, she continued, "Listen, the first thing I did was give Jackie a gun. If I try to bite, she can just shoot me."

As he reached for the keys, Val threw the car in reverse.

Nick jumped back. "Val! You about ran me over."

Tires squealed, and she sped off ahead of us. Clearly, the girl had a mind of her own, and she didn't like being told what to do.

I tapped Nick's shoulder. "C'mon! We gotta catch up!"

He jumped in the driver seat, looked over his shoulder to make sure Claire and I were in back, and stomped on the gas.

I let out a breath, my gaze focusing on the road ahead. "Why's she acting like that?"

Nick gripped the steering wheel tightly. "She's stubborn. It runs in the family."

My heart jumped when I saw Val exit the freeway into the next city.

"Oh my gosh!" Claire said as my brother swerved into the opposite lane. "What's she doing?

She's driving like a maniac! She's gonna kill my cousin!"

"I don't know what's wrong with her. We have plenty of gas, food, and water," Nick said. "There's no reason to venture into one of those cities. I'm gonna have to kick her infected butt when we catch up to her!"

"Not if I get to her first," I said.

He pulled off the ramp and turned left into the city. A sharp jolt rushed through me as we ran over a deep pothole, then another. Nick didn't slow down one bit and rushed to keep up with Val. The place seemed deserted except for a few stray zombies stumbling aimlessly down the street, groaning in unsatisfied hunger. There were no streetlights and no traffic—just eerie silence, darkness, and walking corpses.

Nick looked over his shoulder at us, "I don't like this one bit."

"Neither do I! Venturing into the city is beyond stupid. I really don't want to follow her, but what choice do we have? We can't just desert them."

We watched as Val carelessly swerved around a corner, past an abandoned subway station.

Nick beeped the horn.

"Stop!" Claire screamed, popping her head out the window.

"Try cutting her off," I said.

He sped up and swerved around her as my seatbelt strained against my shoulders. The headlights fell on the other Jeep, illuminating Val's face for a brief second.

In that second, I saw the dangerous look in her eyes. I yelled for her to pull over.

She suddenly turned left and came to a halt in the empty lot of a grocery store where shopping carts were scattered all about.

"All right. She stopped," Nick said. "Let's go talk to her! I'm dying to see what she has to say." Frowning, he pulled next to her and parked the Jeep.

Claire jumped out after Val. "Val!"

"Claire," my brother yelled. "Don't go out there without a weapon!"

"Got the stun gun," she replied.

I didn't believe in giving lectures, but Val needed a good talking-to, and I was going to give it to her, whether she wanted it or not. I opened the door, but my brother yanked my arm to keep me inside.

"Wait! You can't go out there unarmed either." He reached down and pulled a gun from a strap on his ankle. "Take this. I've got another one."

Nick was right—again: Walking out in dangerous territory without a weapon would have been suicide, so I grabbed the gun. "Let's go see what Val's little problem is, and then we'll get back on the road again. And she's NOT driving again, no matter what."

"Exactly." Nick nodded.

"Hey, sis," I yelled.

Like a madwoman, Val grabbed a loose brick and whipped it through the window. Glass shattered with a *boom*, making me lower my head to protect my face. My sister was losing it big time, and I realized Nick and I were going to have to wrangle her back because she wasn't playing with a full deck.

"What are you doing?" Nick yelled, waving his arms in the air.

Jackie came from behind and shook my shoulder. "Your sister's talking all crazy. She says you have a cure for her zombie bite, but she has to turn into a zombie first. She's going mad or something!"

"We do have a possible cure," I said, "but she's right about having to become a zombie first."

She nodded slowly, as if trying to process the words. "The cure...it's in that black bag you were carrying over your shoulder when I first met you. Isn't it?"

"Bingo. Hey, you got a weapon?" Nick asked her.

"I lost my gun when I almost went over the banister," she said, "but Val gave me another one."

"Good." Nick said.

"Let's wrangle my sister back into the Jeep," I said.

"Crap!" Jackie yelled.

My heart leapt when Val suddenly darted inside the store, disappearing into the darkness stretching beyond.

CHAPTER 11

Nighttime had descended a few hours earlier, and the streets ahead of us seemed devoid of life. A narrow slice of the moon peeked from behind thick clouds that looked almost black against the night sky. Without lampposts to show us the way, we knew anything could be lurking in the shadows, waiting to ambush us. Luckily, though, the light of the stars cast just enough light to illuminate our way. My breath misted before me as I jumped out of the car. I left the door open and hurried past overflowing trashcans, toward the entrance to the small building into which Val had disappeared a minute ago.

"Shoot anything that looks suspicious," Nick said. "I don't care how many bullets you waste, just stay safe. We have plenty back in the Jeep."

Even though his back was turned on me and he couldn't see me, I nodded and hurried after him. I didn't know what kind of goose chase my sister was leading us on. Why she had decided to pull off the highway and lead us into a creepy, deserted ghost town at night, only to break into a grocery store, was beyond me, but for her own sake, I hoped she had some viable reason. Nick, however, wasn't as understanding and patient as his little brother.

"C'mon, Dean. Move your butt. We haven't got all of eternity," Nick said, motioning me forward.

"Wait!" Claire said. "We'll never see a thing in there." She whirled around and headed back to the Jeep, then returned with what looked like an overstuffed purse full of flashlights, which she passed around.

Nick met her gaze. "What do you mean, 'we'? You're not going in there with us."

"What? Of course I am." As though to prove a point, she walked past him, calling over her shoulder, "It's your sister, isn't it? You guys might need my help."

I raised my brows at Nick. I'd assumed Claire hated Val, but either they'd suddenly bonded over killing a few zombies, or else she really did dig Nick and was just trying to impress him. I didn't know her all that well, but from what I had seen so far, I was ready to bet my most precious friend and possession—the gun in my hands—on the latter.

"Just be careful. She's been bitten!" Jackie yelled after her.

Claire stopped and turned. "I know. Nick told me everything back in the Jeep."

Yeah, definitely the latter. She probably thinks they share something special now that Nick has confided in her. Shaking my head, I let out a long breath and took off through the parking lot. I stopped abruptly in the doorway of the market when I heard Val's screams echoing through the air. The air smelled of damp earth and rotting garbage, but there was also something else: the scent of death.

I gritted my teeth as I looked at Nick, "Val's going to alert every zombie from here to kingdom come if she doesn't be quiet." If I'd have had a roll of duct tape, or if we'd have been fortunate enough to stumble into a hardware store where they sold the stuff, I would have been highly tempted to use it. My sister's big mouth was going to turn us all into zombie bait.

The bobbing beams of our flashlights swept back and forth as we hurried up the cereal aisle. I only knew we were in the graveyard of Rice Krispies and Golden Grahams because the sign over our heads said so; there was nothing left on the shelves but layers of dust and debris and a box ripped right down the middle of Tony the Tiger's striped head. Then something scurried past to our right and I craned my neck and swept the flashlight over a dark head with long hair. I nudged Nick, then sped up to catch my sister. "Val, c'mon! We gotta go!"

The filthy linoleum, carpeted by an inches-thick layer of dust and grime, barely made a sound as I dashed through the darkness, then stopped. A sickly scent hit my nostrils, making me want to puke. I moved my flashlight around and illuminated the darkness as I scanned the area to spot the culprit...packages of rotting meat.

Val held up a blue box with a picture of noodles and fancy writing. She didn't even turn as she said, "Look! It's smashed. Rodents have been nibbling it as well, so this one's a no-go." She tossed the box on the floor, and it landed with a loud *thud*, then pulled out a giant, moldy piece of steak from its wrapper. To be honest, I wasn't even sure what it was and I didn't know what possessed her to pick it up in the first place. "Is this going to be my new choice of food?" she asked.

"I sure hope not, Val," I whispered.

Ignoring me, she rolled her eyes and threw the steak away. It plopped onto the ground a few feet away and remained stuck to the ground. "It's expired! You can have it, miss!" Val yelled, her voice reverberating from the walls. "And get some clothes on. Who comes to a store dressed in a robe anyway? When you're done snacking, go home and cook your man some brains or something."

"Who's she talking to?" I whispered to Nick.

"I dunno," he said. "But it's kind of freaky. I bet she's hallucinating."

My attention remained glued to Val as she held up a can and rolled it in her hands, continuing her monologue. "And this one's dented. This store sucks! Where's the manager?"

Footsteps echoed behind me a moment before Claire and Jackie appeared and Claire's hand wrapped around my upper arm.

"What's going on?" Jackie whispered.

I shook my head, signaling that I had no clue, and turned my gaze back to Val, who was still regarding a can as though it was a famous painting hanging in an art museum.

"Are you trying to memorize the ingredients or something?" Claire asked, her voice oozing with sarcasm. "Surely you're not counting calories now, are you?"

In one swift move, Val lunged at Claire, hissing like some kind of vampire chick in a horror flick. Claire's arms flew up to protect her face, but Val was stronger. In a single motion, she tossed Claire to the ground and landed on top of her, pinning her to the ground. I had to admit, it kind of freaked me out, almost to the point that I wanted to summon the men in white coats to bring their paddy wagon and lock her up in a straightjacket. After the initial shock, I finally unglued myself from the spot and leapt forward, but Nick was quicker on the draw. He wrapped his arms around her and dragged her up in an iron grip as she kicked and screamed.

"She's trying to kill me!" Claire yelped.

I rolled my eyes. "No, I don't think so. I think she just didn't like what you said. If you knew anything about zombies, you'd know to keep your mouth shut rather than provoke their short temper."

Val's eyes bulged in her skull, and she looked like a serial killer. "You'll be the first to go, Claire! You didn't watch my back, so now I'm going to eat yours."

Nick held her tight and I was thankful for that.

Claire gasped, hiding behind me. "She's mad, freaking crazy! Get that monster away from me," she chanted over and over again. "Get her away!"

"She's not a monster," I whispered. "...*yet,*" I wanted to add but didn't.

"My gosh! It's like she's possessed or something," Claire said.

"Okay, okay. I'm fine! Let me go," Val said quietly. She had stopped struggling and seemed reasonable again, but I didn't trust the sudden calmness.

"You sure?" Nick asked.

She nodded, her gaze sweeping over Claire, and for a moment, I thought I saw a flicker in her eyes. I wanted to shout at Nick to watch out when he pulled away a few inches. Like a wild beast, Val lunged forward again, her hands cutting through the air inches from my face. Claire buried her face in my shoulder, and her hands clutched the shirt at my lower back.

"What's wrong with you?" Nick said through gritted teeth, grabbing hold of Val again. "I trusted you, and you're acting like a psycho again. Calm down, Val!"

I smacked my tongue and peeled Claire off my shirt, and then I shot my brother a look. "You can't trust a zombie. Wasn't that the first lecture you ever taught me? Funny that you'd forget it now."

"I'm not a zombie," Val hissed. "I'm just a girl on a mission."

Yeah, right...the mission of eating a friend. I flashed my beam in her eyes and then gave Nick a sideways glance.

"What?" he asked.

"Her irises are dilated, her eyes bloodshot. The skin on her forehead is beginning to crack."

"The virus is kicking in," Nick said. "She doesn't mean to act like a maniac. I hate to tell you this, but it's only gonna get worse, so you'd better get used to it." He pushed Val past us. His knuckles had turned white where his fingers had sliced into her arms.

She struggled, her legs tangling with his, making it impossible to inch forward.

"Move it, Val," he whispered, "or I swear I'll tie you up and drag you out of here. You won't like that little trip through the express lane. Trust me."

"How are we going to get her back in the Jeep?" I asked.

"She'll either cooperate, or else I'll knock her out using pressure points."

Val hissed and spat but didn't argue. Slowly, she began to take one pace at a time.

When I heard a growl that wasn't coming from my nearly zombified sister, my senses kicked in on full alert. I shined my light around until the beam fell on a pair of glowing yellow eyes that came out of the darkness. "Nick!" I yelled. "Zombie housewife at three o'clock!"

"Don't panic!" Nick whispered. "I've got this."

I squinted to get a better glimpse as I swung the beam around so I could catch any attack. The zombie inched forward, then stopped and bent forward, allowing us a glimpse beneath her dirty white robe. I smirked and moved my gaze from her naked legs to the bulging red veins covering her face. Val's words echoed in my ears, and I wondered if she'd been talking to that half-dressed zombie, advising it to throw on some clothes, but I had no time to ponder her strange comment. The zombie moved again. Slowly, she knelt to the ground and picked up the piece of meat Val had tossed away, then started to lick the spoiled steak in a bloodthirsty frenzy, like a starving stray dog.

Val slapped her forehead. "That's sick! I can't believe that's going to be me in less than a day!"

"Put that thing out of its misery please," I said.

Nick aimed his gun and shot the corpse in the head.

She fell straight back and landed in a large display of macaroni and cheese boxes.

"Will you shoot me too?" Val asked sweetly. "You did just shoot my sister, in a sense. I mean, we're all part of the same happy meat-eating zombie family, right?"

"Stop talking like that!" Nick said through gritted teeth.

She grabbed my collar and shook me, her unnaturally shiny eyes piercing into mine. "What's it like to have a zombie for a sister?" she asked.

I set my jaw and forced myself to stare at her. *What am I supposed to say? The truth? That it completely sucks?* Whatever my brain came up with, it wouldn't be good enough, and I knew it sure wouldn't change anything. "It's not fun—no fun at all! Especially when she breaks into stores at night in the middle of Zombie Land." It was hard to see any life behind those eyes of hers. I was losing her after just so recently finding her, and that hurt me more than anything. "Try and think straight, Val! We gotta go, big sister."

"Big? So now I'm fat, huh?"

"No way!" I shook my head.

"I don't want to become a zombie," she said sadly, knocking over another display, sending several red and white cans to the floor. "Mmm, mmm, good," she mocked, looking at them. "I'm not really into brains as a delicacy," Val said.

Her thoughts were all over the place, and I realized I needed to keep her focused. "You won't be a zombie forever, Val. I've got the cure, remember?" My voice remained calm, but inside I was shaking like a leaf in the wind, hoping that what I was telling her was true.

"You do? Why didn't you just say so?" She yawned. "I'm so tired. What's your name again?"

"I'm your brother, Dean."

"And I'm your other brother, Nick. Now come on, sis. I have a nice blanket and pillow waiting for you in the Jeep," Nick coaxed softly. "Let's go."

"Okay." She leaned forward as though to hug me.

Nick grabbed her arm to put a few inches between us.

If she noticed, she didn't comment on it. She simply said, "Dean and Nick, I love you guys so much. I couldn't ask for better brothers."

I prayed to God she wouldn't bite me while my guard was down. "It's gonna be okay. I promise."

"Why are we here? In a grocery store of all places?" Val asked, as if she had just snapped back into reality. "Are you guys that hungry? Didn't we take enough food from that glass house?"

"I'm not hungry at all," I said, pushing her forward as gently as I could. Luckily, she began to move.

"Then why are we here?" she asked.

"Well, you hightailed it off the freeway to take us on some kind of midnight tour of this place," I said. "I figured maybe you were looking for a fast-food drive-thru."

"I'm losing my mind. You better not let me drive again. I'm so sorry, guys. I-I just don't know what's happening to me." She squeezed my hand and then let it go, as though she didn't trust herself any more than I trusted her. In the very next second, she yelled, "Get away from me! Who are you? I'm not going anywhere with you!"

In an instant, Claire pressed her stun gun on Val's arm, sending my sister crumbling to the ground on jellied legs. "Sorry for zapping your sister and all, but I think we need to get outta here," Claire said.

"It's okay. She was out of control." I scooped her up and realized she was burning up.

Nick shined the light down. "She's out cold. Let's get her back into the Jeep."

We barely moved a few steps before zombie groans came from our right.

Jackie gripped my hand. "We've got company, and I don't think they're here for this week's sales." In spite of her attempt at infusing humor, I could feel her rigidity.

"This isn't good!" Claire said.

"Don't worry," Jackie said. "Val gave me a gun, so we'll be okay."

"I hope you're right," Claire said. She peeked around an aisle, then gasped.

I followed her line of vision, and my own breath caught in my throat. "There're so many of them. That gun of yours better be a dead aimer...and I mean that literally."

We moved forward at a snail's pace, careful not to draw any unwanted attention. About twenty zombies stumbled around aimlessly, knocking over boxes and cans as they rummaged through the stock, looking for any kind of raw meat.

We were almost halfway down the aisle when a zombie's gaze fell upon me. I forced myself to remain calm, even though my whole body screamed to run. "Nick!" I nudged my brother harder than intended. "We're outnumbered. How are we ever gonna get out of here?"

He grabbed my arm and pulled me down the aisle where we hid behind a giant display.

"We need a distraction," Jackie said.

Nick glanced around, as if pondering. "Flour," he finally said. "And it's not for baking a cake."

"Brilliant idea. We can cover them in the stuff," Claire said.

"Perfect distraction," I said. "I saw flour too."

"Where?" Claire said.

Without giving her an answer, I darted a few aisles over, flashing my light on the overhanging signs until I found the right isle. I turned left and started frantically looking until I found it. Just as I snagged a package, a zombie's hand burst through the shelf opening from the other side, grabbing my arm and startling me. My gun clattered to the floor, next to a cellophane bag of broken plastic forks.

Through the shining beam of my flashlight, I looked through the gap, and I saw the zombie's white, lifeless, hungry eyes. My heart lurched. I knew if the thing broke my skin, I'd be in as much trouble as Val. I tried to wiggle my hand free, but it had amazing strength and just tightened its grip, pulling while rattling the shelf. I feared it might draw the attention of the other undead late-night shoppers, but my main concern was freeing my arm without sustaining a wound. I prayed it wouldn't scratch or bite me with its jagged teeth, because I knew that would be more fatal than any saliva dropping on my skin. With my free hand, I tried to hit it with my flashlight over and over again, until my arm hurt, but still the thing wouldn't let go.

Footsteps rushed behind me, and my heart raced. A zombie? *How am I supposed to fight while this thing's got a hold of me?* I glanced over my shoulder and saw it wasn't a zombie. It was only Claire. She was hurrying over to me, holding her stun gun. I bit my lip hard as she stunned the corpse's arm. When it released its cold grasp, I yanked my arm free. "Thank you, Claire! I so owe you."

"Did it get you?" she whispered.

I ran my hands over my arm, fearing that I might find myself in the same predicament as Val. "No blood," I said, letting out a huge sigh of relief. When I suddenly heard footsteps, my gaze jerked up.

"It's okay," Claire said. "It's only the others."

Nick carried Val securely in his arms. "Grab as many bags as you can!"

We all went to work and started grabbing bags of flour. I was pretty sure Nick hadn't seen my little 'shelf battle' with the zombie and I wasn't about to say anything at the moment. There was no time for lectures. Carrying the sacks, we sped down the aisle.

"Our goal is to confuse them, to distract them!" Nick whispered, setting down Val.

We clambered to the top of the shelves and opened the bags. When we threw them, flour spewed everywhere. I coughed from the blanket of white sifting through the air, but our plan seemed to work: The zombies hissed and started to stumble around like big, clumsy idiots, and it looked as if they were completely disoriented from the flour fog we'd created.

"Run now!" yelled Nick, jumping down and scooping up Val.

Nick and Claire darted off ahead of Jackie and me. We were right behind them when an avalanche of cans and boxes tumbled over my head. The shelves had collapsed right down on us, probably from the weight of so many zombies filling the store. I gripped Jackie's hand tightly, peering through the smog of flour. It appeared as if Nick, Val, and Claire had made it out okay, but I hadn't. *Murphy's Law. Go figure.* I glanced helplessly at all the zombies flooding in through the doorway.

"We'll have to find a different way out," Jackie whispered.

I glanced at the zombies flooding in through the doorway and realized we definitely couldn't use the main entrance. From what I had seen so far, the only other way out was the back, where the zombies were gathered. *Crap! We're so screwed.*

CHAPTER 12

From outside, the grocery store had seemed deserted, even peaceful, but there was nothing peaceful about the place. Unfortunately, we had to discover that tiny detail after following Val inside, and now we were trapped. The countless growls and moans cutting through the night made my skin tingle, and my brain was working overtime as I tried to figure out a way to make it out alive. Nick, Val, and Claire had made it out of the store, but Jackie and I were still trapped inside, and it didn't look like we were going to be able to come up with an exit strategy before the zombies noticed our presence. One had already spotted me, and with more flooding in through the front by the minute, the place would grow crowded soon. My heart was already drumming in my ears, and I was sure that if I could hear its terrified *thump-thump* so loud and clear, the zombies would hear it too. It was only a matter of time.

I bit my lip as I glanced around the darkness, then pointed to a high window way over to the right.

Jackie nodded in silent agreement, then took off in the right direction.

Our shoes barely made a sound on the tile floor as we zigzagged through a few aisles and finally made it to the horizontal window, then stopped to peer around. Long shelves filled with cans jutted out of the wall.

Giving Jackie's hand a last squeeze, I stepped on one of the rickety bottom shelves and pulled myself up to the next horizontal surface. "C'mon!" I whispered. It was difficult to shimmy up it without knocking off any of the merchandise with my feet, but we couldn't risk making any noise. The last thing I wanted to do was give away my location to the army of the undead. I placed a foot on the hard surface and held on to the metal rod, then heaved myself up. My clothes made a chafing sound that wouldn't have been noticeable under normal circumstances, but nothing about our circumstances was normal. I held my breath and peered around me, trying to determine if we'd been spotted. The zombies went about their business, fighting and hissing over a slice of foul-smelling meat. Letting out my breath, I tested the shelf with my leg. When I realized it was strong enough to support me, I moved up to the next level, then stopped again when the shelf trembled. A few cans knocked against each other; two or three rolled to the side, but didn't drop to the ground. *Thank God!* I knew if I could keep it that way, we might just stand a chance. The last thing I wanted to die over was a can of black-eyed peas.

Using the shelf as a ladder to reach the top, I climbed up slowly but steadily, taking one step at a time. I was almost up when one of the cans clattered to the ground, the sound reverberating from the walls. Crap! Suddenly, a few zombie heads snapped in our direction, causing my breath to catch in my throat. I prayed their interest wouldn't be piqued but, as usual, luck wasn't on my side. Hurrying as fast as I could, my legs on fire, I dashed up, then reached down to help Jackie. I wrapped my hand around her thin arm to pull her up, and once she reached the top, we glanced down. Because of my fumbling cans fiasco, zombies had spotted us and headed in our direction.

Jackie unlocked the window. We pushed and pulled as hard as we could, our arms straining as we forced the latch, but it was painted shut and refused to budge. I reached for my gun but it wasn't there and I knew it must've fallen out when the shelves collapsed on us.

"Give it another push!" I yelled. "On three!" I began to count, and then hurled my whole weight forward, to no avail. My heart began to race again. I got on my knees and reached down for anything we could use to bust the window or knock the latch off. My hands wrapped around a can of spaghetti sauce, the mushroom variety. It was a bit small, but the edges were sharp enough to do the trick. "Cover your face!" I said to Jackie.

"No need," she said, sliding out her gun from her holster. Pulling the trigger, the window shattered with a boom, glass spraying outside onto the gravel below. The shelves started to wobble as zombies began to rock them from below, and Jackie fell back with a loud yelp.

I quickly grabbed her around the waist to steady her, while holding on to the railing with my other arm. "Wrap your arm around my neck," I shouted through the moaning noise below. When Jackie reached up, I scooped her into my arms and held her tightly against me, then kicked out the rest of the window while Jackie kicked the shelf over. Her body was still pressed against me as we teetered on the edge of the windowsill, dangerously close to the floor below and the hands reaching up to grab us and tear us into tasty, bloody morsels. With a loud *thud*, the shelf crashed on top of the zombies.

I peered out into the night, exasperated. There were no trees to shimmy down, no ladder, no rope, and nothing to aid our descent. Only after leaning out did I notice that directly underneath us, there was a tall dumpster with flat, open doors on the top and metal sliding doors on the side. "We've gotta jump," I said.

Without hesitation, Jackie climbed out and took the plunge.

I followed right after and fell into a giant pile of black bags. I could hear the plastic crinkling beneath me a moment before the reek of rotten eggs hit my nostrils and made me gag. Pushing up, I struggled to grip something hard without spreading the garbage and smell all over me. When I finally managed to sit up, I realized the only thing that wasn't covered in trash were parts of my face. "Are you okay?" I whispered, looking around for Jackie, who'd disappeared into the abyss of garbage.

She popped up and peered over a few bags. "Yeah, I'm fine. You?"

I nodded, even though I couldn't tell whether she could see anything in the pitch black.

"See anything?" she continued.

The moon cast a glow over city buildings, and graffiti-covered walls stretching into the distance. To the left of a broken lamp post, I noticed a long alley strewn with garbage. My gaze scanned the area for any suspicious movement, but everything remained silent. "The coast is clear," I whispered to Jackie.

The loud rustling of plastic bags next to Jackie startled me. Then, a green, rotting hand burst from the boxes and tried to clench the air. My heart lurched. I felt around the trash looking for anything I could get my hands on. All I could find were empty boxes that wouldn't even smash a fly, let alone fight off a zombie.

The oversized container shook slightly on its wheels as the zombie fought its way through the trash and sprung toward Jackie, snapping its jaws. She whipped out her gun and shot it straight in the forehead. Dark liquid squirted everywhere, and the zombie fell sideways. Jackie scrambled up.

I was right behind her, so I helped her climb over the edge of the dumpster, and then followed. "Which way should we go?" I whispered as I scanned my surroundings.

"Let's circle around. Maybe we'll find Nick and Claire...and your sister."

Before I could even answer, I heard a moan and spun around. I gasped. More zombies had spotted us and shuffled in our direction. Jackie aimed her gun, but we both realized there were too many and we wouldn't stand a chance. With my heart pounding, I gripped her hand, and we turned around. "C'mon!" We took off down the alley, and I spied the perfect getaway vehicle, an abandoned motorcycle. Nick had taught me how to ride his motorcycle ages ago. I was a pro and could handle this with no problem. "Think it runs?" I glanced over my shoulder to make sure the zombies weren't gaining on us. Luckily for us, they were slower than turtles, and they were still a good distance away, but I wanted to get out of there before they caught up.

"It won't even start without keys," Jackie said, searching for them in the darkness.

It would have been far too easy for them to have been left in the ignition, I supposed. I glanced down and noticed a leather coat lying on the sidewalk in a bloody heap. I was about to open my mouth to say something about it, but before I could, she had followed my line of vision and was poking her foot into the heap. Bending down, she felt the pockets and pulled out a set of dangling keys. I prayed one of them would start the bike. I hopped on, she hopped on behind me, and I slid the most appropriate-looking key in the ignition. There was a *click*, but the motorcycle wouldn't start. Beads of sweat rolled down my face.

"Try again!" yelled Jackie. "They're getting closer."

"I am!" I said, wondering why the thing wouldn't cooperate. With a terrified glance over my shoulder, I tried one last time. The engine spluttered for a moment, but then it finally started! We sped down the alley, my heart racing. I had always dreamt of riding a magnificent Harley with a beautiful girl, the blasting gusts of wind whipping through our hair. Of course, I'd pictured it more on a highway, not in a back-alley labyrinth, in the middle of the night, with zombies hot on our tailpipes.

We took a few twists and turns, but I really wasn't sure which way to go. I slowed and turned the motorcycle down another alleyway, which ultimately led us to a beach.

"Turn around," Jackie said.

Just as she said it, I heard hissing and moaning wafting through the night air and glanced over my shoulder to see a new group of undead coming out from behind deserted buildings and heading toward us. "Um, scratch that!" I said. "There's no way we're going back."

CHAPTER 13

"The sand! It'll slow them down big time," I said, turning left onto the beach and hitting the gas. I scanned my surroundings. To the left, tall trees stretched into the sky, their crowns swallowed up by darkness. Behind us, a white sign glowed in the darkness, pointing out that it was a private beach and any intruders would be prosecuted. We didn't know what we might stumble upon in either direction, and I wasn't sure which way to take. While I was deliberating, my wheels suddenly squealed, throwing up sand everywhere.

"What's going on?" Jackie asked behind me. Her frantic tone and the way her hands clutched my waist told me she was slowly getting worried.

"Hold on," I said calmly, even though my hands were shaking. There wasn't enough time to dig the tires out. If we were stuck, we'd have to make it out of there on foot. We had no flashlights and, worse, no idea what was lurking around the next corner. Shuffling through the sand, groups of zombies slowly came from every direction, drawn to us like moths to a flame. I assumed they were attracted to the roar of the motorcycle. I met Jackie's terrified gaze. "If we can get free, we can zigzag around them." It was a crazy idea, but it wasn't impossible. They were still at least a hundred feet away, but one particular zombie seemed to move faster than the rest; I wondered if he'd been just recently turned. I kept the zombie MVP in my line of vision.

Jackie pulled out her gun. "I'm going to keep these freaks from getting too close. You just work on getting us outta here."

"Remember, aim for their heads."

"I know," she said flatly.

The motorcycle rattled as I revved it up, the tires digging deep into the sinking sand. Time was running out, and I contemplated running on foot if we didn't get the Harley out within the next minute or so.

"Hey!" she said. "Try not to spin the tires. Digging us halfway to Australia isn't going to do us any good." She squeezed the trigger and missed.

"Concentrate!" I said.

"I am!" she said. She fired again, this time hitting the zombie in the chest. "It's still coming!"

"They will unless you hit them in the *head*!" I yelled. With the zombie inching forward, I needed to get the motorcycle tire out of the sand, but I couldn't focus on helping Jackie and digging our way out all at once.

"Got it!" She slid off the bike. She walked right up to the zombie, until she was only a few feet away, then aimed and shot him right in the forehead, sending him to the ground, where he flailed around for a moment like a dying fish out of water.

"Are you crazy? Get back on the bike!" I yelled.

"I'm not going down without giving us a fighting chance." She aimed at the approaching crowd, and three more fell. Jackie was finally realizing that fighting had become a necessity for life, but she was failing to realize that two people couldn't take on an entire zombie herd by themselves.

"You need to quit playing hero and get your butt back on this bike!"

Reaching down, she grabbed some loose branches from the beach. "I have an idea."

"I think your gun's a much better choice," I said.

"Try to lift the motorcycle when I count to three," she said.

I heaved as hard as I could, but with the sand shifting everywhere, I only managed about two or three inches.

"Hold it up," Jackie said, kneeling down.

I clenched my teeth and held the weight of the machine as I watched her squeeze the branches under the front tires, then move to the back. I held my breath as I dropped the front tire, then lifted up the back so she could stabilize the branches beneath it.

"The branches will provide traction, or at least I hope so," she said.

It was a brilliant idea; I had to give her that. I rocked the motorcycle back and forth, spewing a cloud of sand in the air. Some of the smaller twigs snapped beneath it, making me doubt it would hold. I knew we had to hurry. I could just picture that undead army pulling us off the motorcycle and biting into our flesh, and I shuddered at the thought. "Jump on," I said to Jackie before starting the engine. I could feel the twigs giving way beneath the tires, so I hit the gas. With one last squeal, the tires were free. I turned in the direction with the least amount of zombies and was able to easily pass by them, my heart racing even faster than the bike.

Speeding up, I followed the beach strip, my thighs clutching to it to keep it steady. I turned right. *There has to be an opening or exit somewhere. If we could only find it...* "Look for a gate or something," I yelled to Jackie, my gaze still fixed on the ground. As I turned the bend, I saw that the south side of the beach was also swarming with zombies. To make matters worse, I was sure our loud motorcycle had just rung the dinner bell.

"There're too many of them!" Jackie said. "We'll never get through."

She was right, for I saw no way to break through them without becoming their midnight snack.

Jackie started shooting, and two dropped in our path.

I abruptly turned the bike and zigzagged past a few stragglers. I revved up the motorcycle and sped toward a nearby pier.

Jackie wrapped her arms tight around my waist. "What're we doing?"

"Can you swim?"

"Yeah, sure. I take it we're going for a dip?"

"Yep, hold on." Adjusting my speed, I raced down the pier. The engine revved and the tires squealed as the motorcycle drove into the lake with a giant *splash* and began sinking, pulling us beneath the surface.

Cold water gushed into my mouth and soaked my clothes. Somewhere in the back of my swirling mind, I realized I could no longer feel Jackie's hands around my waist. With deliberate, long pushes of my legs and arms, I broke the surface and spewed out water, my whole body screaming for oxygen. I took giant gulps of air and searched for Jackie. "Jackie? Jackie! Where are you?" I asked between breaths.

A few moments passed, but the dark surface of the water remained undisturbed. I scanned the area around me frantically, fearing the worst. Suddenly, a spluttering noise echoed from behind me. I turned sharply to Jackie, throwing her arms around me.

"You're okay!" She laughed.

I melted into her embrace. "Never been better. I shook my head to push the scary images to the back of my mind. If anything had happened to her, I wouldn't have been able to live with myself.

She motioned toward the shore. "You don't think they can swim, do you?"

"No way! I live on an island. Trust me, those things can't swim, and they know it." My gaze darted over to the shore. Under the bright moonlight, zombies were pacing up and down it, moaning and groaning, just waiting to tear us apart. Lots of them had also followed us up the pier. It gave me the creeps, but I knew they wouldn't come into the lake.

She squeezed my arm. "I bet they'd love it if we were stupid enough to swim back."

"Yeah, but we're not that stupid."

"Let's swim to the other side and get our butts out of here," Jackie said.

I had no idea how big or deep the lake was, but I didn't even want to think about it. With no other choice, I had to remain positive, so I glided forward with long strokes.

After a few minutes of swimming, Jackie stopped. I halted next to her and followed her line of vision, down the water surface to the darkness stretching in the distance. "You see that?" she whispered, pointing at what looked like a shore.

"What?"

She started forward, then swung back. "There's somebody over there."

I was sure it was just more zombies, so we'd have to keep swimming until we found a safe way out. I could see the opposite shore not too far away. Squinting to get a better look, I made out figures in the distance. A second later, a strong breeze carried their shouts to us. My lips curled into a big smile when I realized Nick and Claire were pacing along the shore, waving their hands wildly. "I can always count on my brother!" I pounded the water with my fists, splashing it in all directions.

Jackie smiled. "We're saved!"

I met her gaze when she gripped my shirt tight and pulled me close, wrapping her legs tightly around me. Catching me off guard, she captured my lips in a hot, hungry kiss. I swirled my tongue over hers. My heart pounded as adrenaline surged. I had never kissed such a hot girl before—or many girls, for that matter—and it was the most amazing feeling in the entire world.

She broke the kiss and said with a coy smile, "C'mon. Your brother's waiting."

I smiled. "Yeah, let's go." With powerful strokes, I cut through the water and swam toward shore.

"Hey, we saw headlights, and then a bike drive off into the lake!" Claire called as soon as we were within earshot, only a few feet away. "When we saw it, we raced our Jeeps over here to the other side, hoping it might be you."

"Yeah, with all that screaming to get your attention, I thought we'd attract zombies," Nick said.

I scanned the beach for any shadows, but saw none. It looked safe for the moment, and I was happy when my feet finally touched the ground beneath me. As I waded through the waist-high water, pebbles and sand shifted under my feet. I climbed out, shivering in the cold breeze running over my body. "How's Val?" I asked my brother.

"Sleeping," he answered. There was something in his voice though, some kind of hesitation, as though he was keeping something to himself, but I didn't press the issue.

Happy to have made it out, I let out a sigh of relief and squeezed Jackie's hand, and then my gaze fell on the gun in Claire's hand. "You pack heat now?" I asked.

She noticed my staring and held it up. "Your brother showed me some tips at the house, so I thought this might be the perfect time to put them to good use."

"Yeah, well, Nick can talk anyone into anything," I said.

"C'mon," Nick said. "You know a stun gun wouldn't cut it out here."

"I thought that too," I said, "but then Claire saved my butt back in the store."

"What?" Nick gasped.

"One of those zombies grabbed me through the shelves and I lost my gun. If Claire hadn't come and stunned the freak, I'm sure the thing would've bitten me." I threw Claire a thankful look. "Thanks, Claire."

"Not a problem." Claire slipped her gun into a holster around her waist, then threw an old blanket around me and Jackie. The wool felt so warm against my freezing skin; I couldn't stop shivering.

Nick hugged me. "I'm so glad you two are safe. You scared me to death!"

"Sorry, man."

"That was crazy!" Nick said. "Don't you dare ever pull a stunt like that again. The bike could've dragged you underwater and drowned you."

Jackie laughed. "A stunt? As if we planned it."

I nudged her, smiling. "Yeah, I knew he'd be totally freaked."

"Why wouldn't he be?" Claire asked, as if standing up for his honor. "The last thing we saw was you guys heading off to the lake on a motorcycle with a herd on your butts." She let out a trembling breath. "We tried to distract the zombies by beeping the horn."

"And then Claire's Jeep wouldn't start at first...about giving me a heart attack," Nick said.

"I really think we should be on a lookout for a new vehicle," Claire said.

"Yeah," Nick agreed. "Anyway, Claire laid on the horn like you wouldn't believe!"

Claire nodded. "Some of them turned, but most of them had their eyes set on you."

I found it funny that Claire had tried so hard to deter the undead army. The girl I'd met only hours earlier wouldn't have dreamt of attracting their attention when she could have just run away. It was quite a change, quite an accomplishment. I was sure she didn't do it entirely for me though. It was for Jackie, her cousin. When someone's loved ones or friends are in trouble, they'll go to astonishing lengths to save them, no matter how scary it is. I learned this firsthand with Val.

"We got separated when the zombies knocked the shelves over," Jackie said. "We made an escape out a window."

"Yeah, we were totally freaked out when we lost you guys." Claire wrapped her arms around both of us. "I'm so glad you're safe now."

"Thanks for finding us," whispered Jackie, hugging her tight.

"You think I'd let my BFF and cousin get eaten by zombies?"

Jackie chuckled. "Not in this lifetime."

We all laughed.

Nick insisted I ride with him because he wanted to discuss game plans and routes, so Claire and Jackie drove one Jeep while Nick, Val, and I took the other. We took off, heading for the highway. Val was sprawled out across the back seat, Nick drove, and I rode in the passenger seat.

"You really think Val's okay?" I asked. "She looks so pale."

"She's fine, but I'll tell you one thing. If our crazy sister pulls another stunt like she did back there, I'm gonna..." He didn't finish the thought.

She had definitely put us in a dangerous situation, and I hoped she would stay passed out for a while because I had no idea how to handle her. "When's she going to turn so we can see if the cure works?"

"Soon—very soon."

A thumping sound startled me. Turning sharply, I signaled Nick to keep quiet as I listened for any more strange noises. A second later, the thumping started again, stronger than before. My head snapped in Val's direction, even though I knew she was out cold. With my heart racing in my chest, I whipped out my gun and motioned for Nick to pull over as I prepared for yet another surprise coming from the storage compartment of our Jeep.

CHAPTER 14

We'd been on the highway for at least half an hour, listening to the rhythmic sound of our tires on the asphalt, when a strange noise made me look up. I held my breath and listened. For a whole second, nothing stirred, but then a thudding sound reverberated from inside the Jeep, the strange thudding and thumping we'd heard before. "What the heck?" I mumbled, motioning Nick to pull over and cut the engine. "I think something *is* in here with us."

"I hear it too. Stay calm," Nick said. "Let's not confront *anything* until we're all safely out of the Jeep. That'll give us a huge advantage."

The moment the Jeep ground to a halt, I grabbed Val and jumped out, setting her softly on the grass. If something was in that Jeep with us, I didn't want her to get hurt, especially while she was out cold and couldn't defend herself. I dashed for the back of the vehicle, with my weapon drawn.

Nick reached me in two long strides and placed his large body on the other side of the rear hatch.

Signaling him to keep quiet, I pointed my gun at the storage compartment located behind the second set of seats, and mentally prepared myself to shoot the miserable stowaway between its dead white eyes. I had no idea how a zombie could've gotten in there, but I was going to make it pay. With my eyes glued to the rear hatch, I inched closer and reached to open it.

Suddenly tires screeched on the asphalt behind us, and the doors opened and slammed shut.

"Get back inside!" Nick yelled. "There's nothing to see."

"What's going on?" Jackie asked, ignoring him. "You just stopped in the middle of nowhere."

"Is it Val?" Claire asked, appearing beside me.

I pushed her a step back and peered at Nick's face, which resembled a mask of irritation. "We all have to be quiet," I whispered, "or you might just wake up the monster—and I'm not talking about the zombie in the storage compartment of the Jeep."

As though in answer, a *thud* echoed from inside, followed by a louder one.

Claire jumped back, startled. "What the heck? A zombie? How did it get in there?"

"Probably while Val was on her little moonlight shopping spree." I shrugged. "As to why it would have wanted to crawl in there, don't ask me. I guess they're not claustrophobic or prone to motion sickness."

"Okay, we're opening," Nick said, pointing at Jackie. "Can you stand guard?"

She nodded, pulling out her gun.

"Okay." Nick sighed heavily, then unlocked the rear hatch and slowly opened the compartment door.

I drew a sharp breath and held it, bracing myself for the worst.

Something stirred inside, as though whatever was in there had sat up groggily and tried to maneuver themselves out. Then a voice echoed from within.

I blinked several times before a face came to mind to match the voice.

"Please don't shoot, Nick! Don't shoot, man!" Tahoe pleaded, appearing in my line of vision. His face was covered in darkness, but I would have recognized his hands anywhere, for they were the hands that had almost cost Val her life.

From the corner of my eye, I noticed Nick stepping closer, his jaw clenched in anger. "Nice touch remembering my name, Lake Tahoe, but do you think that's gonna actually save your sorry butt? The tables have turned for you, buddy. Now I'm in charge."

I shined the flashlight in Tahoe's eyes, unable to believe the guy's luck. He'd ventured out into the night, and when we'd watched his friend being eaten alive, we'd all mistakenly assumed Tahoe had been a side dish. I couldn't believe he was still alive, let alone standing in front of us. Either he had to be the luckiest moron in the whole wide world, or else he'd been bitten, so the venom had kept his future kind at bay. I knew which option was more likely. Taking a step back, I pushed Claire behind me, just in case, and focused my attention back on Tahoe. His hands and clothes were bloody, but whether the brown and red stains were from his blood or someone else's, I couldn't tell. If he had been attacked and infected by zombies, I knew Nick wouldn't hesitate to shoot him; at least that would have given Nick the perfect excuse to put a bullet in his head, a fitting death sentence for his attempted murder of our sister.

"You're the scum of the Earth. You know that, right?" Nick pointed his gun directly at the scraggly man's head. "Give me one good reason why I shouldn't pull this trigger."

Tahoe held up his hands, his eyes wide with fear. "Please don't shoot! It was all Earl! I let Dean go so he could help her. Just ask him. I let go!" He pointed at me, his gaze begging me to tell my brother my part of the story.

I'm not gonna play along with his little games.

My brother glanced over at me as if to acknowledge his claims.

"What?" I asked Tahoe. "You want me to remember? Hmm. Well, I'm afraid that might not work right now since I have a little concussion leftover from trying to save my sister from you and your sleaze-ball friend."

Tahoe paled, and a sheen of sweat covered his forehead. His hands clenched and unclenched, and his gaze fixed on the gun in my brother's hand.

"Is that so?" Nick said, grinning.

I inclined my head and tried to keep hard from laughing at Tahoe's shocked expression. "Yeah. Look, Nick, you might hafta draw your own conclusion here since I ain't gonna be of much help."

Tahoe swallowed audibly.

I couldn't help but feel justice had been served by terrifying him, if only a tiny bit. "Okay. He did let me go, technically," I said eventually. "Thing is, I still couldn't reach Val in time, and if it weren't for him and his half-wit friend, she wouldn't have gone through the horror she experienced."

Nick nodded. "Right. An accessory. I think any judge and jury would condemn a man who tried to assist in the murder of an innocent woman." He pointed the gun into Tahoe's forehead.

"Hey! You're not the judge and executioner," Jackie said, grabbing Nick's arm.

Even though I'd sworn it when Val had supposedly died, I didn't believe in cold-blooded murder. Those vengeful thoughts had been nothing more than the result of my emotions spilling over when I thought my sister had been murdered. "Just let him go," I said with a heavy sigh. "He's not worth a wasted bullet. Besides, we need to get back on the road."

"Get out of the trunk, Tahoe!" Nick said through gritted teeth. "Make one wrong move, and I'll shoot you dead in your tracks."

Tahoe slowly climbed out. "I'll just be on my way. Thank you."

"Everybody get back to your vehicles," Nick said, motioning Claire and Jackie back to their Jeep.

"Nick..." I said, hesitating. Knowing my brother, I doubted he'd just let Tahoe be on his merry way, but Nick was hard to read. He'd always been like that, but he was no killer. *Or is he?* "Nick?" My hand wandered to grab his arm, but he shrugged it off.

Jackie picked up on his vibes too. "You can't kill him, Nick. We're not murderers!"

Tahoe coughed and fell to the ground. He'd lost a lot of blood and was pretty weak.

"Nick," Claire said, "you're not a killer. You know that."

He regarded her coolly. "How would you know? You've known me for all of five minutes."

She pressed her fist against her chest, right above where her heart was beating. "I can feel it." Her voice quivered with emotion. "Let's help him get better, and then you can kick him out."

Laughing, Nick shook his head. "Why shouldn't we just leave him here? He'd make a nice little buffet for any zombies who happen to come along."

"You can't just leave him out here to die," she said, her gaze imploring him to listen, "and you can't kill him either."

We were trying our best, but in the end, we knew it was Nick's decision to make. We hoped he would do the right thing. *But do I really know him?* I wondered. What I'd seen of him during our brief stint in Zombie Land had changed my perception of him. He was tougher and colder than I ever imagined he could be.

"They won't touch him if they recognize their kind," Nick said, regarding Tahoe.

"They didn't bite me," Tahoe insisted. "Really, they didn't!"

Nick's eyes narrowed. "But wouldn't that be sweet justice?"

"I'm with you on that one," Jackie said. "He had no qualms about helping to throw an innocent woman over the railing as a distraction to save his own butt."

"I would never hurt anybody!" Tahoe said, shaking his head vehemently. "It was all Earl! I can't begin to tell you how sorry I am for your loss. If I didn't help him and do what he said, he would have killed me too!"

"Not a loss," Claire whispered. "The girl lived."

He gasped. "What? How? I-I mean that's wonderful, but how? Where is she? I'd like to personally apologize."

"Let's bandage him up," Jackie said. "Give him some food and water and a weapon. Whatever happens after that is his problem."

"You want to waste our precious supplies on this loser?" Nick asked.

Jackie stepped toward him, her eyes sparkling with determination. "Yes. I don't want to have his demise on our conscience. That's the only thing that makes us any more human than those things out there, isn't it?"

Nick waved his gun in the air. "This jerk almost cost my sister her life!"

"Listen, Nick..."

"No, Claire! If he and his friend hadn't stopped us, we could've made it out in the nick of time, before the herd came around to the front of the house."

Claire shook her head vehemently. "That's not entirely true, and you know it. I slowed you down in the first place. If you hadn't stayed there long enough to convince us to come with you, you would've been long gone."

"That's different."

A dangerous glint appeared in her eyes. "Why?"

Nick ran a hand through his hair as he contemplated her answer. "Because you didn't *try* to kill my sister," he said after a moment.

Claire's shoulders slumped. She was losing the argument, right or wrong, and she knew it. Whether we wanted it or not, Nick would make the final decision.

"Claire, Jackie, you can't just leave me here," Tahoe pleaded. "Zombies will shred me to pieces. Earl's a psychopath and told me he'd kill me countless times. I believed him after I saw the things he's done in the past. But he was my uncle and I couldn't leave him."

"Oh, you're good," Nick said. "Go on, storyteller. Humor us."

"No, really! It's all true. My father's the chief of police and I was going to tell him all about Earl."

"Right," I said.

"I swear I'm telling you the truth. Earl and I left the city we resided in to go pick up family members stranded in another state. We got sidetracked trying to lose a herd. I planned on getting back home, zombie apocalypse or not."

He was good at making up stories, but none of us believed Tahoe for a second.

"Do you really have the heart to kill a cop's son?" he said. "Not to mention, I have a wife and twin girls. Please think of them before you do anything to me."

"If I was you," Nick said, "I might've tried telling the story with one kid. It's way more believable than twins."

"Please think of my girls," Tahoe added. "They have beautiful blonde hair like their mama. If you met my babies, you'd instantly fall in love with them."

I raised my brows at him when he tried to play the sympathy card. I was sure no one in our group could possibly fall for such a tall tale, yet I could tell Jackie was softening: Her frown and the angry crease in her forehead disappeared, and her hands clutched into fists at her side as she turned to regard Nick. "We need to get going." I said. "Having an argument out here is bound to draw attention—and not the positive kind."

Nick nodded and took another step toward Tahoe, but Claire jumped in front of him as if to block Nick from shooting him. "He has nobody to look out for him!" she said. "You know what would've happened if no one had helped me in my time of need? I'd be dead."

Nick let out a long breath. "Fine. Get the medical kit, Dean."

I sighed. *Is he seriously caving just because of a pretty face?* Then again, I didn't care. I just wanted to do whatever we were doing so we could get the heck outta there. When I grabbed the first aid kit, Claire snatched it out of my hand and began tending to Tahoe's wounds.

"Hurry up. We don't have time for this," Nick said. "Every minute we stick around here just makes a bigger target on our backs."

"Then help us get him into the Jeep so we can leave," Claire snapped.

"No," I said. "Nick's right. Tahoe can't come with us. He's a liar and nothing but trouble. Tend to his wounds like you wanted, and we'll give him a little food and water and some kind of weapon to defend himself, but that's all we're going to do for him."

"Check him for any scratches or bites," Jackie said.

Tahoe wiped a sleeve across his eyes. "I wasn't bitten. Earl stabbed me. The zombies were on my butt, and I saw the rear hatch wide open from where you were packing supplies. I threw out the stuff in my way and I squeezed into the compartment, then shut the door. If I would've climbed into the back seat, they would've seen me. My idea worked. The dummies had no idea where I went."

"And how did you plan on getting out?" I asked.

"I didn't think that far ahead. I just wanted to get away from them."

"Wow," Nick said in a sarcastic tone. "You're pretty smart for a cop's son."

"All I knew was that I couldn't outrun them," Tahoe said. "I was bleeding, and I didn't have the energy to hotwire the Jeep. I was about to pass out. I knew if I fainted in the Jeep, the zombies would've broken in and eaten me. I thought it would be safer to try and hide in the storage compartment, and I must have passed out and not woken up till now."

"He's coming with me," Claire said, determined. "Cut out the tough guy act and try to show a little compassion, because there's nothing you can do about it." As though to prove their point, Claire and Jackie helped Tahoe up.

When he hobbled over and climbed inside their Jeep, I knew there was no changing their minds; we were stuck with him.

Nick's eyes blazed as he pulled Claire aside. "Have you lost your freaking mind?" I could tell that he was a bit miffed at her outright defiance, but the girl had a mind of her own.

"What if he hurts you?" I said.

"Just look at him." Jackie pointed at Tahoe, now slumped over the back seat. "He's a conman, not a murderer. We can handle him. I really don't think he'll hurt us. He's barely in any condition to breathe, let alone anything else."

"True," I said, "but what if he dies? It takes up to five days to turn into a zombie from a bite or scratch, but if one dies, it's immediate. You need to know that." I didn't even want to think about what might happen to the girls if he turned and attacked them.

Jackie's eyes grew wide. "He won't. I grabbed the medical kit, some antibiotics, and pain pills. But just to be safe, I'll let Claire drive. I'll watch him closely. If he dies, I'll shoot him straight in the head."

I pulled her close. "No! This is a bad idea, Jackie—a really, really bad idea."

"I just can't stand by and leave somebody in this condition in such a horrible, lonely, scary place. Please try to understand." She kissed my cheek and hopped in the passenger side.

"It'd make me feel safer if you at least tied him up," I said.

"We can handle it." Claire turned the key and started the ignition. "We'll be right behind."

"Change of plans," I said, peering in through the open window. "Tahoe's coming with us in our Jeep whether Nick likes it or not. That way I know you two will be safe."

Jackie shook her head vehemently. "Nope! Not happenin'. Nick will use any little excuse to kill him and you know it."

"Then we move onto Plan B," I said.

"What's that?" Claire asked.

"Hey, Nick," I yelled. "I'm riding with the girls."

"Okay, that's fine. See if Claire wants to ride with me?"

"Yeah, I want to ride with him," Claire said, opening the door, when Jackie grabbed her arm.

"No you don't," Jackie said. "They're insisting a guy needs to be in each Jeep. We're strong, independent women. We can handle a Jeep just as well as they can." She looked up at me. "I killed that zombie with a bat because I was trying to make a point. From this moment on, I can take care of myself. And I don't need a guy to protect me ever again."

"I'm just trying to keep you safe from a psychopath," I said. "So here's Plan C. You know I won't kill Tahoe, so he and I will ride in my Jeep and Nick can ride with you two."

"I like it," Claire said.

"I don't," Jackie said. "Again, he feels like a man has to be with us so we're safe. Go back to your Jeep, Dean, and please trust me that I can handle this."

A moan echoed from the trees as a zombie stumbled out of the vegetation toward us.

"Get in the Jeep, Dean. Now!" Nick said. He then shot the zombie with perfect aim. "We don't have time to stand out here arguing. Listen, they're big girls. They can make their own decisions."

I ran back to my Jeep and jumped in, slamming the door. "They're trying to be all independent now," I said.

"Not again," Nick said, peering out the window. "Their Jeep just stalled."

We definitely needed to find them better transportation. I let out a sigh of relief as the Jeep suddenly turned over.

Biting my lip hard, I struggled with the decision of leaving the girls with a possible zombie.

"At least we know Val's safe with us," Nick said, shooting her a glance over his shoulder. "We need to stick with the mission and save Val. It's easy to get sidetracked, but we have to stay focused for her sake." I opened my mouth to argue my point, but my brother raised a hand to stop me and continued, "Today has been a horrible nightmare, and I'm dead tired. Let's just go and leave it at that."

The crease on his forehead deepened, and worry wrinkles had emerged around his eyes. He was tired, and I didn't want to add to his problems, so I pressed my lips shut and made myself comfortable in my seat. I wasn't happy about the girls letting Tahoe ride with them, but there wasn't much I could do about it.

CHAPTER 15

The highway was one long strip stretching out into the night, illuminated only by our headlights and the rising moon above. Sitting in the passenger seat, with my head pressed against the cold, smooth window, I stared at the road ahead, my mind scattered in a million directions. I knew I should try to get some sleep, in case I had to relieve Nick from driving, but for some reason, any shred of fatigue seemed to have eluded me. Every now and then, my gaze moved to the rearview mirror to check on Claire and Jackie, following in the second Jeep with Tahoe for a passenger. With nothing stirring, silence engulfed us, just three siblings. *Siblings. Brothers and sister.* It sounded strange to me. Up until recently, it had been just Nick and me. Never in a million years would I have guessed that might change, but then Val came along, and just like that, we had a sister. I still couldn't quite wrap my head around it.

My brother suddenly rolled down the window, jolting me out of my thoughts. "I can't stand the stink in here. We need to get a clean dressing on Val's wound before it turns completely nasty."

"We don't have to stop out here. I'll do it while you're driving," I said, crawling into the back seat. I dug around for the medical kit we'd snagged from the glass house. Inside it, I found all the necessary sterile bandages, antiseptic, and tape.

Suddenly, our sister awoke and sat up.

I stopped, unsure how she'd react to me looking at her wound.

"You're changing my bandage?" she asked groggily. "Because Jackie gave me a new one while I was driving."

"Yeah? Well, we need to put a fresh one on again," I said, clearing my throat. "It's, uh...it looks like it's seeped through."

"Just be sure to wear gloves," she said, pointing to the medical kit. "We don't want to take any chances of you getting infected."

"Yeah," I said quietly. In silence, I grabbed a pair of latex gloves, tore the packaging open, and pulled them on with a snap, just like a surgeon.

"Ready?" she said, pulling her sleeve up. When I nodded, she switched on the flashlight and held it up, instructing me step by step on how to cleanse and change the bandage like she'd done seemingly a million times before.

As I worked, the scent of foul flesh intensified. Taking in shallow breaths, I followed Val's instructions to a T, then threw some tape on it and smiled. Back when we first met, she'd hinted at having some basic medical knowledge, but I'd never had the chance to ask about that. I sensed it was now a good time to learn more about her. "What did you used to do—you know, before all of this?"

"I was a cop," she said, looking at me with an amused expression, as if anticipating my reaction.

It wasn't what I expected her to say, but it did make perfect sense. "I should've known by the way you handle a gun," I said. "So where did you get your medical knowledge from?"

"I was engaged to a doctor," she whispered. "His name was Travis. I used to help him change bandages at the clinic. Infected people swarmed that place. His staff was swamped when the outbreak happened, so he had no choice but to let me assist him, even though he didn't want to and we argued for hours whenever the chance presented itself."

Nick glanced over his shoulder. "Our hospitals, doctor offices, and clinics in South Carolina were also teeming with people who wanted help and demanded to know what was going on."

"Yeah, I imagine every medical facility across the world was jam-packed just like ours. So, whether Travis wanted it or not, I helped out at the clinic when my shifts were over."

"That's dedication," Nick said.

"Yeah, well, we didn't know what was going on at the time. Travis was so sure he could help them, and I was naïve enough to believe him."

She seemed sad to talk about him, and I wondered what had happened between them. *Did things go sour and not work out, or was he killed when the zombie thing went down?* I didn't have the nerve to ask, but she must've sensed my interest, because it didn't take long to get my answer.

She pressed her lips into a grim line. "He's dead. He never shoulda been at the clinic with all those infected people. I still can't believe we were treating zombie victims like real people. They wanted nothing more than to rip our heads off. How could we have been so stupid?"

"You couldn't have known," I said softly, "but what you were trying to do was admirable."

"If only we had known what we were really dealing with, maybe things would have turned out differently. If only I could go back in time and save him."

"I'm so sorry, Val." Even though nothing I could say or do would ease my sister's pain, I leaned in and rubbed her back gently in the hopes that she might draw some relief from it.

Her voice quivered. "They're all dead—all my family in Philadelphia and most of the people I've ever known. I thought I'd lost my entire family until I met you. Now, you guys are all I have left. I thought I couldn't lose more until zombies broke into my home and killed my dogs. That was the moment when I knew I couldn't stay in Philadelphia. I had to get the heck outta there, or else I would've been next."

"Pennsylvania?" I asked.

"Yep. Born and raised." She nodded and smiled, her gaze turning distant. "When I found adoption papers by accident, I was shocked. I demanded answers, and my adoptive parents finally told me about my past and about you. A few weeks later, they died. I spent months traveling around, trying to find you, slaying I don't know how many zombies in my path." She reached in her pocket and pulled out a crumbled Christmas card, then handed it to me.

With trembling fingers, I reached for it and recognized it immediately. "Nick, this picture is of us, last year at Christmas," I said, passing it to my brother.

He glanced at it briefly, his gaze barely brushing it. "The Christmas card with those goofy Santa hats Mom made us wear? Come on! That was so freaking embarrassing."

"Yeah." I studied our bright smiles and glowing faces. *We were so happy.* I shook my head and swallowed the lump in my throat. "How did you get this?"

Slowly, the words tumbled out of her mouth. "Your...er, *our* mom sent it to me."

I gasped, shocked beyond belief. "When did she find you?"

She reached for the Christmas card. Her eyes glazed over, as though she'd lost herself in memories. "We'd been talking for only a few weeks, barely able to share much about our lives, when the epidemic destroyed everything, from the police force to the postal service and radio stations, and we lost touch. At first, the phone lines went dead. When the letters stopped arriving, I feared the worst."

"Mother talked to you? I don't believe it," Nick whispered, in just as much shock as I was.

"That picture kept me going on my long journey from Philadelphia to that island in Ohio," Val said, her hand still clutching the photo. With shaky fingers, she brushed a stray strand of hair out of her eyes and continued, "After I got in touch with our mom, she begged me to relocate with you in South Carolina. That was right before the whole zombie thing happened and you left South Carolina to come to the island to join Grandma."

I nodded, thinking back and remembering how hard it was to leave our old lives behind.

"She said she wanted us to meet and start from scratch, so I went through this zombie-infested landscape in order to be with my new family."

"I'm so glad you did, Val," I said. "Meeting you is the best thing that's ever happened to me. I've always wanted a sister."

She grinned. "And I've always dreamt of having some little brothers."

"Have you met Grandma?" Nick asked casually.

"Yes," Val said. "As a matter of fact, she was the one who called me when we realized the virus was a full-blown zombie dilemma that might just wipe out the world. She told me to get my butt out of Pennsylvania and move to the island, but we stayed behind because we thought we could change something. We were wrong. We should have listened to Grandma."

"I can't believe you met Grams," I said, my jaw dropping. My grandma was the most understanding, caring, forgiving person in the world. It made sense that she would have met Val right away, but I couldn't understand how she managed to keep it a secret. My grams and I were so tight, and I thought she always told me every secret she knew.

"Yeah, she's sweet. She texted me every day before all communication went down."

I smiled, proud of myself. "I taught her how to text." I'd even taught her how to email, and I got a message from her every day when I lived back in South Carolina.

"I know. She told me all about your mad skills."

It seemed as if everyone had already known about Val except Nick and me. I wondered why it had been kept a secret from us. Mom had told me they'd planned on sitting down later that day with the entire family and explaining everything, but it still didn't make much sense why we'd been left out of the loop. My thoughts raced. *So Val didn't just pop up on the doorstep to give us all a heart attack. She was invited.* I could completely imagine Grams begging Val to be with us in our safe haven. Heck, I'm surprised she didn't try to go out and find Val herself, guns blazing. Upon our arrival on the island, I noticed Grandma being more absentminded than ever. I suspected something was bothering her, but every time I'd tried to ask her about it, she'd just clammed up and brushed me off, calling me paranoid. One evening, however, she'd disclosed that she was worried about a girl in Pennsylvania. Her words had made no sense at the time, but now a light bulb went off in my head. Now, it all made sense.

"Our grandma is amazing," she continued. "She showed me a picture of Mom and me in the delivery room. By the look on our mother's face, I know she didn't want to give me up. Dad looked happy too."

"They should've never given you up," I said.

Val smiled bitterly, and for a moment, I thought she was going to agree with me, but then she said, "That's not true, Dean. You know they couldn't have taken care of me. I mean, they were only fifteen years old, just kids themselves. Besides that, Grandma seemed to be losing a battle with cancer, and Grandpa had just died in a car accident. So much was happening that raising a kid was out of the question. Keeping me just...it just wasn't possible."

"Did you ever flat out ask her why she did it?" Nick asked.

"Yes." Val hesitated a bit, considering her words. "She said it was because she loved me so much that she wanted me to have more than what she could give me. She also told me that not a day went by when she and Dad didn't think about me."

"They should've never given you up," I repeated, anger edging my voice. I swallowed hard and stared out the window as I tried to process everything.

She brushed the hair behind her ear and sighed. "Mom and Dad's decision to choose adoption for me must've been a difficult one. Dad said it left them with a sense of deep loss and that they were haunted by it."

Nick kept quiet during most of our conversation. Several times, I noticed him shooting interested looks into the rearview mirror, his tired, bloodshot eyes shining in the darkness. He kept driving at a fast and steady pace, but the way his hand clutched the steering wheel rather than casually lingering on it as usual told me he was taking in every word being said.

Val touched my hand, sensing my sadness. "Hey, it's okay. They gave me to a really great family because they loved me and wanted the best for me. I have no regrets. I had an awesome and fantastic life. My adoptive parents truly loved me with all their heart."

I didn't even know what to say. Maybe I was in complete and total shock that my mom had hidden something so big from us when we were such a close-knit family. I was happy that Val had enjoyed a great life.

Her voice quivered. "I was almost there. My group got attacked in Sandusky."

"You've been through so much," Nick said. "We're here for you."

"Thank you, Nick," she said. "When I lost everyone, Grandma's words rang in my ear. 'Get your butt to the island. You'll be safe. I promise.' So, I decided to come and find you, to meet all of you in person."

I put my arm around her and pulled her close. "I'm so sorry for your loss, sis. I can't even begin to imagine what kind of pain you're in and all of the horrible things you've seen and experienced, but you've got family here. We're not going to ever let you go."

"Well, I wish I wouldn't have gotten bitten on the way, but that was probably fate." She let out a long sigh.

"What makes you say that?" I asked.

She shrugged. "Travis and I thought we could find a cure, so we kept close to the infected, treating them, searching for ways to make them feel better. If this cure works, that means our prayers were heard, and our mission is complete. I can finally focus on helping the infected to get cured."

"See?" I asked. "You are destined for something great, and you'll be famous, because you'll be the first one to survive a bite!"

"Yeah, I can see it in the papers now. 'Guinea Pig Zombie Cop Girl Lives to Tell the Tale.'" She smiled faintly, then yawned. "Gosh, I'm so tired," she said, leaning her head against my shoulder.

"You should rest," Nick said. "We still have a long journey ahead of us, and you should get as much sleep as you can."

Val closed her eyes, as if drifting off to sleep.

I closed mine too, but I knew that my racing mind wasn't going to let me doze off anytime soon. Apart from the tiny detour through the grocery store, we drove without a break for most of the night. When morning came, we made good time until we ran into a major roadblock...a helicopter had crashed into the ground upside down on a major road. This meant we had to take a different route. We had gotten lost and spent the entire day trying to get back on track.

***

After hours of driving, we finally took a break and parked in the middle of a wide and very shallow river. It was Nick's brilliant idea and I loved it. The rushing water was shallow enough to keep us from getting our vehicles stuck, but would wash away any zombie who dared to come brave the strong current. Nick and Val were getting to know each other over lunch on the hood of the Jeep. Val scooted to the edge, her bare feet swaying in the air over the trickling water. Nick never had alone time with Val so I headed over to the other Jeep.

My boots sloshed through the water as I waded through. The sky was a neat shade of blue and a cool breeze blew through my hair. Tahoe was passed out and sprawled across the backseat. Claire sat on a huge boulder nearby and seemed to be in deep thought while Jackie sat on the hood of her red Jeep sipping a bottled water. I loved how the afternoon sun brought out the blonde highlights in her dark hair. A frown creased her forehead and I knew something was on her mind.

"Is everything okay?" I asked, jumping up next to her on the hood.

"Yeah, I was just thinking, that's all."

"About what?"

"I should've never hesitated," she said, setting the bottle down next to her.

"Hesitated?"

"I can't stop thinking about the glass house. The second Earl took Val, I should've whipped out my gun and shot him in the arm or leg."

I reached for her hand. "Jackie, you can't blame yourself. You were just handed a gun. And you never held one a day in your life. How could you expect to be some kind of Lara Croft and kick the bad guys butts? Trust me, that will come in time. 'Cause you have mad skills."

She playfully slugged me. "Not yet, but I will. You can count on it."

"Jackie, you do have skills. You were spectacular when you sprang into action to save our butts. I mean, you didn't hesitate to shoot out that window back at the grocery store, hit the zombie with the baseball bat, walk straight up to that zombie on the beach and shoot him, and the way you took down that zombie in the dumpster was impressive."

"It's a start. But I need more practice with shooting. I sucked back at the beach."

"It was dark and you have absolutely no shooting experience, but it'll come in time. I sucked when I first started, but I've been practicing for a year now. By this time next year, you'll be slinging down zombies like second nature."

"When I watched Val get thrown into that pit of zombies..." Her voice trailed off.

I cupped her cheek. "It's okay."

She blinked away a tear. "When that happened, I swear something inside of me snapped. I thought my actions just killed this poor girl. I was devastated."

"But Val's okay," I said. "Everything turned out fine. Dwelling on that horrible memory is just going to eat you up alive."

"When I thought she died, it was one of the worst moments of my life. I felt like I was struck by lightning. I knew from that second on, I could never be scared of defending myself or my friends. All of this anger boiled up inside of me, and I swore I was going to take down the next zombie I met."

"Uh-huh. So that's why you grabbed the bat out of my hands and pounded that zombie."

"I took out all my frustration and pent-up anger in a few powerful hits. I refused to fear them anymore. Believe it or not, it was a major turning point in my life. I was going to fight to survive. And

I would never hesitate shooting anything or anyone that threatens me or my friends lives ever again."

"We'll fight together," I said.

Her fingers entwined into my hair and pulled me closer, her green eyes shining bright. I kissed her on the lips...slow, gentle, and romantic. Everything felt perfect.

"That was nice," she said. "I'm so glad I met you. Thank you for not wanting to leave me back at that glass house. I know it could've been so easy to just drive away without ever looking back."

"No, it wouldn't have been easy. Not easy at all."

"Really?"

"I was hoping not to leave without you," I said. She smiled.

"And I'm so thankful you didn't freak out about Val's bite. You were so cool about it. I mean, you even rode with Val in the same Jeep."

"I knew she was still a day or two from turning so I wasn't worried. But I didn't expect her to stop at the local grocery store."

"Even still, you stood by her. That means so much to me."

"I felt like I owed Val. So when she ran off into that grocery store, I didn't hesitate going in after her. Even though I know she'd never admit to it, she needed my help."

"She's so much like Nick," I said. "We just met Val for the first time yesterday."

"That's what Claire told me. Nick told her everything. I think it's an amazing story."

"Let's just hope it has a happy ending."

She brushed a stray hair out of my eyes. "It will."

I wanted to believe her more than anything.

"Hey, I also wanted to apologize to you about what happened when we met. I can't believe I hid in the house with Claire. We should've been at your side fighting."

"Seeing those zombies for the first time all by yourselves had to be terrifying. I hadn't seen a zombie since the outbreak a year ago. And when I saw them again, I was..."

"Shaking?"

I laughed. "Let's just say my heart was racing a million miles a minute. We've got a lot in common. I was sheltered over the last year too. And then— *bing, bang, boom!*—we're both thrown into Zombie Land at the exact same time."

"Two newbies just trying to survive another day, huh?" she said.

"Yeah. Why didn't somebody give us a zombie survival handbook?"

She laughed. I loved her laugh. We talked some more. Jackie was so easy to talk to and we had so much in common. After a few minutes, I went back to hang out with Val and Nick. Jackie and Claire gave us siblings some space. I think they both knew that we needed to get to know each other by spending time together.

A growl made me glance up. A zombie with those horrible white eyes broke out of the thick vegetation. The thing that really caught my attention was the axe sticking out of its head. I whipped out my gun, my heart racing.

"There's only one," Nick said, scanning the vegetation around us.

"I can take on one blindfolded," Val said.

I motioned to Val and Nick. "Don't worry, I got this."

"I thought you lost your gun back at that grocery store," Nick said.

"I did. But Val got me another one." I shot her a thankful look and she smiled.

Val cringed as she stared down the zombie. "Wow, if that dude could feel pain...ouch. I bet he'd have a pounding headache the size of Texas."

Just as the zombie stumbled to the water's edge, it lost its balance and was swept away downstream.

"Good riddance!" Nick yelled.

"We better get a move on before more come," I said.

"Dean's right," Val said. "I planned on stopping for lunch, but not becoming it."

Nick motioned over to the girls that we were leaving because it wasn't safe anymore.

And once again, we were all back on the road.

CHAPTER 16

I'd driven for hours giving Nick some time to sleep, but then he woke up and we switched. I stared out at the stars in the night sky. This would be my second night out here in Zombie Land. I don't know when tiredness overwhelmed me, but at some point, my eyelids became so heavy I could no longer fight off sleep. It seemed like I'd only managed to doze off for seconds, minutes at the most, when the horn blew, jolting me. I sat up groggily and looked around, disoriented. "Wh-what's going on?" I asked Nick. "Is Val okay?" My voice sounded hoarse and slurry, so much so that it took me a second to recognize it as my own.

"She's sweating up a storm, but she's out cold," Nick said, cool and calm as ever. "Look up ahead."

I rubbed my eyes to get rid of the foggy sensation and peered out the windshield as Nick hit the brakes slowly. The Jeep came to a halt a few feet away from our obstacle. The headlights shone on a figure in the middle of the road. I couldn't make out his features because a dark hood hung over his face. "Is it a zombie? Run it over, Nick!"

Nick shook his head. "No, it's not a zombie."

I didn't reply because he was right, as usual. I squinted to get a closer look, and as my sight adjusted, I could make out more details.

He was at least six foot, maybe six-two, with a strong physique that boasted of regular physical activity. His feet stood apart, turned toward us, and his hands hung by his side, hidden beneath his coat. Something shimmered at his waist, and it appeared to be some kind of belt buckle. When I inclined my head to get a better look, I realized it was a weapon, pushed halfway up to his shoulder. The guy's hand moved ever so slowly up to the gun, and his fingers hovered there, maybe to signal us he wasn't afraid, but he didn't retrieve it.

"I think he's dangerous," I whispered to no one in particular.

If Nick heard me, he didn't reply. There was, after all, nothing to say. No one could argue that point.

"What is that shadow on the right side of the road?" I said, pointing ahead.

Nick leaned into me and followed my line of vision, to the place where the headlight didn't reach. "I don't know."

Keeping the guy in focus, I peered from him to what looked like a black, shapeless pile cast in darkness. It looked like someone had gathered a mound of firewood, but some of the timber seemed larger than the rest, like whole tree branches instead of twigs. *What would anyone need all that for? If he's trying to barricade the street, why is it all piled over there?* I was inclined to believe it was nothing but a pile of wood, until a strong breeze blew against our windows, carrying with it the unmistakable scent of dead flesh, even stronger and more noxious than the one coming from Val's wound. The latter was probably the reason why we hadn't noticed the stench before.

"Looks like the guy's killed a zombie or two," Nick said, mirroring my thoughts.

"I hope he's not infected. If he's healthy, he might need help," I said hesitantly, almost expecting Nick to ask why I was being so stupid. "Don't get me wrong. I'm not saying we should offer him a ride or anything, but—"

Nick slipped out his gun. "Okay. I want to help him if we can, since the guy looks like some kind of master zombie slayer, but we have to be careful. Even if he's not infected, he's armed, and he might try to steal the Jeep. Times like these will turn otherwise good people into all sorts of things, zombies and thieves included."

"Well, just a thought, but it looks to me like he's pretty good with whatever weapon he's slinging. There are more than a couple dead zombies on that heap," I offered.

Nick put the Jeep in park, flung the door open, and jumped out, then stopped in his tracks. "What the...?"

I peered from him to the figure, who was still standing in the middle of the road.

"Dean, you aren't gonna believe this," Nick said, laughing.

I frowned and jumped out of the car, my hand wandering to the weapon attached to my waist. Out of the car with the headlights no longer reflected by the windshield, I could make out more details.

The guy tossed back his hood and headed straight for us. His military short hair and Army fatigues caught my attention before my brain registered his facial features.

My mouth gaped in sudden recognition. *It can't be!* "Lucas? How did you—"

"Dean!" He came over and slapped my shoulder, laughing.

I noticed spots of blood and gore on his coat, but I didn't pull back.

"You know Rambo?" Claire asked, approaching us from the left.

"Hey, ladies," Nick said. "Next time, wait for me to deem the situation safe before you leave your vehicle. What if this guy was some kind of serial killer or something?"

"And that's supposed to scare me?" Jackie asked. "For all I know, I could be riding with one."

Lucas raised a brow.

"They picked up a straggler we had a run-in with," I explained.

"Let's not open up that can of worms right now," Claire chimed in. "I'm not up for another fight. So, Nick..." She turned and gawked at my brother, wearing the most obvious I-have-a-crush-on-you smile I'd ever seen. "Now, do you know *him*?"

"This is my best friend Lucas. We go back a long way."

"Hey, gals. What's up?" Lucas smiled and gave me a fist-bump, then turned to Nick. "I've been looking for you, man! When you didn't come back to the city, we were all worried. I came with a team, but we all got separated in the woods when a group of zombies ambushed us."

"I'm sorry to hear that. We meant to get in touch, but we had no phone out here in the middle of nowhere," Nick said quietly. "I'm just glad you made it. Can't believe you even found us! How's that possible?"

"I tracked you. Bet you didn't know the bag of vials Dean took were tagged."

I tried to make sense of his words. "Whoa! What? Wait a sec! What tracking device? You never told me about that." I didn't know whether to be pissed or hug the guy. Having Big Brother on my heels felt kind of intrusive, but at the same time, it was nice knowing that someone had known our whereabouts all along.

Ignoring my question, he eyed the girls cautiously, as though to warn us that he didn't want to divulge that information in front of civilians. "I'll explain everything, but how about some introductions first?"

I motioned toward Nick. "Well, you know my brother."

Lucas playfully slugged him. "Nick? That's your name? I've always called you The One-Man Army, dude. You've got more zombie kills than all of us put together. It's good to put a name to that face."

"Stop messing around." Nick rolled his eyes. "I'm still pissed at you. I can't believe you helped my brother break Val out without telling me."

"Come on, man! You woulda done the same in my situation. When Dean came to me, I understood his point straightaway. The girl didn't deserve the death she was going to get," Lucas said. "I felt compelled to help her just as much as Dean did. When we see something going on that just isn't right, we gotta step in and try to do something to fix it."

"Had you told me the truth, I would've helped you," Nick said.

Lucas sighed. "With those high morals of yours, always sticking to the rules and the code? I highly doubt that."

Lucas was right. Nick would've come up with some stupid legal way that wouldn't have worked in a million years. My brother always played by the rules, no matter what. It was his strength in many cases, but it also drove me nuts at times. Eager to change the subject and ease the tension, I continued with the introductions. "Lucas, this is Jackie and Claire," I said. "We met them along the way."

Lucas held out his hand. "Nice to meet you, beautiful ladies."

They smiled and shook his hand.

"And where's this drifter you picked up?"

"Tahoe's sleeping right now," Claire said. "He's recovering from a knife wound."

Lucas cocked a brow. "A knife wound? Who stabbed him?"

"He had a fight with his psychopath buddy. The dude's doing just fine. It looks like it's just a flesh wound."

"You'll have to introduce me," Lucas said. "I'm a good judge of character."

"Don't get too attached," Nick muttered. "We're dropping the idiot off as soon as he's better."

I still couldn't believe Lucas was there, yet there was something else I couldn't wrap my head around either. "Okay, let's get back to the topic at hand here. Don't keep me in suspense. How did I get tagged like a wild animal?"

Before he could answer, a zombie ventured out of the woods, moaning.

Lucas pointed his gun and nonchalantly shot it in the head. "It's not safe out here. Let's get moving, and I'll fill you in on everything. Mind if I drive? We had to leave the cars behind, and I've kind of been hoofing it everywhere. I miss driving."

Nick clapped his shoulder. "You're still the same old Lucas. It's great to see you, man. Even still, the answer is no. I'm driving."

He nodded. "Fine." He then turned his gaze to me. "I didn't know it at the time, but every bag of vials had a tracking device installed."

"I should've known," I said.

Lucas opened the door and peered onto the back seat, where Val lay sprawled, still sleeping, her hair spread around her like a soft blanket. She looked so serene that it was hard to believe she was about to turn into one of those monsters, but there was no denying the inevitable.

"How's your sister doing?" Lucas asked.

"Good as can be expected," I said.

"I can't believe you knew about Val being my sister before I did," Nick said.

"Dean tells me everything. Why do you think I put my neck on the line like that to help her escape? She's family, and I knew I had to help. I just hope the cure works. It hasn't been tested enough, and no one knows what it's capable of." Lucas threw his backpack over the back seat. He scooted Val over and sat down.

"It'll work," I said in a stern voice. *It just has to.*

"Not again," Nick said, glancing out the window.

"What?" I asked.

"The girls are having a hard time starting the Jeep again."

"We need to hotwire them a better car," I said. "Let's keep an eye out for one."

"Definitely," Nick said.

"Okay, looks like they got it started," Lucas said.

Nick pulled out onto the empty road.

Lucas then pulled a thin black computer out of the satchel dangling over his shoulder. It looked like an iPod or something. He turned it on, and it beeped loudly. "See? The bag with the vials is in here."

"Of course it is," I snapped. "I don't get it. There's an entire lab filled with those vials. Why do they care about one missing bag of them?" I asked. When he looked away, I knew something was horribly wrong. *Am I in big time trouble? I bet they saw me on the security cameras! Lucas would never rat me out.* "Did they send your team here to arrest me? And why would they risk their lives just to bring me in?"

"Just the opposite, buddy," Lucas said, avoiding my gaze.

I blinked. "The opposite?"

"Yeah. You're being hailed as a hero for stealing them out of the city."

"Why?" I asked. "What are you not telling me?"

"There's something else." A shadow crossed his features.

I tried to make sense of his words. *Why would I be a hero for sneaking out a bag of vials?* "What's going on, Lucas? Just spit it out."

He bit his lip and then finally spoke. "There's no easy way to say it, but the city's been overrun by zombies."

A shudder shot down my body. "How's that even possible? It's an island, with walls, and those undead freaks don't go in the water!"

"They didn't actually break in. It was the virus itself. Somehow, it accidently got inside, and many people became sick and started attacking everyone."

"I-I don't believe it," Nick said, shocked.

"Too many people were bitten, and an overzealous general even bombed parts of Kelleys Island. The lab is completely demolished."

"No!" I shouted. "How could they do that?"

He swallowed hard. "The formula's gone. All that's left are those vials you stole."

"No! Quit joking," I said.

Lucas nodded gravely. "It's absolutely true, pal. I'm sorry, but you have the only remaining vials."

I froze, numb. Parts of me wanted to believe him, but it all sounded so far-fetched that I just couldn't. We'd been safe for months on the island, but now all was lost. Our safe haven had been compromised, infected, blown to bits. I sucked in a trembling breath as my mind contemplated his words over and over again.

"No! I can't believe this," Nick said, his harsh tone jerking me out of my trance.

"I was on zombie patrol inland, battling a herd in a tank, shooting as many of those smelly, decaying freaks as I could. I missed the whole thing so there was no way I was exposed to the virus."

My heart lurched as horrible images and thoughts and worries flooded through me. "What about Mom and Dad? Grams? Dr. Hamming? My friends and family?"

"Lots of people escaped to South Bass Island. I think your grams and your parents were with them, but Dr. Hamming is dead. As of now, Dean, you hold the only cure in your hands."

"I don't believe this," Nick said, slowly letting out a breath. "It's impossible."

"I assure you it is entirely possible and entirely true, crappy as it is. You're our only hope, Dean. General Rika didn't send my team to capture you, but to bring you back to safety, along with those precious vials."

"Is the island totally destroyed?" I asked, fearing his answer.

Lucas hesitated. "All the zombies have been killed. We're rebuilding the parts of Kelleys Island that were bombed. The south side, where you live, was untouched, so I'm sure your family's safe, but they don't know how long the restoration will take."

"I hope they weren't infected," I said quietly.

"Like I said, a lot of people escaped to the other islands around Lake Erie. The important thing is that we managed to avoid an epidemic."

"But you don't know specific names," I said. It wasn't Lucas's fault, and I knew I shouldn't be taking my anger and helplessness out on him, but I couldn't help it. Not having answers frustrated me big time. In a brief moment of anger, I punched the window until my knuckles ached.

"It's a big mess over there," Lucas said. "Everything's in total chaos, but I plan on going back and helping the island get back on its feet. We just have to be more careful about letting anyone new onto the island. Stricter guidelines have been put in place."

"How much stricter could they get?" I'd already felt like I was living in a prison.

"Every resident has to carry an electronic ID badge. If you leave the island and come back, you have to be put in isolation for one week for observation."

As much as it infuriated me, I was willing to do whatever it took to be safe. Nick and I questioned Lucas for the next hour, but that interrogation didn't change anything. For all I knew, my parents and my grandma were dead—or worse, undead. I wanted to scream from the emotional torment ripping through me like a knife. *No! They aren't dead! They aren't infected! Not my family!* I didn't believe that for a minute, and neither did Nick. I had to quit thinking about everything, because my mind was turning to mush.

We took turns driving through the night so everyone had their turn for a catnap. When it was my turn to ride in the back, as much as I tried not to think about things, thoughts of my parents wandered into my head. I wondered if they were okay and when we'd be reunited. I thought about them giving Val up for adoption. I wasn't even sure why that popped into my head, but it did. I still couldn't believe I had a sister, and even though my parents had had their teenage reasons for giving her up, I was still bitter about missing out on all those years I could have had with her. I hadn't had the chance to grow up with a big sister. Maybe part of me wanted to make up for it by protecting her and saving her life, now more than ever. Knowing my parents, even if they had only been teenagers at the time, they wouldn't have given Val to just anyone. I knew my grandma would have made sure Val had a loving, caring, safe, happy home. I only wished I would have known about her. *Why did she have to be a big secret? Was that really fair, keeping our sibling away from us like that?* But there was no use dwelling on things I couldn't change. I had to keep my mind focused on getting to the next city. Nick, Val, and I had become fighters, and somehow, I knew we'd get through it together.

Beams of sunshine shone through the trees, and mist billowed and swirled all around us. Morning had come so fast! Val was sleeping quietly in the back seat next to me, and I was thankful for the chance to focus on my thoughts and form a plan. There was no way I could have dealt with any of her crazy antics at that moment.

Lucas shook his head, jamming to songs on his iPod, and Nick drove us down the highway, past deserted towns.

"Great! Another obstacle," Nick suddenly said, breaking the silence.

Black skid marks caught my attention as I peered through the windshield. Further down the road, cars and trucks had crashed and were now abandoned on the little stretch of road. *What the heck happened here?* I wondered.

CHAPTER 17

The sun shone brightly in the early morning. Through the windshield, we peered at the scene before our eyes. Even though months must've passed, the car accident looked like a picture frozen in time with countless vehicles piled up on top of one another, stretching out as far as my eyes could see. Scraps of metal were strewn all along the road.

I swallowed hard and pointed at the mess, even though Nick had already gotten a good look at it. "Whoa! Look at that. I've never seen such a big collision before."

"There's broken glass everywhere," Nick replied with a frown.

I could sense the implication in his words: That glass could have led to a flat tire or two, and we had no time for obstacles.

"We can swerve around some of the cars to get past," Lucas said, hesitating.

I stared at a crumbled blue car that was resting upside down. The thing that scared me the most was that I didn't see one dead person, and I knew there weren't exactly any clean-up crews or EMTs around—at least not human ones. I didn't even want to think about where the bodies had gone.

"What's going on?" Val asked from the back seat.

I wrapped my arms around her shoulders to pull her close and pointed ahead of us, explaining the situation.

Val's jaw dropped open. Her hands wrapped around my arm, either to support herself from the shock or to keep me in place. Either way, she was distressed.

"We'll be okay," I said.

Nick swerved around a red sports car and slammed the brakes, tossing us forward.

I pushed my hand against the driver seat to steady myself and Val, only then noticing the beads of sweat rolling down her face. In the soft glow of the sun, her skin pallor reflected the light. Her grip was more flaccid than before, as though she was losing strength, which she probably was. My heart went out to her. "Could you hit those brakes with a little less vigor?" I asked my brother.

"Sorry," he muttered. "It looks like the girls blew a tire. We better go help them."

I craned my neck to see what he was talking about. "Pull up closer," I said.

Nick shook his head. "I'm not parking on all that glass. You want us to be the next ones to get a flat tire? No way. We're not moving from this spot.

Once we get the girls moving, it'll free me to swerve around in the grass."

"Makes sense," Lucas said.

"Stay here," I whispered to Val, who nodded, wide-eyed. "If you hear or see anything, don't move. Don't get out of the car or do anything stupid. You hear me?"

She nodded again.

I wasn't convinced that she'd listen, but taking her word at face value was about all I could do.

"Hey, Nick," she called. "Can't we just have them ride with us? We can all fit in here I'm sure."

"And lose a perfectly good vehicle loaded with supplies just because they have a flat tire?" he retorted.

"He's right," Lucas agreed. "We can change it in less than fifteen minutes. It's no biggy and not worth losing a Jeep."

Nick opened the car door to step out, but I tugged at his arm and nodded my chin toward Val. "I still think we should park a little closer to the girls."

He narrowed his gaze the way he always did when he was irritated. "Why?"

"Because she's not doing so well, and I'd like to keep an eye on her," I whispered so Val wouldn't hear me.

"Park here," Val said. "I can change that tire in a hurry."

"Remember what we talked about? Nick and I got this." I took a deep breath to calm my nerves.

She wasn't doing well at all. The girls' Jeep was at least fifty feet, maybe a hundred, down the road. Nick wasn't doing us any favors by stopping so far from where we were heading.

Val shook her head and tried to squeeze past me.

I grabbed her around her waist to hold her in place. "Where do you think you're going?" I hissed.

"Look at that accident." She struggled in my grip, but her attempts were feeble. "You'll need backup. I'll call this in."

Nick shot me a look that warned me our big sis was drifting back into La La Land, and I couldn't have agreed more. "Val, you're not at work," Nick said.

She flopped back down. "I'm so confused. I can't even tell what's real anymore."

"Go back to sleep," I said, brushing her hair out of her eyes. "I'll take care of things until you're better."

She nodded, her eyes shining unnaturally again. "I'm so sorry. You must think I'm a horrible partner. Just don't take my gun and badge, okay?"

It was so sad to see her like that, and I felt like shouting and kicking at something. Instead, I just bit down hard on the inside of my cheek until I thought I drew blood. "Just promise you'll get some rest."

She peered over my shoulder, her gaze clearing a little. "I'll try. Hey, am I imagining things or is this the dude who arrested me and threw me in that hole back on the island?"

Lucas's fingers reached up, as though to touch her cheek. When I shot him a venomous look, he pulled back. He smiled, but his eyes never left her as he spoke, "Yeah, that'd be me, the one and only. But don't worry. I'm on your team now."

Val met my gaze. "Slap the bracelets on that perp!"

"This is Lucas," I said patiently. "He's a friend, not a perp. He's one of the few friends we've got left."

She grabbed the collar of Lucas's shirt. "My mistake. But, hey, will you do me a quick favor?"

He smiled. "Sure. Just name it."

"Tell Claire she's safe." She leaned back into the back seat.

I could see she was overwhelmed with tiredness by the way her brows drew together with a tiny crease forming in between.

Lucas cocked a brow at me. "What's she talking about?"

"I've taken her off my hit list," Val said simply.

"That's good." Lucas nodded.

She licked her lips, as though she was thirsty. I raised a water bottle to her mouth, but she shrugged it off. "Yeah, it's good. For her. This might be one fight she couldn't win."

"Why's that?" Lucas asked, as if humoring her.

"Because once I change into a zombie, I'll probably end up bored and determined and particularly hungry. Combine that with the fact that I won't be very choosy as to what or who I eat and how I get my next meal, and you'll have a deadly combination."

A dark shadow crossed Lucas's features for a second, but it disappeared quickly, and his easygoing smile was back in place. "You'll be the first pretty zombie," he whispered. "I think that makes up for the deadly part."

With her confused gaze focused on him, she leaned back into the seat and wrapped her arms around her waist. Her lips moved still, but no words came out.

Lucas inched closer, until his fingers almost touched her cheek. He shot me a questioning look. When I nodded, giving him permission, he brushed a stray strand of hair out of her face and leaned in to whisper something in her ear.

I strained to listen, but I couldn't make out his words.

Val's fingers clutched his forearm, and her head bobbed once, then again.

Lucas reached into his backpack and pulled out a mini black bag. Unzipping it, he pulled out a syringe and a vial full of blue liquid.

"What're you doing?" I yelled at him, already picturing the worst. Whatever he'd said to her, I could only hope he hadn't asked her for consent to kill her, or he would have been the next to go.

"She needs it," Lucas said.

Nick pushed me aside, taking charge of the situation, probably fearing what I might do if Lucas didn't explain himself immediately. "You can't just whip out a needle and not explain to Dean what it is."

"It's Tyrima," Lucas said, as though I was supposed to know what he was talking about.

"What the heck is that?" I asked.

"It'll take a few hours to work, but once it kicks in, she'll feel better. I'd rather give her the last vial than see her suffer." He met Nick's gaze. "You cool with that?"

"Yeah, do it," my brother said.

"Nick!" I shot him a glare. "I hope it doesn't slow down the process because we need her to change into a zombie as soon as possible so we can give her the cure."

Lucas fumbled with the equipment while my brother steadied Val, who assured me, "It won't slow down the zombie transformation one bit, but it'll help her keep her mind until the very end. It'll just take a little while to kick in."

"It's safe," my brother reassured me. "We've used it on the front lines to get important information from people going loony from zombie bites or scratches."

Nick obviously knew what he was talking about, and I trusted him. Val was my sister and I hated to see her suffer going through this zombie transition. I slowly nodded my consent, albeit not quite convinced. "Okay, but if something goes wrong, I'll hold you responsible for it."

"I would expect nothing less," Lucas said, turning to Val. His voice became softer, more soothing. "Hey, like promised, this is going to help you, but you need to trust me. It's going to keep you from losing your mind. Nick told me about the grocery store incident."

Val's voice came so low that I had to crane my neck to hear her. "I don't want to put the others in danger. If you can help me keep my mind a little longer, please do whatever it takes."

Lucas nodded and gripped the syringe tightly.

The serum caught the light and shimmered blue. Val's gaze fell on it, and her face paled like a ghost. For a moment, I thought she might be sick, but instead of showing fear, she broke Nick's grip and jumped out of the Jeep, yelling, "You touch me with that thing and you're a dead man."

"Val, we're trying to help you," I said.

"I'm going to bite Lucas," she said. "He'd better watch out because I'm pretty hungry."

"No you're not!" I said.

"I repeat, suspect is armed and dangerous," Val said. "All Philly PD units be advised; suspect is armed and dangerous! I need backup immediately."

Nick gripped her arms from behind. "Quick! Do it!"

She let out a long growl a moment before Lucas pierced her skin, injecting her with the serum as she thrashed about, calling him every name in the book. I knew it was a temporary fix, but we had to do what we could to keep Val sane and calm. She was starting to get weird again with all that growling and hissing, just like back at the grocery store. It was for her own good, and I knew if she could think straight, she would've agreed with me.

Val's eyes fluttered shut as she slumped back into Nick's arms.

"Okay, she's out cold," Lucas said. "I didn't know a girl could even talk like that. Where did she learn that kind of language?"

"She was a police officer back in Philly. Couldn't you tell from the cop lingo?"

"I seriously thought she just watched too many cop shows on TV." Lucas grinned. "If she had her gun, I bet she'd have shot me dead."

"Lucky for you, Nick disarmed her earlier," I said.

"Did you see the hate in her eyes?" Lucas asked.

"C'mon, man. She can't help it. She's not herself. She's just mad that you dragged her out of our parents' house and threw her in jail, and now you just injected her with something."

"Yeah, I put her in jail, but I was just following orders!" he said. "And did she forget I helped you get her out? Without me, you wouldn't have gotten anywhere! She'd be dead right now."

Reloading my gun, I smiled. "Yeah, we'll remind her about that later, but right now, she's kind of grumpy."

Nick rested his rifle on his shoulder. "Yeah, really grumpy."

"Zombifying will do that to a girl." I slipped my weapon into my holster.

I looked up at the towering pines along the road. The jungle-like ground was covered in a blanket of green ferns and colorful wildflowers. "You guys keep watch, and I'll change the tire," I said. A gust of cool morning air brushed through my hair. For a quick second, I considered getting a jacket, but I just wanted to get the heck outta here.

Lucas nodded and took off after Nick. I watched them with my weapon aimed, making sure I had their backs. Glass and metal crushed beneath their feet, the sound reverberating in the early morning.

Half the distance in, my brother turned and waited until I had caught up with him, then grabbed my arm. "Just a sec."

"What?" I asked, following his line of vision as he scanned the area. As I gazed around myself, it made me think I was living in a dead world of chaos and twisted metal. I wondered what had happened to the drivers and their companions. *Are they dead? Turned into lost souls who never asked for that kind of sorry existence? Souls who were never given a choice, just handed a monstrous fate?* I stared at an empty baby seat still strapped in the car and tried not to think about what had happened. There was no dried blood, so I hoped that meant the people were able to get away in time. It sure was a different world out there; my brother was right about that. Back home, I'd had no idea how bad it was. Now I was getting a taste of it firsthand. I wondered if the people out there even knew about the safe cites around the U.S. *Maybe the government should have a rescue mission to help those who are still stuck out here in this disease-ridden place.*

"All's clear." My brother motioned for me to continue, and we reached the Jeep in no time.

Sure enough, the rear passenger-side tire was flat as a black rubber pancake. I grabbed a jack out of the trunk while Nick fetched the spare. The girls stood at the rear of the car and kept watch. They both offered to help, but I assured them we had it under control. I placed the jack under the side of the Jeep and hooked the crank to it, then started cranking it up.

"It's so freaky out here," Nick said. "What a place to break down. I don't like it. There's no visibility."

"Me neither." Thick fog swirled around everywhere, putting my overactive imagination into play.

"Don't worry," Lucas said. "I'm keeping a close eye out. Kind of reminds me of a Stephen King novel though. Remember the one where a thick mist descends from the mountains to cloak the land in fog?"

Nick chuckled. "Yeah. I saw that movie, and now's not the time for a recap. Creatures lurking in the mist? They're real, and they're called zombies. You can't scare me with that Stephen King crap. I've seen worse than that movie in real life."

"You're not kidding," Lucas said, nudging me. "Hey, we aren't scaring you, are we?"

Their chitchat wasn't exactly settling my nerves, but I wasn't going to admit it. I set my jaw and rolled the bad tire out of the way, muttering, "Just keep a lookout, okay?"

"Sure," he said. Just as I glanced up at him, Lucas suddenly threw his head back and pointed his gun into the trees. "There's something up there. See it, Nick?"

Nick stepped closer and peered into the overgrown vegetation. "Yeah, I think I see it, but I'm not sure what it is."

I tilted my head to look at a black patch of shadow in the trees. I had no idea what it was, and frankly, I wasn't keen on finding out. The mist and eerie silence added to the scary atmosphere and made us feel like we were on pins and needles. "We better hightail it outta here," I whispered. "If whatever that is gets a good glimpse of us, it might decide it wants to join our little crew—for dinner."

"It's probably nothing," my brother said, "but let's hurry up, just in case."

I didn't like the "just in case" part. Rubbing a hand over my face, I let out a breath to calm my nerves, then focused back on the tire.

"Hey, I got a good look," Nick said. "It's only a deer foraging for food so you have nothing to worry about."

"Good," I said, relieved.

The Jeep door slammed behind us.

Groaning inwardly, I looked up at Val dashing down the street toward us.

"What are you doing here?" Nick growled.

Ignoring him, she wiped her forehead with her sleeve. "I can smell it." Her nostrils flared as she sniffed the breeze that washed over us, as though to prove her point.

"Get back in the car, Val," my brother said. "We got this."

"The smell's getting stronger by the minute," she said.

"Okay, I'll bite," Lucas said. "What smell?"

She spun in a slow circle, sniffing the air like a dog. "Death, terror, affliction, torment, horror—"

"Way to use a thesaurus, Val, but you're tinkering a little in the dark side there," Lucas said.

She met his gaze as the sunlight reflected in her eyes, giving her an eerie glow. "One of humanity's greatest fears is the terror of death. You better flee while you can, because the living dead are on their way!"

Lucas nudged me. "She always so dramatic?" His tone was nonchalant, but I could tell her words were getting to him from the way his gaze scanned the area around us.

I shrugged. "How much longer before that shot starts working?"

"Maybe a few hours."

I nodded. "Good. The faster, the better."

Val walked a few steps closer to the forest. "There's more than one."

"Your sister's kind of freaking me out," Claire said, pacing around the Jeep as her gaze scanned the trees around us.

"She's hallucinating," Nick said.

"I'm keeping a close eye out," Jackie said. "Just in case she isn't."

Val spun around. Spots of decaying flesh mottled her once perfect skin. Thin flaps of greenish skin peeled from her face. Her bloodshot eyes met mine. "They're coming," she hissed.

I swear she looked like she was possessed. I tried to ignore her and tighten another lug nut.

Lucas patted me on the shoulder. "Focus, okay? She's hallucinating. Nothing's coming."

"Lucas is right," Nick said. "It's all in her head."

"I'm going to call this in," Val said. "We'll need backup and medics on the scene as soon as possible. How could anyone have survived such a horrible pileup? Have you checked for survivors?"

"Let's get her back in the Jeep," Nick said.

She shot him a look. "Bite me."

"Please, Val. You need rest," Nick said gently.

"No! And why are you looking at me like that? It's my face, isn't it? It is! I can't help the botched-up chemical peel."

Nick gently grabbed her arm. "Come on. Let's get you a bottle of water from the Jeep."

She yanked her arm away. "Listen, Sergeant, just because you took my badge and gun, that doesn't mean I can't fight as a civilian. They're coming! Don't you smell them? I do!"

Nick ran a hand through his hair, seemingly frustrated.

"Play by her rules," I whispered. "It might help."

He moistened his lips and nodded, then turned back to her. "As your commanding officer, I order you to get back in the patrol car so we can drive back to the station. I'll expect a full report."

"You're a dirty cop, and I'm going to prove it. I saw you taking a bribe from a major drug dealer, and then you had me raid that house, where a million bullets happened to come my way. In case you haven't learned by now, I'm hard to kill." Her voice thundered. "I'll spend the rest of my life taking you down. You're going to regret the day you messed with me."

Jackie and Claire suddenly yelled for us to get back in the Jeep. Out of nowhere, six or so zombies moaned and broke through the thick blanket of fog. Val's nose told no lies.

"We can handle a few zombies, right?" Nick asked casually as he aimed to make his famous lethal headshot.

"Oh yeah. No problem. Dean, you done?" Lucas asked calmly over his shoulder.

"Almost!"

"Just hurry!" Claire said.

Gunshots echoed as they all fired away.

My hands trembled. *Get it together. Concentrate!* I tightened another lug nut.

"It's not just a few. More are coming!" Lucas shouted. "Dean, that looks good enough to me. Let's roll!"

I scrambled to my feet. A zombie in a torn suit walked toward me, his head leaning to one side. He had a metal rod protruding from his head, and bite marks ran across his green arms and neck. Behind him and out of the fog, more zombies stumbled toward us.

Val jumped straight into their path, with no weapon. "I'm going to arrest every single one of these sorry thugs. You have the right to remain silent..." The girl had guts. She started taking one down with her bare hands, using impressive karate chops and lethal roundhouse kicks like in those old Kung Fu movies. She sent the zombie rolling across the asphalt. If I hadn't been so utterly terrified, I'd have been cheering her on.

Nick grabbed me by the upper arm. "Let's go! Who has the keys?"

"Me." Claire jammed her hands down her pockets and whipped them out. Jumping into the front seat, she tried to start the Jeep, but it just clicked when she turned the key. "It won't start!"

"What?" Jackie asked in a frantic tone. "You're kidding, right?"

"No!"

"Let me try then." Jackie pushed her aside and turned the key.

The engine spluttered but didn't start. It wasn't good, because I knew we'd never make it to the other Jeep without being mauled to death.

Nick covered Lucas while he popped open the hood to see what the problem was.

"There doesn't seem to be anything wrong with it," Lucas yelled over the gunfire.

"Have you checked the belt?" I yelled back, firing away, hoping to stall the zombies until Lucas could fix the Jeep.

"Negative."

I frowned as I tried to focus on doing two things at the same time. I knew a bit about cars—not quite as much as Lucas, but enough to possibly be helpful. I thought if I could take a peek under the hood, maybe we could figure it out together and get the thing up and running again.

Jackie stood close by, with a determined look on her face. She wasn't the best marksman yet, but she was going to stand next to me and help me fight. I admired that. If there had only been two or three zombies, I would've let her have a go at it, but this wasn't the movies. There was no way she could take down all those zombies after one fighting lesson. "Get back inside the truck!" I yelled.

"I'm not leaving you." She aimed and fired, letting out a round of shots, but she only managed to hit a zombie in a blue, sparkly party dress.

It threw its head to the side and let out an angry roar but didn't drop to the ground. The thing kept coming at her, this time with more vengeance than before.

CHAPTER 18

Stopping near the car pileup had been a bad idea. I'd known it all along, yet we had to help the girls change their tire. *If only we'd just picked them up, squeezed them inside our Jeep, and driven away before we managed to raise half the undead population in the area.* But Nick and Lucas didn't want to lose a good vehicle loaded with precious supplies over a simple flat tire.

Swallowing hard, I peered around me. The sun was breaking free from behind the clouds, but the fog made it difficult to see into the trees. Lucas continued to try to fix the Jeep and the rest of us gathered in a circle, pressing our shoulders and arms together so we could watch all angles as the undead neared us, their calls breaking the silence of the morning. From the corner of my eye, I noticed a zombie in a fancy sequined dress, heading straight for the girls. Jackie and Claire began to shoot, but their bullets did nothing to slow down the corpse.

"Headshot!" Nick yelled.

"I'm trying," Jackie said, frustrated.

But we had no time for trying. I took aim at the party girl zombie, measuring her raised arms and swaying body as she hobbled toward us. My gaze moved to her undead white eyes, and I pulled the trigger, nailing her right between them. Dark blood squirted in a wide arc, landing not far away from us. As I watched the zombie drop to the ground in a crumbling, bloody heap, adrenaline rushed through me.

Jackie grabbed my arm. "Dean! Your sister! Look!"

Val gripped a zombie's hands behind his back and was telling the thing he had the right to remain silent. She hauled him over to the Jeep and opened the door.

"Val!" Claire yelled. "That's not a police car. You wanna kill Tahoe?"

It wasn't that I particularly cared for the guy, but I couldn't just let her kill him. For one, we needed all the backup we could get. Also, there was the tiny inconvenience of him turning into a zombie if he was bitten; one more zombie might have been just one too many. I rushed over and shot the zombie in the head. He dropped down, crashing at Val's feet, and I poked him in the ribs just to make sure.

Val yelled in my ear, startling me. "How dare you? Where's your code of honor? You can't take justice into your own hands like that."

I couldn't believe she was taking her job so seriously, even in the throes of delirium. I wanted to scream; my only sister was turning into a monster right before my eyes.

Claire let off several rounds, but she did not hit any zombies. We needed all the help we could get, but she was really just wasting ammunition, so I motioned her back into the vehicle.

"Try and start it!" I said.

She opened the door, jumped in, and pulled Jackie in with her.

Rolling down the window, Claire asked, "Hey! Can't you just hotwire this thing?"

"Hot wiring just starts the car without a key," I said. "You can't hot wire a vehicle that isn't working." I then turned my attention to Lucas. "Well? Anything?" I asked, shooting him a questioning look over my shoulder.

"Claire, turn the key," Lucas said, ignoring my question.

I assumed he was either too busy and didn't hear me or that he had bad news and didn't want to tell me; I would have wagered on the latter. "Nick, cover me," I said. "I'm gonna have a look under the hood."

"Lucas's got it under control," Nick said. "Besides, I can't cover you both." His tone betrayed his tension.

I took a few steps to my right, arguing with myself about whether or not Nick could handle it. Suddenly, I saw a figure passed out on the grass, her long brown hair spread around her in disarray. Sudden recognition hit: It was Val. Zombies were stepping over her, some of them tripping, their feet burying into her flesh and kicking her limbs. They'd obviously accepted her into their clan. If Nick or I had been over there, they certainly wouldn't have ignored us and kept on walking. Those zombies would have ripped our throats out without hesitation. Even though I'd seen them bonding and recognizing their own before, it still creeped me out.

I had to help her, no matter what, so I aimed and fired until I had a clear path to reach Val. My feet moved quickly, minding the broken glass and dead zombies, until I was a step away. Kneeling down, I gently scooped her up in my arms and slung her over my shoulder, then sprinted back to the Jeep. Val's eyes turned in their orbits as I laid her in the back seat and slammed the door shut, making sure to lock it to prevent her from venturing out again.

The Jeep sputtered and started, but then it stalled, refusing to turn over.

Lucas frantically cursed.

More zombies broke out of the woods, as if they were multiplying by the minute. My heart began to race, pounding adrenaline quickly through my veins. *We have to get out of here right now!* I knew, but I began to lose hope as Claire turned the key again and again, to no avail. Just when I thought the car was beyond saving, though, the engine started.

Lucas let out a loud, "Woo-hoo! Got it!"

"Get your butts in here NOW!" Jackie said, rolling down the window.

Lucas slammed down the hood. "Listen to Jackie. Get in there and lock the door."

"You too!" I said, not about to leave him or my brother out there to die like some kind of martyrs. Even if the tire wasn't finished, we could still drive away. Even if we weren't able to drive as fast, we'd still move faster than the clumsy zombies could on their decaying feet. None of the corpses would be joining the Olympic track team anytime soon, that was for sure.

"I'm coming!" Lucas said.

I shot another zombie right in the forehead, then gave him a hard kick in the gut. He fell straight back, sailing down to the ground, his badly shredded arms flailing. I slipped inside the truck, but I refused to lock the doors until I knew Nick and Lucas were safe inside.

"Hurry!" Jackie shouted.

Claire screamed out the window, "Nick! Lucas! Get in here! I'm leaving, with or without you two." She laid on the horn to prove her point, but I knew it was just a bluff; she wouldn't ever leave them behind.

After a few more shots, they jumped into the Jeep, tumbling over sleeping Val, an unconsciousness Tahoe, and me in the back seat.

Once they were all inside, I frantically locked the door.

"Drive!" Nick yelled.

Lucas rolled down the window and started firing. "Yeah! Run the bony freaks over!"

Claire shifted gears, and we were about to take off, fixed flat or not. She peeled out, but we didn't get very far with all the zombies pounding on the glass and rocking the Jeep. Before we knew it, we found ourselves helplessly sandwiched next to a semi.

Claire kept gunning it, squealing the tires, but the Jeep wouldn't move an inch. "It won't budge!" she wailed. The engine roared, but we remained wedged, even after Claire jammed her foot on the gas over and over again.

"You're destroying the pedals," Lucas said calmly.

"I don't care!" she yelled at him. "They're not working anyway."

"Claire, you need to listen to Lucas," I said. "We need this Jeep to get away from here."

She nodded, and her expression softened a little, as though his words made sense to her.

A zombie with black hair and bald patches of bloody scalp crawled onto the windshield and began slapping at the glass.

My heart raced. I gripped Jackie's hand and gave it a reassuring squeeze, though I wasn't sure whether it was meant to calm her or myself. I didn't want to go out like that, surrounded by zombies who couldn't wait to get their paws and their nasty rotting teeth on us. Then, an idea struck me. "Nick! We can climb out through the sunroof onto to that semi next to us."

"It might work!" Nick tucked a gun in the waistband of his jeans and slung the rifle back over his shoulder.

"What about Tahoe?" Claire asked. "We can't just leave him."

I glanced down at Val, lying on top of him. "Val's smell will repel the zombies. As long as he stays under her, he'll be safe. Even if he turns, they won't attack each other."

Jackie sucked in a deep breath, and I gripped her hand tight. "You can do this."

She nodded, and Nick slid the electronic sunroof open and climbed out. He reached down to help Jackie and Claire, and I was right behind them.

Claire stumbled, almost losing her balance, but she clung tightly to Nick.

"Don't look down at them," I said. "Concentrate on getting to the roof of the semi."

Nick wrapped his arm around her waist, trying to steady her.

I balanced on the roof of the Jeep waiting for the girls, Nick, and Lucas to get on top of the truck. As I did, a blue-veined, beyond-creepy hand grabbed my foot, trying to force me to lose my balance. I thrust my boot into the zombie's face, sending him flying back into the crowd. "Hurry up, you guys!"

More zombies grabbed for me, and I lunged to temporary safety on top of the eighteen-wheeler. I wanted to jump and run off into the woods to try to lose the suckers, then circle around and get back to the Jeep Val was in. Val was safe for the time being, but I knew if we didn't get her out of there, we might miss the turning and our chance to administer the antidote when the time came. The problem was, the semi was completely surrounded, so that little plan of mine wasn't going to work.

Chills swept through me. I glanced down at the zombies crowding us. Swarms of hands were reaching up to grab us, and countless others pounded the steel walls of the truck, causing an unnerving clatter. Groans, gurgling, and moans came from everywhere, making the hair on my neck rise. It was worse than being trapped inside the glass house. At least there, we'd been safe on the balcony after the stairs were blown to shreds, but in this situation, there was no safety net. I felt like I had done nothing but fight to survive since we'd crashed in the middle of what my brother called Zombie Land. I had been naïve to the dangers all around me, and I felt like an idiot—a terrified idiot.

Next, the hungry zombies began to rock the truck. Claire and Jackie let out long screams, and I couldn't blame them. We had no idea how to get out of that predicament. Desperate for some kind of escape, I swept my gaze over the area one last time. When I did, I saw it: a hornet's nest, hanging just above us. I picked up a loose branch and poked at it, trying to find the entry hole.

"What's that gonna do?" Lucas asked. He aimed his gun and began shooting at the zombies who were rocking the truck.

"There's a method to my madness!" *I hope.* I used the stick as a baseball bat and swatted the nest as hard as I could, right into the group of zombies. Granted, they wouldn't feel the pain of the stings, but I hoped it might be enough of a distraction to allow us the time we needed to get away.

A mass of angry hornets immediately swarmed the zombies, and the undead began to swat them away. It didn't cause the zombies to retreat, but it did distract them from rocking the semi-truck. We huddled close together.

I looked at the others. "At least I gave it a try. Anyone have a Plan B?"

"We could try and make a run for Nick and Dean's Jeep," Lucas said.

"No way!" Claire hissed. "If they so much as grab our sleeves, we'll be dead in no time."

"I agree. It's way too risky," Nick said. "We can't possibly take a chance like that. If we could only divert them to the back of the semi, I could move toward the front and see if I can slip into the driver seat and try to hotwire this thing."

With a serious look, Lucas gave him a fist bump. "I like it, but if you get it running, just don't go too fast. We'll all fly right off the top."

"Maybe the keys were left in the ignition," Jackie said, hopefully.

"It could be out of gas, especially if the driver left it on when he was dragged out." Tuning out, hundreds of thoughts raced through my head, until I came up with a better plan. I swatted at a few stray hornets that were headed our way, and I screamed my lungs out for Val. Everyone caught on quickly and started yelling for her too.

I thought maybe she could bring the other Jeep around, the one Nick and I had driven, and open the sunroof so we could all slip in. It sounded like a great plan to me. I saw Val walking toward us to the back of the semi through the sea of zombies. They didn't pay her one bit of attention, and her appearance—greenish skin and long, stringy hair— was allowing her to blend in with them.

"Get my Jeep!" I yelled to her.

Squinting, she pointed a gun at the gas tank. She obviously had her own plans, but I didn't like them one little bit. I was sure she wasn't thinking straight. *Did that shot Lucas gave her even work? She's still deranged!*

"What in the world is your sister doing?" Lucas yelled.

She peered up at him, droplets of sweat pouring down her face. "I'm going to fry these suckers."

"Yeah, and us too!" Jackie shouted down.

My brother shot Val a glare. "Don't you dare!"

I waved my hands up and down, trying to get her attention. "No, Val!"

Ignoring us, she shot a hole in the gas tank, and a river of fuel began to trickle down into the dirt. She pulled a pink lighter out of her pocket and was preparing to throw it to spark the flame when Tahoe appeared behind her.

He grabbed the lighter out of her hand. "Don't throw it until they're clear!" He motioned for us to jump as he shot the zombies blocking our path.

Val elbowed him in the ribs and grabbed the lighter, throwing it into the trickling gas on the ground.

"Holy crap!" I shouted.

"GO!" Lucas gave me a hard shove that made me stumble forward. "It's gonna blow!"

CHAPTER 19

I couldn't believe Val had shot the gas tank and thrown a lighter into the trickling gas. *What was she thinking? The semi's gonna blow up any minute!*

As we jumped off the truck, Nick, Lucas, and Val started shooting at the zombies to clear a path for me and the girls. Everything moved so fast that it seemed to be a blur before my eyes: bodies dropping to the ground in front of us, us jumping over them to get to safety (whatever safety we could find in such a situation), and our voices slicing through the morning as we called instructions to each other. Glancing over my shoulder, I was thankful to see the others right behind me. It was about all I could hope for, but the moment of weakness left me unprepared for the attack.

A zombie's jaws snapped just inches from my neck when a bullet hit him in the head, sending him crashing to the ground. Almost choking on my breath, I shot Tahoe a thankful look and forced myself back into the moment, a hundred thoughts racing through my mind. I didn't necessarily like the guy, but I had to admit that Tahoe was covering us like a champ, mowing down anything that got too close to us. Had he not been there, that thing would have taken a sizeable chunk out of my throat, and I would have become one of them. Tahoe quite literally saved my neck.

"Get away from the truck!" Nick yelled a moment before a loud *thud* echoed through the air.

The roaring blast sent me tumbling through the air. I landed on my stomach as hot air rushed into my lungs. Everything throbbed, but at least my brain seemed okay. *Or is it?*

Groaning, I lifted my head off the ground and turned to peer at the exploded truck—or what was left of it. The stench of burning zombie bodies made me gag. Instead of the truck, I saw snapping jaws and flailing bodies in the flames, their flesh burning from their bones as they held on to the hot metal. The Jeep the girls had been driving was covered in leaping flames that seared everything in their wake. If Nick hadn't been so paranoid about running over glass, we would have had to fight our way out of there on foot. Finally, I was thankful Nick had refused to budge on that, even though we gave him a bunch of gruff for it.

"You guys okay?" I called out to the others.

"Everyone's here!" Tahoe yelled back.

I scrambled up, and we all hopped into my Jeep. Just as I slammed the door shut, a burning zombie pounded on the glass. I had never locked a door so fast in my life. When the zombie slammed its pasty, ugly skin against the glass, I shuddered. "Let's go!" I shouted to Lucas, who now sat in the driver seat.

Lucas backed up, turned around, and hit the gas pedal so hard that the Jeep jerked forward.

As we sped off down the road, I glanced out the back window at the shocking scene stretching behind us. Billowing, thick smoke twisted into the air, interspersed with burning bodies. Their pained moans gathered to a crescendo that was only nearly drowned out by the Jeep engine.

Closing my eyes, I leaned back and let my nerves get the better of me. As we moved away from the burning heap, my hands began to shake from the aftershock. I couldn't believe we'd survived— again. It had been a tough one, and there had been times when I wouldn't have bet on us living to tell about it, but we had.

***

At one point, the highway became an impenetrable maze of tangled vehicles. I would've insisted on driving through, but as usual, Nick made the better decision, and Lucas followed it through. We backtracked through the woods, and I swear we lost hours because of it, but no one complained. Everyone was still in shock, realizing how close we'd all come to losing our lives.

Val stayed out cold for hours, so I assumed she'd used up all of her energy. How the girls and Tahoe could sleep while we rode over one bumpy road after another was beyond me, especially with

Lucas's music playing on his iPod in the background.

My brother met my gaze. "You're so lucky I didn't park close to the girls like you suggested. If we had, this Jeep would've been toast."

"Yeah, yeah," I said. "You're awesome...and always right. You want a medal?"

"No, but some respect would be nice."

I smiled. "You know I respect your decisions. Heck, I'd probably be dead if it weren't for you."

"I'll watch your back," he said, "even if you're a royal pain in my butt sometimes."

I chuckled and closed my eyes again. It wasn't long before I drifted off, and by the time I woke up, the windows were rolled down, and the sunroof was wide open. The sun cast a warm sensation on my face, while a cool breeze whipped through my hair. I opened the glove compartment and fumbled around, then pulled out a nice pair of men's sunglasses and slipped them on.

"Oh yeah," Nick said, shooting me a sideway glance. "Now you look cool."

I noticed he and Lucas must've switched seats at some point, and I wondered how long I had been out cold, unaware of anything around me. I chuckled. "They give me character."

"They make you look older," Nick said.

"Yeah?" I asked.

"Yep."

"Well, my life has been turned upside down. I guess I do feel more mature. I can't believe the crap we've been through. It's mind-blowing, you know?"

"I feel ya, little brother." Nick let out a long breath, giving me the impression that he had something else on his mind.

"What's wrong?" I finally asked.

He refused to look at me, keeping his gaze focused on the road. "I'm sorry I yelled at you when we first crashed, and I'm even sorrier I even suggested that you should kill Val. That had to be tough, knowing she was our sister."

"It was horrible," I agreed, "but I should've just told you the truth. If I had, it would've never even crossed your mind, I'm sure."

He grimaced, his gaze still focused on the road. "It probably would have, but I might've given her another day to live. Letting my sister turn into one of those things...well, I just couldn't let it happen. The only thing that stopped me was the knowledge you have a possible cure."

I considered his words carefully. *Would he really kill his own flesh and blood if I didn't have the vials in my possession?* I reasoned that Nick must have thought he was saving her from a fate worse than death, and perhaps he was right. I knew I would have rather been shot dead than become one of those things.

"I don't blame you for anything," Nick said. "Yes, you broke some rules and went outside of protocol, but you saved Val's life, and I couldn't be more proud of you."

"Gee, thanks," I said.

His lips pressed into a grim line, but I could tell something else was bothering him.

"What?" I asked.

He shook his head and ran a hand through his disheveled hair, speaking out what I had been trying to push out of my mind ever since boarding that helicopter. "What if the cure doesn't work, Dean?"

I clenched my fists, hoping against all odds that it would work. "It will," I said with less conviction than I wanted.

"But what if it doesn't? I don't think I can bear having a sister one day and having to put her down humanely the next day. It's just not fair—not freaking fair at all! I never even got a chance to really know her."

"I dunno," I said. "All I know is that we'll get through this." I tried to keep my voice from quivering.

He nodded in agreement and didn't say another word. He'd never shown me his emotional side before, and I could tell how hard it was on him. I decided not to pry any further; I left him alone and didn't talk about it any further. Besides, I knew if we continued discussing such touchy subjects and sentimental things, a tear might slip down my cheek, and I wasn't about to let him witness that.

We drove for another hour before something caught my eye. The Jeep drove past a zombie, hunched over a dead deer on the side of the road. I didn't have much time to grasp details, but in the brief second our eyes connected, a chill ran through me. I knew I would never get used to their cold, dead eyes. A few years back, my buddies and I had enjoyed a good laugh and chatted about how the world was going to end. We'd even joked about a zombie apocalypse, but we didn't think that would really happen, not in a million years. I'd come to realize as of late that life does throw curveballs we never quite expect. The girls slept. Lucas and Nick glanced at the venison-devouring zombie for a second, but then their attention drifted off like it didn't even faze them. *There's something seriously wrong with this world when we can drive by a zombie feasting on a deer on the side of the road and accept it as normal. Yeah, this is seriously messed up!*

The world seemed to be crumbling all around us, and the undead army seemed to be growing in numbers daily. Sooner or later, though, they would have to run out of healthy people to infect. My hopes were that we could take the remaining healthy people out of the equation. I wanted to get them into safe cities, even build more cities if we had to. I didn't understand why the authorities weren't trying to do just that. It seemed simple to me. I figured the leaders needed to focus on solving major problems first and then deal with after-effects. Getting help to everyone in Zombie Land had to be hard, if not impossible.

The living dead would eventually die, and survivors could rebuild, but in the meantime, the healthy people out there needed help. They were always on the run or hiding out. I quickly learned that it was an everyday battle to survive, with death lurking around the corner. Life was rough and totally sucked out there, but there was little I could do about it. Whether I wanted to or not, I'd have to deal with it, and I could never give up on thinking humanity might stand a chance after all. Whatever happened, I knew I'd never get accustomed to the things we witnessed out there. My head ached. Thinking about the last days' events, Mom and Dad, and trying to save Val was driving me insane. I needed sleep—some peace, if only for an hour—but sleep felt as though it wouldn't come for a long time. Trying to block the image of the half-eaten deer out of my head, I eventually drifted off to the girls' shallow breathing. It felt as though I had only closed my eyes for a few minutes when someone shook my shoulder hard, jerking me out of my slumber. What?" I groggily opened my eyes to Nick towering over me. "Where are we?"

"Look up, sleepy head," Nick said, pointing up to an air traffic control tower. "It's an airport. I think this would be the best place to stay the night and get some rest."

Without another word, I followed him out. It was late afternoon and we'd been driving all day. My whole body felt cramped. I squeezed out and stretched my legs, thankful to get out of the truck. I glimpsed at our surroundings. To the right, there was nothing but woodlands. To the left was a tall, gray building. In front of us, there was a ramp that probably served as a runway. Apart from the usual sounds, such as chirping birds and a soft wind rustling the leaves, the area seemed completely deserted. And I couldn't believe this would be my third night out here in the middle of Zombie Land.

No planes were out, but a giant steel hangar lined the north side of the field. For some reason, the hangar doors were slid open, as if somebody was in a quick hurry to leave. I craned my neck until I could see right in. Everything was empty.

Nick was right: The control tower was the perfect place to spend the night, and I felt like we would be safe. "We can see a zombie coming from anywhere."

Lucas playfully slugged me in the arm. "Yeah, but the best part is that we can talk and be as loud as we want."

I gave him a fist-bump. "Yeah!"

"I like it!" Jackie said, grabbing a box of food from the trunk. "I can whip up some dinner with this stuff. How about cold chicken noodle soup with crackers, baked beans, and Spam?"

"Mmm. A meal fit for a king." Claire laughed as she grabbed some candles and other supplies.

I got a crowbar out of the trunk and wedged the lock until it finally snapped. I agreed to stay downstairs with the girls while Nick and Lucas checked things out. We left Tahoe sleeping in the back seat; we weren't about to carry his sorry butt up all those stairs. But then a thought struck me: *Wait a minute...he did save my life back there. Maybe I should cut him a break and not ride him so hard.* I decided if he didn't come up by dark, I would go out and get him. I owed him that much.

"Your brother is so brave," Claire said, wearing a big smile. "He's not afraid of anything. When I'm with him, I just feel so safe."

I smiled and decided to put her on the spot. "You have a thing for Nick, don't you?"

Her cheeks grew red. "Yeah, he's really sweet."

Jackie grabbed my arm and smiled. "So is Dean here."

I flung my arm around her shoulder and pulled her close, my heart racing. "Is that all I am to you? Sweet?" We'd shared a rather passionate kiss, and now I was standing there with my arm around her, so I was pretty sure there was more to it than "sweet".

"Is there something wrong with sweet, mister?" she chimed, meeting my gaze.

"No, but I'd rather be sexy and irresistible."

She batted her eyelashes like a puppy dog. "Should I rephrase?"

"Oh brother," Claire said.

"Yes, please do." I shot her a playful look.

She wrapped her arms around me and stared into my eyes. "Dean, uh, what's your last name?"

"Walters," I said.

"Dean Walters, you are sexy and irresistible *and* sweet, and I like you. I also trust you, and I consider myself lucky to have met you."

"That's more like it." I softly kissed her lips. "But I could say those same things and more about you." My lips brushed hers again. When she leaned into me, I put some distance between us. "No, let me tell you what I think about you." My voice grew slightly husky. "You're gorgeous and clever, brave and adorable."

Her face lit up, and her lips curved into the most beautiful smile I had ever seen.

"Get a room, you two!" Lucas said.

Jackie turned around and playfully punched him. "Shut up!"

He chuckled. "Just because we're in the middle of a zombie apocalypse doesn't mean you can't get arrested for public displays of affection."

We all laughed, and the mood seemed lighter.

"So I take it everything's safe up there?" Claire asked.

"All clear," Nick said.

We went out to the Jeep to get Val. I scooped her up from the back seat. She was still out cold, but she looked a lot paler, and she was sweating profusely.

Claire and Jackie glanced over. "Is she okay?" Jackie asked.

"It's all part of the process of becoming a zombie," I said.

Nick nodded. "We'll prepare her bed upstairs."

Claire didn't waste a minute. She was right by his side, holding some pillows and blankets and a box of supplies to be carried up.

"Here, Claire, let me help," Nick said, taking the box before he turned and looked at me. "You got the vials in case sis changes?"

I nodded. "Yep." Carrying Val, I climbed up what felt like a million flights of stairs, but eventually, we reached the open space overlooking the airstrip below, and I could finally lay her down.

Claire hurried to cover her with a blue blanket.

Val opened her eyes briefly and said. "Hey, do you know what a lobster feels like when it's boiled?"

I shook my head. "Not really."

"I do."

I could tell she was roasting, so I took off the blanket and chuckled at her attempt at sarcasm, something she'd obviously inherited from our mother. "There. I hope that's better. Just get some rest, sis."

She closed her eyes and drifted back to sleep.

The view from the top of the control tower was amazing. I could see from every direction. I picked up a pair of binoculars from a desk and realized I could see as far as the woods stretching in the distance. Nothing would get past us.

"We're taking those," Lucas said, pulling me aside.

"I'm sure nobody cares at this point."

He opened my black bag and inspected the vials. "Everything looks good here."

"Of course. I've been guarding them with my life."

"Keep up the good work. You're doing great."

I nodded. "Well, there's a lot on my shoulders, I'll tell you that."

"Yeah, I know. It's to be expected since we're the world's only hope for survival."

"No pressure or anything."

His expression darkened. "Seriously, Dean, you're doing a fantastic job. You really are a hero."

"I wonder if they'll even work. You really think we've got the cure?"

"If not, it's the closest thing we do have. We've got to get those vials to the scientists in Washington. This is the most important mission of our lives."

I bit my lip hard. "I know."

His eyes glimmered with hope. "We're gonna be able to help so many people. We can't think of this as the end of the world. We need to think of it as the beginning of a new life...for everyone."

"I hope it's the miracle we've all been praying for," I agreed.

He zipped up the bag. "Well, there's only one way to tell. We need to test it on your sister."

"That's the plan," I said.

"For her sake, as well as the sake of all humanity, I sure hope it works like we want it to."

"Doc ensured me this is the final formula, and I believe he was telling me the truth."

Lucas nodded gravely. "Yeah, me too."

Jackie's laugh drifted over, and we both smiled. She was joking around with Claire and Nick. When I met her gaze, she smiled; she had the cutest smile, teeth gleaming white like a Hollywood movie star.

"Hey," Lucas whispered, "Jackie's really cute."

"Yeah, she's hot, smart, funny, and super sweet. I like everything about her."

"She seems perfect for you. I guess time will only tell."

I shook my head. "Yeah, she looks a lot like, uh..."

"Who?" he asked.

"A lot like my *next* girlfriend." Maybe I was jumping to conclusions. After all, we hardly knew each other, but I was smitten. I wasn't going to rush anything, especially with everything we were going through. We'd just take it nice and slow. Besides, my main focus right now was saving Val and getting home.

"She's all yours," Lucas said. "Besides, I like your sister. She's pretty when she isn't threatening to eat me."

"I could tell you like Val," I said.

"The second I laid eyes on her back on the island, I was totally blown away. It sucked that I had to arrest her. I really hated that. Would it bother you if I asked her out sometime when this is all said and done?"

"It's fine with me if you wanna go after my sister. You're the most honorable guy I know." I playfully slugged him. "Just don't go pulling pranks on her the way you do to the guys back on the island."

"She might like a guy with a sense of humor."

I laughed. "Yeah, or she might punch you in the face."

CHAPTER 20

The airport control tower was the best possible place for us to rest and stay the night. The highest story boasted fantastic visibility, allowing us to see any approaching zombie from a mile away. We weren't worried about single zombies though. Our main priority was not to draw any attention; we had to avoid a herd. Scanning the area below the tower, I realized that even if a whole bunch of them tried to corner us, there'd be enough time to jump in the Jeep and race down the airstrip that led to the main road.

"What are you thinking?" Jackie whispered from behind me.

I smiled but didn't turn to face her. "Nothing Earth-shattering. I just realized we can get from the airstrip to the main road by taking a few different directions."

She rubbed my back gently. "Always plotting ahead, aren't you?"

I inclined my head, not sure where she was headed. "Sometimes."

She laughed. "Relax. It's a compliment. I wish I was more of a planner rather than jumping in headfirst without thinking of consequences. I might've saved myself a bit of trouble in my life."

"And I wish I was more carefree," I said, finally turning. My gaze fell on her lips first, then trailed up to her beautiful eyes. "My paranoia's something I learned from Nick. Did you know he's already plotted our escape plan in case we have to evacuate?"

She cocked a brow. "Impressive. I haven't even planned my dinner yet."

I laughed and pulled her against my chest, marveling at how good she smelled. "That's something I like about you." My heart picked up in speed at the realization. I liked a lot of things about her—a whole lot of them.

We settled in, and Claire laid out a red and white blanket on the floor. Jackie dished out cold chicken noodle soup, baked beans, and Spam, just like she promised, on paper plates. I lit some thick white candles and put them in the center. Girls usually dig candles, and I had a strong hunch Jackie would like them too.

"Our first romantic dinner," she said.

I grinned while everyone sang, "Awww!" trying to make light of a tough situation. I laughed as I drank a warm, flat Pepsi. I was so hungry and thirsty that I didn't even care. I could have eaten a whole other can of baked beans, and I didn't even like them.

The stairs creaked as someone walked up them. We all exchanged shocked glances.

Jackie ran to the window and glanced out. "I don't see any zombies around and it looks like Tahoe isn't in the backseat anymore."

My heart raced as I rushed to the door. "Who is it?"

"It's me."

"Lake Tahoe?" I asked. I was so thankful it was a human's voice and not a zombie's moan and heavy breathing. At this point, I just needed a little breather from all that kind of crap. I'd only been out here for three days and seen enough to last me a lifetime. Of course, after a good night's sleep, I'd probably be ready for more adrenaline rushes tomorrow.

"Funny. Just let me in. My side's killing me."

Hesitating, I opened the door. Even though he had saved my life, I was still ticked at him for almost killing Val. How can someone forget something like that? I knew I needed to forgive him. And I would...in time.

Jackie offered him a plate of food and a beer. He sat next to us like he was part of our gang, as though all was forgiven and forgotten. Personally, I couldn't wait to be rid of the mountain man once and for all, and Nick's expression told me he thought the same.

Keeping to himself, my brother downed a beer, then another, as though alcohol could help him forget his worries. The city we'd lived in for the last year had been destroyed. We didn't even know if our family had survived. He didn't usually drink, so I could only assume it was all quite devastating for him. As much as I understood him, I didn't like him drinking while continuing to play tough. We needed to be on alert, but after everything we'd been through, a beer was nothing. Heck, we all decided to have one. Nick didn't even speak for the first hour we were there. He just drank while Lucas kept guard using the binoculars we found. Finally, he said, "I've been thinking. I know my parents had to make it out safe, and I'm not even going to waste another minute worrying about it."

I nodded. "I agree. Mom and Dad had all kinds of escape plans and drills. We'll find them, no doubt about it." I lifted up my can and smiled. "To survival and new friends."

Jackie's brown eyes twinkled, and we all clanked cans.

"I'll toast to that," Tahoe said.

Val even opened her eyes. "How can anyone toast in this day and age? I've lost so much and so many people I cared about." The pain was evident in her whisper.

"She makes an excellent point," Lucas said. We all nodded as he continued, "Death lurks around every corner, making every breath a choice. We fight to live another second, another minute, another day. All of us come from different backgrounds and walks of life, but we all have one thing in common." His lips pressed into grim lines.

"We've all experienced the loss of a loved one. Let's stop making toasts and just live to see another day."

There was a moment of silence as we all contemplated his words. Somehow, he hit home with every single one of us. I wrapped an arm around Jackie to draw her close, and she snuggled into my shoulder.

"I can't argue with that," Nick said, "not after losing countless friends and even my childhood girlfriend."

"I've lost friends too," I managed to choke out.

Nick lifted his chin. "This one goes out to Sam Moalny, who was killed last month in the line of duty. He was a great patriot, humanitarian, and loyal friend. And this also goes out to all those who have died in vain to this wicked epidemic that has taken place all over our world. Our loved ones are gone but never forgotten. This thought goes out to them. May you rest in peace."

"Thanks, Lucas," Val said quietly.

He smiled. "I didn't do anything."

"You understood what I meant." She leaned back against the pillows and closed her eyes again. For a moment, silence ensued, and I believed she had drifted off to sleep, but then she opened her eyes again and smiled. "Hey, if I said anything crazy to you, just forget it, okay? I wasn't thinking straight. Also, I think I might've attacked you. It's all fuzzy. I'm trying to put the pieces together."

"Then you're not going to eat me?" Lucas asked.

Her face blushed. "No way. Did I really say that?"

He smiled.

I chuckled. "That...and a little more."

"Yes, with a very descriptive cursing vocabulary," Claire added.

"I'm sorry, Lucas," Val said. "I talk like that in front of the guys on the police force to blend in, ya know?"

"Don't worry about it," Lucas said.

"That shot took a while to work, but it finally kicked in. I can't thank you enough. Nick filled me in about how I fought you over it. I'm sorry I was such a bear. Also, thanks for breaking me out of that medical prison."

He threw his arms up in the air. "Well, it's about time you gave me some credit for that great escape."

"You did a fantastic job of planning it." She shot him a tiny grin. "You'd be kind of cute if Uncle Sam would let you grow your hair out."

"What? You don't like the buzzed look? What do you expect? Are you looking for some brooding sap or some Fabio from the cover of one of those romance novels?" He made a fist and the huge muscles bulged in his arm. "I'm a born and bred soldier, and this is a soldier's hairdo."

She grinned. "If you're ever interested in going out with me, you'll have to grow out your hair."

He grinned back. "Are those your final terms?"

"Yep."

"Then it's settled. I'll grow out my hair for one date with you."

She smiled. "Deal. Hopefully, by the time that happens, I'll be back to normal too." She walked back to her bed. "I'm going to rest over here for a bit." She pulled the cover up to her chest and closed her eyes.

"Get some rest," Lucas said, carrying over a second pillow and propping it under her head.

Tahoe approached. "Hey, Lucas, I need a minute with Val, okay?"

Lucas cocked a brow.

"It's okay," Val said. "I want to hear what he has to say."

Tahoe apologized for Earl and even his own involvement. His words were mumbled, but whatever he said, it seemed to make Val smile. I regarded her from the corner of my eye, unable to believe what I was witnessing. A few times she just nodded, and then she raised her arm to touch his shoulder, as though all was forgiven and forgotten. He said something under his breath, making her giggle and then laugh, reminding me of the old Val I'd met not long ago. He irritated me, but I let him chitchat with my sister because he seemed harmless. I knew Val could handle him, but I couldn't help inching closer to tune in.

Val was telling him about the cure and that there was hope for her life. He squeezed her hand

and gave her words of encouragement. Even though she seemed tired, her mind was clear, and it had been hours since she last growled, hissed, or said any off-the-wall things. I was happy the shot had worked after all. If it hadn't, she would have been taking down Lucas or Claire and trying to bite their necks at that very moment; or else she would have been trying to arrest me, thinking she was a cop hot on a case. I chuckled to myself at the thought.

"Hey, Lake Tahoe," my brother said, "I'm watching you."

"Love the nickname," he said. "I guess I'm stuck with it, right?"

Lucas and Nick started telling us Army stories about their narrow escapes with death and zombies. Tahoe even joined, sitting at Val's side as he told some stories of his own. I used to think my brother was an exaggerator, but after all I'd seen, I knew the stories were true. I wondered if the guys back home would believe me when I told them about the glass house or the multitude of zombies that surrounded the semi-truck we stood on top of. Those were the crazy kind of stories Nick used to come back and tell us, and we'd always thought he was full of it. Of course, I had never said that to his face.

Nick squashed the beer can he was drinking from and threw it across the room, making the basket. "Yes!"

"Woo-hoo!" Claire squealed. "He shoots; he scores, and beats the buzzer at the last second to win the game."

"He's so getting a championship ring," Jackie said.

Nick laughed, then grabbed another beer and took a swig. "So, Claire, what's your story?"

Jackie almost spat her drink out in a fit of laughter. "Dean used that line on me earlier, back at the house. Is that some kind of brother pick-up line?"

We all laughed, and I elbowed her playfully.

"I just want to know more about you, Claire," Nick said. "I don't know a darn thing except that you're twenty-one, smokin' hot, and gorgeous."

"That's the corniest thing I've ever heard," Lucas said.

I laughed. "It is, isn't it? But he gets so daring once he's had a couple of beers."

Jackie chuckled. "Yeah. He's not beating around the bush now, is he?"

Nick stumbled over and wrapped his arm around Claire as he slumped down next to her. "I like the direct approach."

"If he gets on your nerves, Claire, just let me know," Lucas said. "I can throw his butt on the other side of the room."

"I'm fine, Lucas." Claire grinned and turned her attention to my brother. "I'm from New York City. Jackie and I aren't only cousins, but also roommates."

262

"Cool," I said. "Nick and I are originally from Myrtle Beach, South Carolina. When all this happened, we got relocated."

"Did you like it there?" Jackie asked, chiming in.

I nodded. "I miss the ocean big time. My buddies and I used to surf all the time. We had fun, but we also had goals in life." I grabbed her hand and squeezed it gently. "I really wanted to be a broadcast sports reporter. I wish we could all go there. I'd love to show you the beach and how to ride a wave."

"Oooh, I would love that," Jackie said. "By the way, sports journalism is a cool career choice."

I pointed at her. "Thanks, but back to you."

"We used to attend Parsons before the zombie thing went down," Claire said.

I cocked a brow. "Never heard of it."

"Fashion school," Jackie elaborated, brushing a strand of hair back. "It's not what you think. It's more than pattern-making and sewing courses. I was taking classes in fashion photography and journalism."

"Yeah," Claire said. "It's one of the oldest institutions of its kind offering undergraduate and graduate degrees. We were taught valuable industry knowledge while designing innovative clothing and products. Parsons is credited with launching the careers of various fashion legends like Marc Jacobs, Donna Karan, and Tom Ford, and so many more."

Jackie seemed quite enthusiastic about it, and I wished I knew more about her career choice, but given that I'd grown up among boys with absolutely no fashion sense, I was glad to even know what fashion school was.

Nick grinned, probably getting as little out of it as I was. "Well, that explains the cute outfits."

Claire nudged him and batted those long eyelashes of hers. She really liked my big brother, and she wasn't embarrassed to flirt with him.

I met Jackie's gaze. "I think you'd make a wonderful fashion photographer."

My heart began to race as Jackie flashed her bright smile. "Thank you," she said. "I started taking pictures at ten. I thought about the great adventures I could have taking beautiful pictures all over the world. But as a teenager, I began to love fashion, so I thought I'd just combine my two great loves."

"You gotta do what you love," I said. "Did you work as well?"

Claire cut in. "Yeah. Jackie and I worked as wedding gown models in some of those wedding shows. We got to wear beautiful gowns and have our hair all pinned up in some elaborate up-dos."

Nick reached for her hand. "I bet you made the most beautiful bride."

"Thank you, Nick," she said. "We weren't allowed to move one muscle or even blink."

Jackie chuckled. "Yeah, and Claire kept giving me this silly look, and we'd end up busting out in laughter. She always got me in trouble."

I shot Lucas an amused look.

"What were you doing when all of this happened?" Lucas asked.

Jackie looked off, as if remembering a horrible event in her life. "We were actually on a photo shoot as wedding models for a fashion magazine in Hershey, Pennsylvania when the virus broke out."

"Why would you leave New York City to go to Pennsylvania?" Nick asked.

"The title of the article was 'Chocolate, Wine, and Weddings'," Jackie said, "so they chose to do it in the chocolate capital of the world. Everything turned to chaos. We couldn't get back to New York City. There was gunfire everywhere. People started killing and eating their friends and neighbors, and there Claire and I were in these fluffy wedding dresses."

"We hid out in the basement of a pet store," Claire said. "The poor animals were going nuts. The glass door was shattered, so we let them go so they'd have a fighting chance. Leaving them locked up in those cages would have been a death sentence for sure. I watched the parrots squawk and fly off into the sky, and I envied them."

"I remember where I was too," I said. "I was stuck at the top of a Ferris wheel with a date. Innocent people were being killed below, and I couldn't do anything to help them."

"That's awful," Jackie said.

"It was like something out of some B-grade horror movie, and I thought maybe I was dreaming. Hours later, Nick and my dad let me down. My date ran in the other direction and I haven't seen her since. Nick then flew our parents and me to Kelleys Island where my grandma lived."

"So you're a pilot?" Claire cut in, her gaze meeting Nick's. "I dig pilots."

A soft hue of red covered his cheeks, and for a moment, I wasn't sure if it was from the alcohol in his blood or the compliment from a pretty girl.

I cleared my throat. "Anyway, my grandma owned a bed and breakfast and a small cottage. About 200 residents lived there before the outbreak."

"My best friend from school went to Kelleys Island two years ago," Jackie said. "She went fishing, sea kayaking, and hiking. And even took a trip to that amusement park, Cedar Point in Sandusky. I remember all the pictures she showed me. It looked like a lot of fun. Kelleys Island is a tourist attraction, right?"

I snorted. "It used to be. It was the perfect place to hole up, considering we were completely surrounded by water. It's a great island and we love it. I just wish Nick was around more."

"And where'd you take off to, Nick?" Claire asked.

"I was home on leave from the Army, but when this zombie thing happened, I chose to fight over here in Ohio," Nick said. "With everything happening, the Army was cool with it. I wanted to give back, to save the people who weren't dead yet."

"Me too," Lucas said. "I had lots of connections so I got stationed at Kelleys Island too. Nick and Dean's family...well, they're like the family I never had."

Claire gripped Nick's hand. "That's very honorable to serve your country."

He leaned in and whispered something in her ear that made her laugh.

Jackie squeezed my hand and I smiled. We talked about everything, and I learned so much about her. She'd been born and raised in New York City, and family and friends meant everything to her. She also loved burgers with all the fixings, and she demanded gobs of mustard, just like me. She used to jog Central Park every morning at six a.m. with her brothers, and she loved cats. She'd always wanted a dog, but her landlord wouldn't allow it. She wore pajamas and pink slippers every night— or at least she had before the zombies took over.

"I've got one question," said Val, looking at Jackie and Claire.

"Val!" I said.

"You're awake," Jackie said. "How are you feeling?"

"Like a zombie is eating my intestines." She cringed. "Well, you asked. Anyway, here's my question."

"Yes?" Claire said.

"This zombie thing has been happening for a year now. Why were you dressed so fashionable when we met?"

"We ran until our group found an abandoned mansion," Jackie said. "We got comfortable and didn't see more than a handful of zombies for over eight months."

"There were giant closets filled with the most gorgeous designer clothes," Jackie said, "so we started relaxing and letting our guard down. We dressed up every day and did our hair and makeup. All the girls in our group did. We were led into a false sense of security. I know now that it was a big mistake. We should've been training to fight, but the men treated us women like china dolls. They took care of us, and I guess we let them."

"At three o'clock one afternoon, a window shattered," Claire said. "I'll never forget it to this day."

Jackie sipped her beer. "That was the end of our group...and our time together. A herd broke in and killed everyone else." Her voice wavered. "We barely escaped."

I wrapped my arm around her and pulled her close. It had to be awful. I couldn't even begin to imagine what that night must have been like for them, mourning the loss of their protectors and running for their lives with no supplies or weapons.

"I'm sorry," Val said, looking out the window.

"Isn't the sunset gorgeous?" Jackie asked, changing the subject.

"Yes. And I want to watch it one last time before I...before I die," she said between breaths.

"How can I deny my wonderful sister her last wish?" I rushed over to help her up. "Technically though, you're not really dying, Val." I scooped her up in my arms and brought her next to Nick. We all sat together and watched the sun sink into the horizon.

"That was beautiful," she said and looked up at me, then at Nick. "Hey, guys, what if the cure doesn't work?"

I gripped her hand tightly. "Don't even think about it."

A tear ran down her face. "I don't want to die, Dean. I want to live to see another sunset."

"Shh." I wiped her tear away and pulled her into my arms. "You're my sister, and Nick and I are going to do everything in our power to save you."

"You've got to trust us," Nick said.

She smiled, but I could see the hopelessness in her eyes. "I'm not giving up yet."

Nick touched her hand. "That's my girl."

"Just promise me one thing," she said.

"Anything," I said, meaning it.

"If the cure doesn't work, I want you or Nick to...one of you have to put the bullet in my head—nobody else!"

Tears welled in my eyes as I met Nick's gaze; he was choking up too. I tried to compose myself because I didn't want to cry in front of everyone. "I...we promise." It was the hardest promise I'd ever had to make to anyone, and I hoped it wasn't one I'd have to keep.

She sniffled. "Thank you."

I squeezed her hand. I prayed against all odds that the cure would work, but if it didn't, I knew I'd have to keep my promise, no matter how much it hurt.

Val let out a sigh. "I wish we could've been a real family, that we could have grown up together."

"Well, we're a real family now," I said, "and that's what counts."

"Tell me about Mom and Dad," she whispered.

I laughed. "You remind me a lot of Dad, with that temper of yours. I think that's a family trait."

Nick chuckled. "I'm the worst. I punch walls when I get pissed off."

"My adoptive parents were as sweet as can be. I knew I didn't get my temper from them."

"You're funny and sarcastic like Mom, but tough like Dad," Nick said.

"And you're a fighter, just like Mom," I said. "When she had cancer, she never gave up. She beat it years later."

"Mom almost died?" she said.

Slowly, the word came out. "Yes."

A tiny gasp escaped her throat. "Why didn't she tell me about it?"

I sucked in a deep breath as I considered my words. "Even though the ordeal was over and done with, maybe she didn't want to worry you." I shrugged. "I honestly don't know."

"I'm glad she made it," Val said softly.

"Me too." I nodded. "Imagine if she didn't. Then I might never have met you, and she would've died without having a chance to meet her only daughter." I met her gaze. "During chemo, she said she only had one regret about life. She wanted to meet Valarie again. Yeah, she called you by your formal name. I thought she was talking about an old high school friend."

"But it was me." She let out a sob. "I never cry like this. It's the virus. It's doing crazy stuff to my emotions."

Lucas put an arm around her, and she playfully slugged him.

"Hey! I'm willing to let that one slide," he said, "but I'm warning you, if you try to bite me, our little friendship is all over."

Val smiled. "You don't look like the type of guy that dates zombie chicks."

He shot her a gleaming grin. "I'd date a zombie, as long as she didn't treat me like a piece of meat, though I'm not at all opposed to a little nibbling."

"C'mon," she said. "Be serious. You know I want your braaaaains."

"You know what else I like," Lucas said. "Zombies aren't quitters. I mean, if they want you, they'll keep coming after you...and I love being chased!"

"That's a no-brainer."

We laughed some more as we continued to tell jokes and stories. For just a little while, we let go and allowed ourselves some fun; we knew that soon enough, we'd be back to fighting for our lives. Settling into our beds hours later, when the sun had long set and countless stars dotted the skyline, we decided to take turns standing guard to make sure no zombies crossed the perimeter and to watch out for Val changing while the others slept.

***

Morning had finally come. The sun beamed in, and we all immediately got to packing the little bit of supplies we had.

"Okay, I'm starting here. You guys split up. Check every corner and crevice so we don't leave anything behind," I said, glancing around one last time.

"Where's Lake Tahoe?" my brother asked.

I peered at him, surprised. "He's not with you?"

"I thought he was with you." He shrugged. "He's gotta be around somewhere. Let's just pack up the Jeep. He'll turn up."

Ignoring the sudden uneasiness in the pit of my stomach, I grabbed a box and some blankets and looked out the window. My heart lurched. "Nick! Lucas! The Jeep's gone," I yelled, my voice reverberating from the walls.

Val's eyes darted about, not really focusing on anything. The way Nick regarded me told me he knew before I even opened my mouth.

"He must've left during his short shift of staying awake and guarding. We're so screwed," I said. My heart lurched in my chest as I checked our belongings, or lack thereof.

I swear Val's face turned another shade of red as she wailed, "He took our food, water, guns, freakin' everything!"

"He didn't take the stuff we dragged up here," Jackie said, swinging a backpack over her shoulder. "We've still got some food and water and some guns."

Nick grabbed my arm and pulled me aside, whispering so the girls wouldn't hear him. "Where's the serum?"

I scanned the naked floor, willing my eyes to see something that wasn't there. "I-I don't know. The bag's gone!" I managed eventually. "I thought you or Lucas had it."

"We'll find another vehicle," Lucas said, "and catch up with him. I still have the tracking device."

"You're right." My heart raced, thumping in my ears like a drum. "We can't stay here."

"We'll have to leave on foot," Nick said, "and I mean right NOW!"

A chill washed over me. We were right back where we'd started: running for our lives and in dire need of transportation. And now, we didn't even have the cure in our hands. Val's life depended on those vials, and without them, my sister was doomed, dead and gone forever.

"What are we waiting for?" Val asked.

"Let's get outta here…and find those vials," Nick said.

I couldn't have agreed more.

The End of Installment One

To be continued in the next book, *The Zombie Chronicles: Book 2*

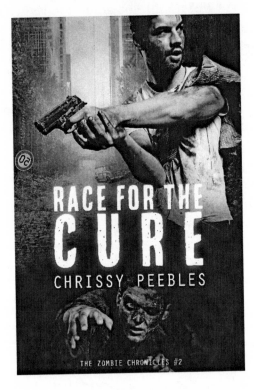

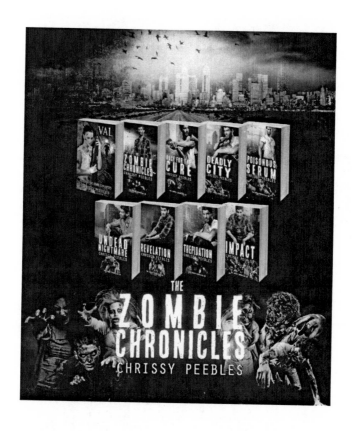

Read Sample Chapters of Val!

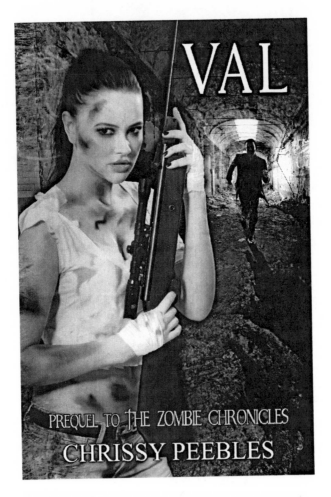

CHAPTER 1

I sped down the streets as thunder boomed and lightning flashed. The windshield wipers were swishing back and forth a million miles an hour as rain dumped down from the dark sky. When I punched the gas, I felt the tires slip on the slick pavement. The truck shuddered, but I quickly gained control.

"What are you doing? We almost crashed!"

"Not even close," I argued.

Jack swallowed hard. "Looked pretty close to me."

"Don't be such a wuss, Jack."

"Val," he barked, "we need to turn around...now!"

"No," I snapped. "We've come too far."

He muttered something under his breath, then said, "As if *you* have any say. Have you forgotten that this is *my* truck?"

"We're not going back," I said firmly.

"It's crazy to be out here in this mess—not to mention that you're wasting my precious gas."

"Quit whining."

"Maybe I would if you'd let me drive."

"You're too slow, and every second counts. Time is of the essence, as they say, and you drive like a ninety-year-old woman."

"Maybe, but at least I don't have a lead foot! There is something to be said for safety, Val. You drive like...a maniac."

I shot him a side look, and he about freaked.

"Hey! At least keep your eyes on the freaking road, Val! And, for goodness sake, slow down!"

I whipped around the corner as the tires squealed out in terror all their own. "For all we know, Sammy's already dead, yet you're whining about gas and speed limits!" I ignored my petrified passenger and kept the pedal to the floor.

Jack went on and on, ranting about why we should turn around and go home. He was wearing on my nerves, and I was just about to throw him out on his butt when I noticed the roadblock up ahead: Multiple cars had crashed. I eased on the brakes and stopped the old pickup.

"No way we're getting through there," he said. "Ya ask me, I think it's some kind of omen. I *told* you we should go back!"

"Omen? I think it was enough of an omen when our cozy little civilization crashed and burned and zombie hordes began sweeping across Earth and—"

Jack rolled his eyes and cut me off. "Now who's whining? Do you always have to be so...melodramatic, Val? But anyway, back to the point at hand. We're not gettin' through, and you're not taking *my* truck on a demolition derby."

I blew out a long breath. "Then we try another way."

His frown turned into an expression of alarm. "No. This is where I draw the line," he said. "I'm *not* going into the city...and don't even ask me why, because you already know."

Worry flooded through me. "Jack, can't you see that something's wrong. Sammy shoulda been at my house hours ago. We have to go!"

He sighed. "She's probably out buying green hair dye for her next new look."

I shook my head. "You're really something, you know that? A girl's life is at stake, and—"

"Okay, seriously. We're talking about Sammy here," he cut in. "She's a moody teenager with blue hair and—"

"Turquoise," I corrected.

"Blue, turquoise...who cares? She has freaky hair, pierced lips, and even a pierced nose. You know how flaky she can be. She's a rebel without a cause."

"She *has* a perfectly relevant cause. There are zombies out there, or have you forgotten that? Besides, she's done so much to help you on supply runs."

"Maybe, but the girl is lippy and nothing but trouble. She was trouble before the zombie apocalypse, and she's worse now. Did you forget that she crashed your car only two days ago?"

"Only because she was running from a zombie pack," I reminded him. "I can just get another car. They're a dime a dozen these days."

"Why do you always stick up for that juvenile delinquent?"

I gripped the steering wheel tightly. "You don't know her like I do. I've babysat her since she was five years old. Sammy's like family."

"Is it fun to arrest your *family*?"

"That only happened twice, and she learned her lesson."

"Then why'd she keep running away from home, living on the streets?"

"Cut her a break, would ya? Sammy's had a rough life."

"So what? She's misunderstood?"

"Something like that," I said, backing the truck up.

Jack peered ahead and pointed to the lumbering figures walking clumsily around. "It's worse every time we come out here."

"I know. Their numbers are increasing every day," I said.

He gripped my arm. "Val, that's exactly why I'm not going into the city. It's way too dangerous. There're hardly any survivors left. The ones who haven't been shredded to bits have already flown the coop. You need to face the fact that the heart of Philadelphia is dead. It's time to move on."

"How can you say that, Jack?" I retorted. "This is our home."

"Not anymore," he whispered. "It hasn't been for a year, since Z Day."

"So you're just gonna give up?" I said.

"Give up? Heck, Val, you, me, and Sammy—we've already lost our entire family. The zombie population has tripled in the last few months. You know it's a death sentence to stay here. Plus, like you said, we don't even know if Sammy is..." Overcome with emotion, he trailed off for a moment, then continued, "They're gonna take us out one by one, until we're all dead. We're their only food source, and humans are getting quite scarce."

"I've gotta get Sammy out of the inner city. She'll be safe with me."

"Just because you live on the outskirts of Philly, that doesn't make it any safer."

I looked away, knowing he was right. I loved living in Chestnut Hill. It was located in the northwestern corner of Philadelphia, PA, ten miles from City Hall. I lived in the official Historic District that boomed with historic homes, parks, gardens, museums, 200 antique stores, art galleries, boutique shops, cafes, and fine restaurants. My place wasn't the fanciest but I loved it nevertheless.

"I know it's not any safer. It's getting harder and harder to survive out here."

"A big group of us have been...well, we're talking about leaving next week. I think you should come with us. You'll never make it out here alone."

I looked at him like he'd gone as mad as the mindless undead who were devouring people. "No. I'm not leaving my home."

"Then you'll be dead before the end of the year, just like all your loved ones."

His words pissed me off, and I threw the truck into park, opened the door, got out, and stood there in the rain. "You obviously don't know me as well as you thought, Jack. I don't run away from my problems."

"Val, what the heck are you doing? Get back in here. They're out there!"

"I know, and if one comes anywhere near me, I'll shoot its rotting head off!"

"They'll gang up on you. You won't have a chance."

I slung my rifle over my shoulder. "I'm going to go find Sammy—with or without you."

His eyes widened in fear. "It's way too dangerous. Let's give her some more time. If she doesn't show by tonight, we'll take a team and go look for her in the morning."

I shook my head. "Uh-uh. She could be dead by then."

"She's been late plenty of times before."

"It's her seventeenth birthday. She wouldn't have missed the little party I planned for her, and she had to know I'd hunt her little butt down for being a no-show. Something's wrong, and I'm gonna find out what it is."

"Get in the truck!" was his only reply.

"So...is this goodbye or what, Jack?"

His face hardened. "It very well could be if you take one step into that city."

"I really could use somebody to watch my back."

"Val, it's just...look, you know Suzy is nine months pregnant. I can't take a foolish risk like that. I'm gonna be a father, and I need to behave like one."

"I get it. I do. You'd better go though. They're coming."

"Val, what's with you? Do you enjoy flirting with death? Have some kind of death wish?"

I shrugged. "I do what I have to do to survive...and to protect the ones I love."

"So do I, and that's exactly why I can't go."

I gave him a halfhearted smile to make him realize I understood, and then I walked off. I couldn't force him to drive me into the city, as he had a lot to lose. But I wouldn't desert Sammy out there either. My only choice was to go solo. As I walked away around the tangle of cars blocking the main street, I heard Jack screaming, pleading for me to come back, trying to talk me out of going. Still, I wasn't about to turn back.

Several zombies stumbled around, but I quickly ducked behind an abandoned armored truck. I was dressed perfectly for the occasion, with all the right accessories: a tactical black vest, with a cross-draw holster secured by a side-release buckle for quick access, in case I needed my handgun. I had four pistol magazine pouches and three double-stack pouches that held a lot of ammo. A knife was strapped to my leg, and my trusty rifle was within reach right over my shoulder.

I peeked out from my hiding place and took a deep breath, scanning the area for potential threats. The corpses were heading toward Jack, who was still screaming, but when he saw them, he had no choice but to speed away, peeling out on the pavement. I hated that he wouldn't go with me, but he had his reasons. The one good thing for me was that his yelling had distracted several of the zombies, allowing me to get by rather easily.

I pointed my gun in front of me and walked briskly, darting my gaze around to keep a close eye on my surroundings. I turned left, walked down the street, then made a right. I was thankful that the rain had let up, but after that mini-monsoon, water was still dripping from my hair.

Four zombies shuffled toward me, and I briefly wished again that Jack had come with me for backup, but I knew I could handle that quarrelsome quartet on my own. I calculated my options. The key was not to be too loud or make too much of a commotion, as I didn't want to invite more undead guests to the party. I knew gunshots would be like a dinner bell. While the zombies were clumsy and weren't capable of rational thought, their ears seemed to work just fine. The last thing I wanted to do was send out a dinner invite where I'd be the main course. I quickly debated whether or not to use firepower, and I decided guns were my best option. Even if more did show up, I was on the move, and my legs and brain worked a whole lot better than theirs.

CHAPTER 2

I raised my gun and took careful aim, hoping for precision shots every time. I fired off my first shot, and the bullet lodged deep in the first zombie's cranium. The thing fell into a huge mud puddle with a *splash*. Water dripped down my face as I carefully trained my weapon on the next zombie, who was walking with an unsteady gait. Just as I let off that shot, its creepy companion ambushed me from the left. When I turned in that direction, I met its grotesque gaze; it immediately went into a frenzy, lunging at my face in bloodlust and unquenchable hunger. I felt like some kind of zombie-age Terminator with my rifle as I pulled the trigger. The gun packed an enormous blow, embedding pellets all throughout the creature's deteriorating face from point-blank range.

I took the fourth one down quickly, only to discover that a fifth had joined the throng. My power-charged bullet sliced through the air with a *whoosh* and landed in the zombie's left cheek. It moaned as raindrops poured down its slimy black hair and oozing face. Much to my surprise, it kept walking, locked on me like my flesh was some kind of homing beacon. I fired again and shot it straight between the eyes. This time, it fell backward with a *hiss*. I silently and quickly moved through the streets, hiding behind anything I could use for cover.

About ten zombies blocked my path, but every other exit would take me too far out of the way. I didn't want to be in that city any longer than I had to. The most efficient strategy would be to take them down, to clear myself a path. So, I knelt down behind a black vehicle and aimed, then fired off a round that sent them straight back to Hell. The second they were down, I leapt up, my heart pounding. I nudged them in the side, just to make sure they were dead before I walked over them. When they didn't move, I nudged them again. Once I was sure they were permanently out of commission, I stepped over them carefully and headed down the street.

When I spied three more walking freaks, more shots cut through the air. I quickly slung my rifle back over my shoulder, ran down two more streets, turned left and then right. The rain began to pelt me again as I took another left turn at full speed and squatted behind a red car. My breath froze in my throat. Moans, hisses, and growls echoed through the rain as it finally began to let up again, coming from a huge group of thirty or more. Peeking out, I watched them shamble around like they were in a daze. I slowly crept back, not making a sound, ready to look for an alternative route to Sammy's apartment building.

As soon as I rose to my feet, bony, black fingers gripped my shoulder. My stomach clenched, but I found the strength to spin around and kick it in the chest. As it stumbled back, I quickly aimed my rifle at its chest, but I knew I couldn't make that much noise with that huge horde lurking around the corner. I kicked it again, much harder this time. It flew back into telephone pole, then slumped down. I rushed over and slammed my boots into its skull. Another one came from behind, and I smashed its head in with the butt of my gun. As soon as it hit the ground in a bloody heap, I took off down the street. I glanced around and sighed in relief; the coast seemed to be clear.

Just as I was about to walk a little farther, I noticed several red dots of light bouncing around. "Laser tag? Great," I tried to joke, glancing upward at the snipers on the rooftop, survivors who had their laser-sighted weapons trained on me. I was sorely outnumbered and a stranger to them, so I didn't want to agitate them or end up in a standoff. I waved my arms in the air to let them know that I was human and meant them no harm. "Don't shoot!" I screamed.

The man with a baseball cap and beard stared at me for a long, hard moment, then waved.

When I saw the group lower their weapons, I shrugged in relief, then ran away as fast as I could. I turned down Cypress Street and made my way, cautiously, to a small apartment building.

The door was propped open with boxes, and Sammy's neighbor was carrying a large one down the stairs.

"Mrs. Jaleno, have you seen Sammy?" I frantically asked.

"What!? You've gotta go!" she said in a panicked voice.

"Why? What's going on?"

Fear flashed across her face. "That gang! They'll be back any minute."

Another neighbor, carrying a blue crate, rushed past me with a terrified look on his face. Others were frantically loading their cars with their belongings in a hurry. I looked around in complete disbelief; everyone was terrified, running for their lives.

"What's going on?" I asked.

"They're taking over," she said. "They gave us one hour to get our stuff, and they said if we're not out by the time they get back, we're as good as dead. We're lucky they're giving us that. Other gangs would've killed us right on the spot and stole the clothes off our backs."

I cocked a brow, not believing what I was hearing. "Are you sure they weren't just—" I started to ask.

"They already killed four people," she said.

"Is Sammy okay?" I asked as she hastily walked off.

She didn't answer.

"Mrs. Jaleno, where's Sammy?" I asked louder.

When she didn't answer, panic set in. I ran down the corridor and stopped at Sammy's apartment. The door was ajar and slightly cracked, which I didn't take for a good sign. With my gun drawn, I eased inside. Murmurs echoed from the bedroom, and I swallowed hard as a droplet of sweat rolled down my face. *Is it a zombie? Was Sammy one of the four who were killed? Oh my gosh! Is she a zombie now?* I couldn't handle losing Sammy. My heart pounded as I took small footsteps toward the closed bedroom door.

Listening intently, I suspected what the outcome might be. If Sammy was a zombie, I would have to shoot her. The thought made me shudder. I had promised to protect her, told her I'd always have her back, and she was all I had. Her family had been murdered a year earlier, and I'd become somewhat of a big sister to her. *If she's dead, that's it,* I thought. *I'll pack up my dogs and go with Jack and the others, leave Philadelphia behind forever.* If Sammy was gone, there was nothing left for me there but death and despair.

As my fingers curled around the doorknob, I held my gun steady. I took a deep breath and pushed the door open.

Instantly, someone knocked the gun out of my hands, catching me by surprise. A jarring impact hit me in the gut, knocking the breath out of my lungs.

Pain exploded across my stomach and I could hardly breathe. Trying to catch my breath, I looked up.

Sammy was tied to a chair, with a gag in her mouth, and all she could do was shoot me a terrified look.

"Sammy?" I whispered as I tried to stand up after the harsh kick to the midsection.

The taller man was dressed in black, and his blond, greasy hair was tied back in a ponytail. The other had acne scars, and his hair was short and black, with a matching, scruffy beard. I recognized them right away as gang members, and I was sure I'd arrested the blond before on deadly assault charges.

The blond pointed a gun at me and smiled. "Well, well, well. What do we have here?" He turned to his friend. "I think I recognize that pretty policewoman."

"Pretty? Ya ask me, she looks more like a drowned rat," the other man said.

"Hey, Officer," the blond said, licking his nasty lips, "maybe you oughtta frisk me. I can see you don't got your nightstick, but I might have one you can borrow."

Disgusted, I asked between gasps, "What do you want? What is she doing here, tied up like that?"

He looked at me with a cold glare. "What do we want? Well, sweet thing, we want this apartment, and we'll have it. We already gave everybody their eviction notices."

"You said you'd give them an hour," I said.

"Yeah, and we did, but since this one insisted on givin' me some lip, I figured I'd better hold her till Runo gets back. He's gonna feed her to one of them slimy freaks to show the rest of the tenants what happens if they defy Runo."

"You can have the apartment, if that's what you want," I said. "Just let us leave, and we'll never come back."

The man looked at his buddy and laughed. "Seems she don't get the gist of what I'm sayin', huh?"

"Nope," his friend said, then spat a nasty, black, sticky ooze of tobacco remnant on the floor.

"Well, Smurfette, here's, gotta pay for her smart mouth," the blond said. "If ya run your mouth, you die. Them's the rules, honey," he said.

The black-haired one looked at me and shook his head. "Can you believe she walked through all them zombies to rescue this mouthy little—"

"Hey!" I said, sickened by their total disregard for me and for Sammy.

Ignoring me, the blond continued, "Apparently, she don't know the number one rule."

"I do," I said. "Always have an exit strategy."

He laughed, looked me up and down, then licked his lips again. "Nope."

"Well, please enlighten me. I'm dying to know what I've been doing wrong all this time."

His gaze narrowed. "Rule number one is pretty simple, darlin'. Don't have one ounce of sympathy."

"And why not?" I asked. "It's the only thing that makes us different from those zombies out there."

He laughed. "Heroes don't simply survive, Copper—not in real life anyway. That only happens in those Hollywood flicks. You wanna live, you might have to step on some people along the way...and you sure as heck can't let people go around mouthing off to you," he said, glaring at Sammy, who just rolled her eyes at him.

The guy with the acne chuckled. "I'm thinkin' the zombies might like to munch on a little pork. I say we feed the officer to 'em too."

"Hmm. I wonder how long she'll last," the blond said, scratching his chin.

"Longer than the last one, I'm sure."

"Sounds like a plan. We'll charge admission."

Sizing up my opponent, I looked him in the eyes and showed him no fear.

"Don't stare at me like that, Miss Piggy. You're about to die," the blond said.

I knew his threat wasn't empty. He knew who I was, and the fact that I carried a badge put me on the opposite side of the law than that gang. They would torture me fiercely, then kill me. All anarchy had broken loose, so the thugs had the upper hand. They could do whatever they wanted—to me or anybody else.

It's now or never, I thought. With driving speed and power, I delivered a heel-of-the-palm strike to the blond's chin. His head jerked backward as I painfully slammed his lower teeth into his uppers. When he fell back, his head slammed into an oak dresser, and blood began gushing out of his head.

Horrified, his friend pointed the rifle at me.

In a blur, I grabbed hold of the barrel and quickly pulled it to the side with force. I held it downward, then punched him in the face and kicked his knee until it bent backward in a very unnatural, painful contortion. I placed my other hand under the gun and began twisting it, forcing him to let go of the trigger long enough for me to wrestle the weapon from his hands. I then backed up and pointed the rifle at him. "Untie her...now!" I demanded.

"All right, lady! Just don't shoot me," he said.

"Then don't tempt me or try my patience. Do it!"

He rushed over and untied the ropes and removed the gag.

Sammy stood and rubbed her rope-burned wrists.

The man looked at me, inching ever closer. "I did what you told me to, Officer."

"Come any closer," I said, "and you'll be roasting S'mores in Hell!"

Without saying a word, Sammy grabbed a bronze statue and hit the man over the head, dropping him to the ground like a bag of cement.

The men were hurt, but I was thankful I hadn't had to resort to murdering them, especially in front of Sammy.

"So...Lucifer's been shopping or what? Chocolate and marshmallows in Hell?" Sammy asked, smirking.

"Graham crackers too."

"Right," she said. She then opened her closet and nervously reached for her Glock, a holster, and a knife.

"Hurry up, Sammy!" I said, nervously looking around.

"I am."

I walked into the living room and peeked out the door. There were at least a dozen gang members flooding into the lobby, a major flaw in my escape plan. I'd hoped we'd get out before they came back, but we'd had no such luck.

"What's up, Runo?" someone asked.

"Runo?" Sammy said, walking up behind me. "If their leader's back, he'll be looking for Dumb and Dumber any minute," she said, nodding to the bedroom where the guys lay on the floor.

I softly closed the door and deadlocked it. "You're right. We definitely can't go out that way," I whispered. "There are far too many of them."

"Can't you just karate chop 'em all? I mean, you were doing some killer moves a minute ago, like some kind of ninja superhero."

"Sammy, it's about the same as standing on the tracks while a huge freight train barrels straight for us. We can't possibly take on a freight train, no matter how many martial arts or self-defense tactics we know."

"Then what do we do?"

"Simple. We get off the tracks."

"Open up," a guy said, following an unexpected knock on the door. "It's Runo."

Startled, Sammy and I exchanged horrified looks.

CHAPTER 3

"We need a distraction," I whispered.

"Please don't hurt me," Sammy yelled. "Why are you doing this? Get off me!" she said, then let out a few more loud screams for dramatic effect.

"Heh. Sounds like our boys are havin' a little fun," Runo said.

Without saying a single word, I motioned Sammy to one of the bedroom windows. I climbed up the dresser and peered out. It looked clear, so I opened the window, then quietly popped out the screen.

"Hurry!" she whispered.

As I climbed out the window, a zombie moan sliced through the air. A corpse in a checkered shirt and ripped jeans climbed out of the overgrown vegetation. The smell of rotting decay hit me full force. Another one, with a green, bald head, came from the other direction.

"C'mon!" I said, then started to help Sammy out through the window.

Suddenly, she looked at me strangely. "Wait! I have to go back," she said.

"No!" I whispered. "Not a chance!"

The zombie reached out for me, and I let go of Sammy. As soon as I did, she darted back into the apartment. A chill shot down my spine as the gang beat on the door. Using the rifle as a bat, I smashed the zombie's face, until it dropped to the ground, motionless. A naked corpse with exposed skin and muscle snapped its jaws within an inch of my face. I jumped back and clobbered it, and the thing hit the grass with a loud growl. Next was a zombie in a red sweater. I swung, delivering a forceful blow to its neck.

A face-eater with blood dripping from several parts of its face met my gaze. It was dressed in a blood-soaked, white dress, with one matching heel barely strapped on its foot, and it took uncoordinated steps toward me, letting out a feral snarl. Its buddy's chest was torn open, its muscles and ribcage on display like some kind of cadaver in a university dissection test. The nasty, bloodthirsty pair charged forward, gnashing their teeth and pawing wildly at me, the main target of their murderous rampage. I rammed my gun through the first one's left eye socket, instantly dropping it, but the ribcage man just kept coming. I whacked its head, then kicked it. A sickening *crunch* sliced through the air as I stomped its skull.

"Behind you!" Sammy shouted.

I spun around and kicked one zombie in the chest, but another one teetered toward me from the right. I quickly fractured its skull by delivering a powerful blow to its left eye. "C'mon!" I screamed, grabbing Sammy's hand.

The mindless corpses just kept coming, and the growl and screams of the diseased echoed behind us.

As we took off through the back parking lot and cut through the bushes, somebody jumped out and tried to grab me. "Where ya goin', honey?" asked the man, shooting daggers at me from his cold eyes and brandishing a knife at me. "Hey! I know that blue-haired freak. She attacked my friends."

I sucked in a deep breath as the blade glittered in the sun that was now peeking out between clouds. I would only resort to deadly force if I absolutely had to. Blood pounded inside my head, and I quickly jumped back, grabbed his wrist with my left hand, and gouged his eyes with my right.

He screamed in anger and disbelief that he'd been bested by a girl.

With quick reflexes, I moved behind him, grabbed his jaw, and jerked him down to the ground, then held him there with my knee on his head.

Sammy walked over and pointed her gun at his head, ready to blow him away, but she didn't have to, because I reached for my handgun and knocked him out.

Another guy reached for me, and I punched him in the throat, dropping him to the ground as he gasped for air.

His friend suddenly came at me with a bat, a surprise ambush. I ran toward him and invaded his personal space, so close that my nose almost touched his. His eyes widened in shock, as if it was the last thing he expected me to do. I knew he might still be able to hurt me, but at least he wouldn't have that much momentum behind his swing. I conked him in the head with my rifle. As he fell to the ground, I looked around, glad to see that no more of them were coming.

Sammy clapped softly. "Pretty amazing to see you in action, Val," she said.

"C'mon."

We jogged down two streets, then started to walk briskly.

"I'm surprised you didn't shoot him," she said.

"He's a kid, probably not even eighteen. I wasn't about to kill him."

"Why? Because he has his whole life in front of him? I doubt that, with all these flippin' zombies. Heck, I doubt any of us do." She looked at me in admiration. "I bet you could take somebody three times bigger and stronger than you."

"It's not about strength, Sammy. It's about knowing where the pressure points are, the weaknesses."

"Like?"

"The eyes, knees, neck, and, my personal favorite, the genitals."

"Sock 'em in the balls, eh? I love this. There might be a zombie apocalypse, but I get to hang out with the coolest zombie-fighter there is. Girl power at its finest!"

I chuckled. "Gee. I'm flattered."

"Well, the best part is that you genuinely wanna make this hellhole a better place," Sammy said. "I keep trying to tell you that you can't, but you keep trying, keep helping people. Even in all this chaos, you've got the compassion of a saint."

"A saint?"

"Yep. The saint of kicking butt—lots of it."

I laughed. "Hmm. I'm not sure there is such a thing."

She chuckled and shrugged. "I don't judge. You let me be who I am, and I'm gonna do the same for you. You never question my hairstyle, my clothes, or my makeup. You just...love me unconditionally."

I wrapped an arm around her. "Always have and always will."

"You've babysat me since I was five. Have I always been a pain?"

"Only the biggest ever."

"And you're honest too. I love that!"

We continued to speed-walk, as I was eager to find the best escape route to get out of the city. I didn't know if the zombies or the thugs were worse. As we walked, we passed several dead, rotting zombies. Clearly, they'd lost the battle against the survivors, as black liquid oozed out of the bullet wounds in their heads. The only cleanup crew for that road kill were the birds that picked at their torn legs and the flies that buzzed around the decaying feast. It looked like something out of a warzone, entirely hideous, and when I dared to peer closer, I saw only maggots.

One zombie, with twisted legs, lay on the sidewalk. It reached for my leg and chomped its teeth in anticipation of just one little bite.

"Not gonna happen," I said, then shot it right in the head.

Gagging, Sammy glanced down. "The smell's unbearable."

"Yeah, I know. Living in an undead world's not exactly glamorous—definitely not for the faint of heart."

"This sucks. We're surrounded by death and gore. I've tasted hell up close and personal, and it's left a bitter taste in my mouth that no amount of toothpaste or mouthwash will ever get rid of."

Taking shallow breaths, Sammy and I stretched our shirts over our mouths and noses to help us escape the stench of rotting flesh. We jogged past the horrendous scene, stepping over torn limbs and chunks of flesh that had obviously been ripped off not too long ago.

Sammy blinked. "Wow. I survived the collapse of civilization. Wouldn't that make a cool t-shirt?" Before I could answer, she continued, "It's like...watching a horror movie, in living color, every single day. Talk about 3D! Every time I take a walk, I see dismembered body parts all over the place. That's not exactly helping my nightmares."

"That's why you're gonna move in with me," I said.

"Thanks, Val. I can really use a friend right now. Everything is just so...well, it's weighing heavily on me. I just want our world back. I can't deal with all this gore."

I wrapped my arm around my young friend. "It's a daily struggle to put the pieces of our lives back together again, but I swear that we will."

"So you say," she whispered.

"It's just gonna take some time, Sammy. Zombies can't last more than one to three years."

"It's been a whole year already, and there are still plenty of the bloodthirsty ghouls out there," she retorted.

"They'll eventually rot out. Nobody can fight Mother Nature, not zombies. We just have to survive till then."

She stepped around a half-eaten, rotting arm on the sidewalk. "So, the zombie head-squashing continues."

"For a while longer."

She glanced at my ring finger. "Hey, where's your rock?"

"I haven't been engaged for a year now. I put it away for safekeeping."

"Ah. I get it," she said.

"Travis is gone, and I know it's time to move on. It doesn't mean I'll ever forget about him. He'll always be...in my heart." I shook my head, trying to rid it of the painful memories. "But anyway, I don't really wanna talk about this."

"Okay. Then tell me how you got here," Sammy said.

"Jack brought me."

She raised a brow. "Really? Where's good ol' Jack now? I'm dying to hear one of his longwinded lectures."

"He ditched me."

"Idiot! But don't worry. We can use Annie's car," she said. "It's about four blocks from here, and she keeps the keys under the seat."

"We can't just take her car," I said.

"She won't need it again," she whispered sadly. "She's dead."

"Oh. I'm so sorry."

"Most friends don't last these days. It's a fact of this zombie-infested life."

"I'll last, Sammy."

"Promise?" she said.

"I promise. I won't ever leave you."

"Pinky-swear?"

I wrapped my little finger around hers. "Yep. I'm afraid you're stuck with me forever, kiddo."

"That's okay. I like forever."

"There's something I need to tell you," I said hesitantly, not sure how she was going to take the news. "Jack told me that he and most of the others are leaving next week."

Her jaw dropped. "Leaving? Where're they going?"

"I'm not sure. I didn't get the details. Maybe we can stop by and find out."

"Do you really think the grass is greener on the other side?"

"That depends. Honestly, I'd rather water the dead grass I'm standing on."

"Until a zombie's dead, rotting hand bursts through the dirt and grabs your ankle."

"I don't know. I'm not sure leaving is the answer."

"Hmm. I'm kinda on the fence. Do you think there really are any safe places left?"

"Jack seems to think so."

"So we should listen to that uptight idiot? That dummy would pitch a tent on the rim of an active, lava-spewing volcano."

"Yeah, I know he's made some mistakes, but we all have."

"Does he really think we can survive out there with an unstoppable horde of flesh-eating monsters on our butts every second, every minute of every freaking day?"

"I don't wanna leave, but it's getting worse here every day. I just want what everyone else wants," I said.

"And what's that?"

"Sanctuary, a refuge from all this...hell."

A feral snarl caught my attention. When I turned, a grisly eating machine with blood oozing down its face stepped out from behind a parked truck. It looked as if its skin had been boiled off, and it was wearing a demonic expression on its face as it limped on a twisted ankle. It had no teeth, no nose, and only part of a black tongue.

I sealed my lips tight, then raised my gun and fired. The weapon packed a deadly punch, and blood and biological debris flew everywhere when the hole was blasted in its foul head.

Sammy continued talking, as if it was a common occurrence; sadly, it was. "I know I shoulda held my tongue back there," she said, "but those gang members were pissing me off. They killed people right in front of us."

"And that wasn't a clue to keep your mouth shut?"

"They had no right to just walk into my place and kick me out."

"It's not safe in the city. I warned you. That gang's nothing but trouble. They've been harassing everyone."

"They usually leave us alone," she said, "but since the zombies attacked the other place they were staying, they came knocking at our doors. The gang-bangers do whatever they want, like they own the place."

"That's why I didn't want you to stay here."

"But it's my home," she said.

"Like Jack told me earlier, not anymore."

"Don't say that, Val!"

"It's the truth. Even those jerks won't make it too much longer if they don't get out. The zombie count is too high. I've been telling you that forever. I hate to leave, but we've gotta go where there are less of them. They've been showing up in your neighborhood pretty frequently lately."

"I know, but I'm not sure it's safe anywhere right now." She knew I was right; she just hated to admit it.

Since I wasn't in the mood for an argument, I changed the subject. "Love your hair, by the way," I said, walking on, admiring her two turquoise, braided ponytails. Some of our group didn't get Sammy, but I loved her unique style. She wanted to be different, and that she was.

She smiled. "Thanks," she said. She was dressed a t-shirt and denim shorts, and her blue eyes sparkled under her thick, long lashes.

"That makeup really makes your eyes pop," I said.

"A li'l black eyeliner always does the trick."

Something crashed, and I lifted my gun. Sammy aimed her gun, too, and glanced around, motioning to me not to say another word. The noise was coming from the alley to the left. She motioned me not to say another word. In a blur, two figures darted past us. Sammy fired once, barely missing two women in ragged clothes, who screamed hysterically.

"Don't shoot!" I said. "It's just survivors."

Sammy shot them a look. "You gotta talk. Geesh! I thought you were zombies. Everybody knows you gotta say something."

"Sorry," I said.

"Yeah, us too," the younger of the women said, then grabbed her friend by the arm and ran off.

"You almost blew her head off!" I scolded.

"Sorry," Sammy replied, her voice wavering. "I know I gotta be more careful, but I really thought she was one of those freaks. Gosh, what would I have done if I'd killed that poor girl? I'd never be able to live with myself."

"I know your nerves are frazzled, but take a minute to think," I said.

"I did that once, and my boyfriend's dead because of it," she said sternly.

"It's a judgment call, Sammy—each and every time."

"I think I'm losin' it, going crazy," she said.

"You're not alone in that. Think about everything we've been through. We lost family and friends, people we cared deeply about. We try to carry on, but it's hard knowing that they were viciously murdered. When we think about that incredible loss we've experienced, it's a miracle we don't lose our sanity."

"But I can't even...I can't sleep," she said. "For starters, I can't take the nightmares. Then there's all the sadness. And, finally, I'm scared to sleep because I know *they* don't."

"I'm in the same boat. I woulda stocked up on caffeine pills if I had known sleep was going to be so terrifying."

Cars revved behind us, and shouts cut through the air. My jaw tensed as I glanced over my shoulder to see what the commotion was. Armed men were approaching us on foot, carrying baseball bats and four-by-fours. One man was standing in the bed of a truck, pointing a 9mm at me that sent a cold shiver of fear down my spine.

"Oh no. What now?" Sammy whispered.

"I don't know, but we've gotta lose these idiots...and fast, before we're all zombie food."

End of Sample

CPSIA information can be obtained at www.ICGtesting.com
Printed in the USA
LVOW08s2148031215

465282LV00001B/38/P